MEDIEVAL
CARTULARIES
OF GREAT BRITAIN

MEDIEVAL CARTULARIES
OF GREAT BRITAIN
A Short Catalogue

by

G. R. C. DAVIS

Godfrey

1724

LONGMANS, GREEN AND CO
LONDON ♦ NEW YORK ♦ TORONTO

LONGMANS, GREEN AND CO LTD
6 & 7 CLIFFORD STREET LONDON W I
THIBAULT HOUSE THIBAULT SQUARE CAPE TOWN
605–611 LONSDALE STREET MELBOURNE C I

LONGMANS, GREEN AND CO INC
55 FIFTH AVENUE NEW YORK 3

LONGMANS, GREEN AND CO
20 CRANFIELD ROAD TORONTO 16

ORIENT LONGMANS PRIVATE LTD
CALCUTTA BOMBAY MADRAS
DELHI HYDERABAD DACCA

First published 1958

Made and printed in Great Britain by
William Clowes and Sons, Limited, London and Beccles

CONTENTS

PREFACE

MORE than a quarter of a century has elapsed since medievalists first began to discuss the making of this book, and exactly twenty years have passed since it was 'provisionally accepted for future publication' by the Royal Historical Society. Formidable obstacles have had, meanwhile, to be overcome, and credit for its ultimate completion and publication is due mainly to the support that it has received from the large body of friends which it has always been fortunate enough to possess.

A list of acknowledgements of specific contributions of information about cartularies follows this preface. I would like to refer separately to the more general debts which the book owes, amongst others, to the late Professor W. E. Lunt and the late Dr. G. Herbert Fowler who, independently of each other, formulated the original proposals from which it springs; to Mr. W. A. Pantin and Professor C. R. Cheney, who planned the earlier stages of its actual compilation; to Professor V. H. Galbraith, Mr. H. M. Colvin, the Rev. J. C. Dickinson and Dr. N. R. Ker, who for many years have given it valuable moral as well as practical support; to Mr. Philip Grierson and Professor Denys Hay who, as successive Literary Directors of the Royal Historical Society, have helped it materially along its way to publication; and to the printers and publishers for the skill with which they have solved many difficult problems of presentation. A special debt is due to the Trustees of the Leverhulme Research Awards, who accepted financial responsibility for a programme of research involving travel of more than five thousand miles, and by doing so brought much within the realms of possibility that could not otherwise have been attempted.

I owe more personal debts of gratitude to the Trustees of the British Museum, to Sir Thomas Kendrick its Director and Principal Librarian, and to Mr. A. J. Collins and Dr. B. Schofield, successive Keepers of Manuscripts, for the help and encouragement which they have given me in my own work upon the book; to Professor Francis Wormald, who first directed my attention to the study of cartularies and initiated me into their mysteries; and to many colleagues in the British Museum for the generosity with which they have placed their knowledge on specific points at my disposal.

In spite of care, the book will inevitably be found to contain many errors and omissions. For these and other defects I alone am responsible. Notes of corrections and additions, for incorporation in any future edition, will be welcomed.

G. R. C. DAVIS

Department of Manuscripts,
The British Museum, W.C.1

ACKNOWLEDGEMENTS

THE catalogue which follows could not have been made without the help and good will of a very large number of people, many of whom must necessarily remain unnamed. Special acknowledgements are due to the owners and custodians of the manuscripts it lists for the generosity with which they have made them available for examination, often at great personal effort and inconvenience, and to the following for their help in establishing the present whereabouts of manuscripts and in supplying information about them:

C. K. Croft Andrew (Yorkshire North Riding), the late R. L. Atkinson (Historical MSS. Commission and National Register of Archives), R. M. Beaumont (Southwell Minster), E. O. Blake (Ely cartularies), T. S. Blakeney (Coxford cartularies), M. F. Bond (St. George's, Windsor), Miss N. R. Briggs (Bodleian Library and Essex), T. J. Brown (privately owned MSS.), Miss E. Brunskill (York Minster), D. Charmian (E. Suffolk), Professor C. R. Cheney (Cotton and other MSS.), Sir Charles Clay (Yorkshire cartularies), I. P. Collis (Taunton), H. M. Colvin (a number of privately owned MSS.), M. le chanoine G. Coolen (St. Omer).

J. Conway Davies (Durham Cathedral), L. M. J. Delaissé (Belgium), the Rev. J. C. Dickinson (Augustinian cartularies), Miss B. Dodwell (Norwich Cathedral), C. R. Dodwell (Lambeth Palace), A. I. Doyle (Durham University Library and Ushaw College), H. D. Emanuel (National Library of Wales), F. G. Emmison (Essex R.O.), Mrs. A. M. Erskine (Leicester Museum), The Very Rev. S. J. A. Evans, Dean of Gloucester (Ely), Levi Fox (Shakespeare's Birthplace Library), R. Sharpe France (Lancashire R.O.).

Miss J. Gibbs (Lacock cartularies), Miss A. J. Godber (Bedfordshire), Miss M. Grace (Norwich Central Library), I. E. Gray (Gloucestershire), T. Gray (Carlisle), M. Gysseling (State Archives, Ghent), J. H. Harvey (Winchester College), W. O. Hassall (Bodleian Library), Virginia Hayes (Lexington Public Library, U.S.A.), T. P. Highet (Manchester), R. H. Hilton (Gloucester and Stoneleigh Abbey cartularies), C. Hohler (Nutley cartularies), A. E. J. Hollaender (Guildhall Library, London), J. C. Holt (Nottingham University Library), Felix Hull (Kent R.O.), P. L. Hull (Cornwall R.O.), R. F. Hunnissett (PRO., uncatalogued material), R. W. Hunt (Bodleian Library).

H. C. Johnson (PRO., uncatalogued material), N. R. Ker (privately owned and other MSS.), P. I. King (Peterborough and Northamptonshire), Miss J. C. Lancaster (Coventry cartularies), Miss M. M. Larter (a privately owned MS.), C. T. McInnes (Scottish R.O. and elsewhere), C. A. Malcolm (an untraced Scottish cartulary), Miss L. M. Midgley (Lichfield and Staffordshire), A. N. L. Munby (Phillipps MSS.), Professor R. A. B. Mynors (Balliol College), W. O'Sullivan (Trinity College, Dublin), W. Park (National Library of Scotland), F. J. Patrick (Birmingham Reference Library), W. D. Peckham (Chichester cartularies), H. L. Pink (Cambridge University Library), N. S. E. Pugsley (Exeter City Library), the Rev. J. S. Purvis (Monk Bretton and Pontefract cartularies).

Miss E. Ralph (Bristol R.O.), M. G. Rathbone (Wiltshire R.O.), R. L. Rickard (New College, Oxford), W. Robertshaw (Bradford Art Gallery and Museums), C. D. Ross (Cirencester Abbey and other cartularies), Mrs. M. J. Rowe (Bury St. Edmunds and W. Suffolk), J. Saltmarsh (King's College, Cambridge), P. H. Sawyer (Rochester cartularies), H. C. Schulz (Henry E. Huntington Library), Miss E. J. Scroggs (privately owned MSS.), the late R. J. Slack (Shrewsbury), Miss M. D. Slatter (Lambeth Palace), K. F. Stanesby (Burton-upon-Trent Museum), L. E. Tanner (Westminster Abbey), F. Taylor (John

Rylands Library), E. K. Timings (PRO.), T. D. Tremlett (Eton College), Mrs. B. D. M. Carpenter Turner (Hampshire).

W. G. Urry (Canterbury), Miss V. Walker (Nottingham Public Library), P. Walne (Berkshire R.O.), C. E. Welch (W. Sussex R.O.), J. R. W. Whitfield (Hertfordshire R.O.), Miss D. M. Williamson (Lincoln and Lincolnshire), Anthony C. Wood (Warwickshire), Professor F. Wormald (Beverley cartularies), T. S. Wragg (Chatsworth), A. Shaw Wright (Hereford County Library), Miss J. A. Youings (Exeter, Devonshire, and Cornwall); also W. Greenway (St. David's MSS.), K. B. McFarlane (Magdalen College).

INTRODUCTION

CARTULARIES are registers of muniments, that is to say of the title-deeds (*carte*), charters of privilege (*privilegia*) and other documents which are kept by landowners as evidence of their personal or corporate rights. They are made primarily for purposes of reference and information; their name derives from the Latin word *c(h)artu(l)arium*, or *registrum cartarum*, by which in the Middle Ages they were commonly known.

The importance of medieval cartularies as a source of information about the Middle Ages has long been recognised, and their contents have been drawn upon for a variety of purposes; over the field as a whole, however, it has always been difficult to discover which of them still exist and where these are to be found. This book is an attempt to provide a brief survey of the present state of knowledge, and takes as its scope the cartularies made for religious houses and private individuals or estates in England, Scotland and Wales before the Reformation, which are known to have survived it. Borough cartularies have not been included, but the term 'religious house' is used in a wide sense to include bishoprics, cathedrals, collegiate and parish churches, secular colleges, hospitals and houses of the military orders.

THE NATURE OF CARTULARIES

Medieval cartularies are usually in the form of books, or sometimes in that of rolls, and the elaboration with which they are executed varies. Occasionally they display great elegance (e.g. Nos. 3–4, 454, 617, 1042, in the catalogue) and have exceptionally fine bindings (e.g. Nos. 24–5, 872, 892, 1042, 1187); more often they are written with merely business-like competence in ordinary charter-hand, and if they still retain their original covers these consist of limp parchment or of plain wooden boards covered with skin, often with fastening clasps or thongs. In most of the earlier examples, the titles and initial capitals of the entries, and sometimes other headings, are in colour—usually red or blue; but after the fourteenth century the use of colour for this purpose becomes less frequent and it is replaced by the ordinary black ink of the text, sometimes with elaborate pen-work decoration for emphasis (e.g. Nos. 992–3). Tables of contents are common, but indexes are rare. When cartularies were compiled, space was often left blank at appropriate points so that additions could be made, and sometimes they seem also to have been left unbound so that extra leaves or quires could be inserted as necessary. An indirect result of the latter practice was that cartularies which were originally quite separate and distinct could, in the course of time, be combined or become confused (e.g. Nos. 320, 501, 528–9, 642–3); a further result has been that odd leaves and quires containing totally unrelated material have been apt to intrude into them (e.g. Nos. 11, 24, 685, 1047).

THE DATES OF CARTULARIES

The earliest surviving cartulary from a religious house in Great Britain dates from the first half of the eleventh century (No. 1068, pt. 1) and, like the only two other known eleventh-century examples, comes from the Benedictine Cathedral Priory of Worcester. Extant twelfth-century examples number fewer than thirty, but are more widespread in their places of origin and not obviously confined to any particular order or type of establishment (see e.g. Nos. 23, 254, 399, 596, 801, 811, 934). The majority of those listed in the catalogue date from the thirteenth and fourteenth centuries. Many later examples survive, however, to show that they were still regularly being made as occasion arose in the fifteenth and sixteenth centuries, mainly as revisions of earlier compilations. The first recorded secular cartulary (No. 1224) dates from the early thirteenth century; most are fourteenth century or later, and in a few large estate offices they continue to be compiled down to the present day.

TYPES OF CARTULARY

A number of different types of medieval cartulary existed which for present purposes may be distinguished and classified as follows:

General cartularies. The most common type of cartulary contains transcripts or calendars of the entire muniments of the individual or house for which it was compiled, normally in the order in which these were kept. While it is sometimes clear that no fixed order in fact existed, in most cases the documents were arranged in groups or bundles according to the places to which they referred, or to their subject-matter, or to their grantors. Occasionally a chronological or some other order was adopted, and not infrequently a mixture of several orders. The detail of individual schemes of arrangement varied according to circumstances, not the least of which were probably the size and shape of the chests, presses or other receptacles used for storage, and the number of documents each was able to hold. In religious houses, however, certain categories of charter were often treated as special classes, notably the foundation, royal, papal and episcopal privileges, and sometimes fines, compositions, material relating to churches or tithes, muniments of lands and revenues assigned to obedientiaries, and the like. Of the alternatives mentioned, some form of topographical arrangement appears to have been by far the most common, supplemented in the case of religious houses by perhaps two or three special classes of the kind described, which in the cartularies are generally placed at the beginning or, less often, at the end. For examples of this arrangement, see Nos. 168, 294, 531, 557, 782, 832–4, 1106–7. For examples of arrangement by grantors, see Nos. 5, 91–2, 213, 801; by subject-matter, Nos. 895, 913, 1100; and chronologically, No. 497.

Special cartularies. From their nature, general cartularies could sometimes be of great size, extending to three or four volumes (e.g. Nos. 327–9, 414–9) or occupying single volumes of enormous dimensions (e.g. Nos. 1013, 1087). In order to reduce them to manageable proportions, or for other reasons, it was often found convenient in large religious houses to make separate cartularies for individual sections of the muniments, such as the royal, papal, episcopal and other important privileges (e.g. Nos. 420, 817, 1035, 1042), the material for particular places (e.g. Nos. 99–104, 533), or that relating to a single endowment such as a chantry (e.g. Nos. 592–3, 886). Separate cartularies were also often made of material relating to the lands and revenues assigned to obedientiaries, but in this case their scope was sometimes extended, for ease of reference, to include relevant supplementary material from other sections of the muniments (see e.g. the entries for Bury St. Edmunds Abbey and Durham Cathedral Priory). Occasionally, as perhaps at Bury St. Edmunds Abbey, it may be suspected that the entire muniments of a religious house eventually came to be covered by special cartularies of this kind, and that no attempt was afterwards made by it to maintain a general cartulary.

Cartularies of rights, privileges, etc. In large religious houses, separate cartularies were also sometimes compiled, of which the contents are apparently confined to copies of documents which were, or might be, of value in dealing with constantly recurrent administrative problems or disputes. Their scope and formality vary, and occasionally they are hardly distinguishable in appearance from casual memoranda-books. The types of document of which they tend to include copies are royal, papal and episcopal privileges of special significance or interest; compositions, ordinations and other material relating to churches, tithes, pensions and rents; records of legal proceedings, and occasionally also statutes of the Realm. They rarely include copies of title-deeds of land. The name given to them here is taken from the introductory heading of York Minster 'Doomsday Book' (No. 1088), one of the more elaborate examples. Other examples are Nos. 6, 326, 381–2, 615, 759, 885, 992–3, 1071.

Chronicle-cartularies. Cartularies of a more literary type were sometimes made in religious houses for the general instruction of their members. These take the form of a narrative chronicle of the house concerned, incorporating copies of its royal, papal and other more important charters and privileges. They tend to become, however, as they proceed, a bare sequence of copies of charters without connecting material. They often survive in more than one MS. Outstanding examples are Nos. 3–4 (Abingdon), 198 (St. Augustine's, Canterbury) and 366–8 (Ely).

Cartularies in Gospel-Books etc. An early custom existed of copying royal and other important charters into Gospel-books (e.g. Nos. 177–80, 199A, 1137). The significance of this practice (of which further examples, omitted from the present catalogue, are described by N. R. Ker, *Catalogue of MSS. containing Anglo-Saxon* (Oxford, 1957), nos. 6, 20, 22, 402) is discussed by F. Wormald, 'The Sherborne "Chartulary"', *Fritz Saxl Memorial Essays*, ed. D. J. Gordon (1957), 106–7. One entire catalogue is known to have been placed in a Gospel-book in the eleventh century (No. 1069, Worcester). Other cartularies of such special types of charter were sometimes made in Benedictine monasteries, mainly in the twelfth and thirteenth centuries, to be bound up with Passion narratives, collects, Gospel lessons and prayers (No. 892, Sherborne); with the Rule of St. Benedict (No. 192, pt. I, St. Augustine's, Canterbury; cf. No. 807, Reading); with a kalendar, life of St. Aethelwold, and the 'Inquisitio Eliensis' (No. 364, Ely); or with the 'Passio SS. Wulfhadi et Ruffini', a chronicle of the house, an extent and a rental (No. 758, Peterborough). Perhaps slightly apart from these should be placed a similar cartulary from Malmesbury, written to be bound up with John of Salisbury's life of St. Thomas of Canterbury and two treatises on the book of Genesis (No. 641).

Inventories. These have the primary function of finding-lists and enumerate the contents of muniment rooms, press by press and bundle by bundle. Usually they do no more than cite brief titles of documents, but sometimes the existence of seals is also noticed. Occasionally they include abstracts of contents and may have been intended to serve the additional purpose of a cartulary. They have special value for the light that they throw on the way in which muniments were arranged and kept. Good examples are Nos. 161, 333–42, 887, 929.

OTHER REGISTERS ETC.

Besides cartularies there were, of course, many other types of medieval register of business and lands such as act-, letter- and memoranda-books, registers of legal proceedings, feodaries, rentals and surveys. With these the present catalogue has not set out to deal, and their numbers are so great that systematic treatment of them would be impossible. The brief references which have been necessary to many of them, because they have at some stage of their history been wrongly described as cartularies, because they have descents which throw light on the fate of cartularies now lost, or because they have similar claims to a place in the picture to be presented here, should consequently not be regarded as complete.

THE DESCENT OF CARTULARIES

In the history of cartularies, as of other books and records, destruction and loss have prominent places. During the course of the Middle Ages, large numbers of them were deliberately destroyed or dismembered by their owners, or were consigned to limbo to perish unheeded, because they were beyond further revision, replacements for them had been made, and their usefulness as works of reference had passed (see e.g. Nos. 95, 164, 324–5, 580–2, 831, 1010). When the monasteries were dissolved in the sixteenth century, many more were destroyed indiscriminately through the ignorance or indifference of those into whose hands they fell. In all ages fire and other mishaps, damp, decay, the rats, the tallow-chandlers and the waste-paper merchants have taken a steady toll of them (see e.g. Nos. 85, 249, 275, 277, 440, 551, 595, 620, 888, 908, 959, 1039). Of many only single leaves or quires now survive to attest their former existence. Those which still exist cannot be regarded as more than a small and only partially representative proportion of the total number originally made.

In the survival of individual cartularies, much has been due to chance. Many of them owe it mainly to the good fortune by which they have remained undisturbed, and often unnoticed, in the muniment rooms and other places of safe-keeping where their makers put them. Some, it may be suspected, have been spared from destruction or limbo primarily on account of their attractive appearance, their imposing size, or similarly fortuitous attributes. Of the factors which have contributed more positively towards their preservation, the most important have been the value which they have possessed to landowners, since the Middle Ages, not merely as reference-books but as actual evidence of title, and the attention which they have received from antiquaries.

Cartularies have value as evidence of title to the extent that they can often be produced as substitutes for the documents copied into them, when these have been lost or destroyed and when no better-authenticated copies are available. Examples of their potentialities and limitations in this respect in modern English law are given in *Roscoe's Digest of the Law of Evidence on the Trial of Civil Actions* i (20th edition, ed. J. S. Henderson, 1934), 13–14. In view of the frequency with which muniments were mislaid in the Middle Ages, or are recorded to have perished from decay and other causes, this value is likely to have been recognised at an early date. Certainly by the fourteenth century it was being openly referred to when cartularies were compiled (see e.g. the preface of No. 312; cf. those of Nos. 866, 1131), and by the sixteenth century it had become well-established. An instance of the production of a cartulary in a tithe-dispute in 1574 is described, from original documents in York Diocesan Registry, with the texts of the attestations which were made, by J. S. Purvis, 'New Light on the Chartularies of Monk Bretton', *Yorkshire Archaeological Journal* xxxvii (1948), 67–71. When the monasteries were dissolved, and large quantities of their records were destroyed, the new owners of monastic estates were consequently quick to lay hands upon such cartularies as could be found, in order to use them in this way; the number which passed at the Dissolution into the permanent custody of the Exchequer was small, and out of a total of fewer than thirty which are now preserved among its records in the Public Record Office, either in their entirety or as fragments, some at least can be shown to have come to it in other circumstances and at much later dates (Nos. 225, 527, 753, 788, 979, 1001). For similar reasons, monastic no less than secular cartularies have had a natural tendency since the Dissolution to follow the descent of the estates to which their contents relate; as lately as the nineteenth century they were still being produced in evidence in the law courts (e.g. Nos. 371, 530–4, 536–41); in comparatively recent years, instances have occurred of their transfer with estates as part of their title-deeds (Nos. 681A–2, 1079) or, if they have strayed, of their having been bought back when an opportunity to do so offered itself (No. 409). As a result, about one-third of all the cartularies recorded in the catalogue have remained down to the present day in the possession of landowners, although now more usually with the status of heirlooms, curiosities or of pious relics than of working records. Many more have no doubt also perished in their hands, having failed to achieve such a status when their practical usefulness as evidences was thought to have passed.

The antiquarian value of cartularies was recognised later than their value as evidences, and took second place to this in time, if not in importance, as an influence upon their movements. Since the earliest antiquarian extracts from them are genealogical, and occur in the now widely scattered collections of such heralds as Robert Glover (1544–88) and Ralph Brooke (1553–1625), it was perhaps discovered in the latter part of the sixteenth century by members of the College of Arms to whom they were produced as evidence of pedigree. Their usefulness for wider purposes was, however, quickly realised, and by the end of the sixteenth century they had become objects of active and persistent antiquarian search. As their immediate value as evidences decreased, they began gradually to be allowed to leave the muniment rooms and offices where they had hitherto been kept and to pass by gift, loan or sale into the libraries of scholars and collectors. Of the date and circumstances of individual removals of this kind, which have continued down to the present day, the known details are recorded in the catalogue and no generalisations will be attempted here. It is, however, to be noted that when their connexions with the estates for which they had been made were severed, all restrictions on their movements ceased, and that the directions of these became diverse and completely unpredictable. In terms of numbers, the most outstanding of the collectors through whose hands they have passed have been Sir Robert Cotton (d. 1631), Robert and Edward Harley, 1st and 2nd earls of Oxford (d. 1724, 1741) and Sir Thomas Phillipps (d. 1872), who between them at some time owned nearly a quarter of all the manuscripts listed in the catalogue; but among the earlier of many others whose names are included in Index II, special mention should perhaps also be made, on account of their pioneer work in searching them out, of Lord William Howard (d. 1640), Sir Simonds D'Ewes (d. 1650), Roger Dodsworth (d. 1654), Christopher baron Hatton (d. 1670), Charles Fairfax (d. 1673), Elias Ashmole (d. 1692), Anthony à Wood (d. 1695), Bishop John Moore (d. 1714) and Peter Le Neve (d. 1729).

The instinct of antiquaries is, however, to preserve rather than to possess, and to other types of collector cartularies have rarely made more than a sporadic appeal. The movement of cartularies from muniment rooms into private libraries had hardly begun before opinion was voiced that, like the many valuable literary manuscripts from monastic libraries which were simultaneously being passed from hand to hand, they would be more securely housed in public repositories, if these could be created, and would also be more permanently accessible to those who wished to use them. Consequently, efforts were soon being made to gather cartularies together in such places as the Cottonian Library, for which Cotton himself long strove to achieve public status, and to which they continued to be added long after his death (e.g. Nos. 56, 90, 302, 648, 700), and at St. Mary's Tower at York, which was destroyed with much of its contents in the siege of 1644 (cf. Nos. 517, 655). From such beginnings, the movement slowly gathered strength until at the present time nearly two-thirds of all the cartularies listed in the catalogue are to be found in public or quasi-public libraries and record offices of various kinds. About half of this total are housed in the British Museum (f. 1753) alone, to which they have come partly as individual gifts, bequests or purchases and partly with collections such as those of Cotton, the Harleys, the 1st marquess of Lansdowne (d. 1805), or of the 1st marquess (d. 1813) and 1st duke (d. 1839) of Buckingham at Stowe, which were in turn to some extent built upon the collections of earlier antiquaries. Other large quantities are preserved in the Bodleian Library at Oxford, mainly as a result of the acquisition in the late seventeenth and eighteenth centuries of collections such as those of Dodsworth, Fairfax, Wood, Ashmole, Bishop Thomas Tanner (d. 1735) and Bishop Richard Rawlinson (d. 1755); in the University Library at Cambridge, mainly as a result of the gift by George I of the library of Bishop John Moore; and in the National Library of Scotland (formerly the Advocates' Library) at Edinburgh, mainly by gift of members of the Society of Advocates. Smaller and more scattered numbers exist in the libraries of Oxford and Cambridge colleges, the Society of Antiquaries, the College of Arms, the Inns of Court, and similar institutions, to which they have been presented by their members. The number of those which are known to remain in the hands of private collectors has become extremely small.

All sight has been lost, however, of more than a hundred cartularies which have been reported, in some cases perhaps inaccurately, to have survived the Dissolution and to have still been in existence at least as late as the seventeenth century. One such lately reappeared among the records of the Court of Arches, where it had lain unnoticed since its deposit in a lawsuit in 1670 (No. 404). Another, unseen apparently since the beginning of the nineteenth century, was found by a collector at an Oxford bookseller's in 1934, having been brought there from a country house with which it was not previously known to have had connexions (No. 5). A third, originally from Norfolk, was discovered about the same time by another collector in a London junk-shop (No. 281). A fourth had been given to the town of Lexington in Kentucky by one of its inhabitants in 1806 (No. 500). Others again are known only to have been borrowed from their owners and not returned (e.g. Nos. 296, 669). Some of them have no doubt been destroyed.

That further cartularies await discovery, of which the existence has not hitherto been recorded, can be shown only by the way in which they continue from time to time to appear (e.g. No. 30). But since the contents of comparatively few private libraries and muniment rooms remain completely unknown, their number and importance will perhaps eventually prove to be less great than is sometimes supposed. The possibility that some still remain in bricked-up priests' holes (No. 801), ruined towers (No. 1294) or similarly romantic hiding-places, must now be considered remote.

FINDING-LISTS OF CARTULARIES

On account of the background of movement, accident and uncertainty which has been described, finding-lists of cartularies have for long been indispensable to those who wished to use them. The following, in chronological order, are the more important or widely known of those which have previously appeared, and systematic account has been taken of them in the compilation of the present catalogue:

SIR WILLIAM DUGDALE, 'Catalogus Registrorum omnium modo existentium per totam Angliam (Domibus Religiosis quondam spectantium) et in quorum manibus'. An unpublished MS. list in Oxford, Bodl., Dugdale 48 (*SC.* 6536), fos. 54–64. Apparently compiled *c.* 1649, with later additions and corrections. The basis of all that follow. **Cited as** (*D*).

R. DODSWORTH & SIR WILLIAM DUGDALE, *Monasticon Anglicanum*, 3 vols. (1655–73). Prints extracts from cartularies, with notes that supplement the preceding at a few points.

THOMAS TANNER, *Notitia Monastica; or an Account of all the Abbies, Priories and Houses of Friers, formerly in England and Wales. And also of all the Colleges and Hospitals founded before*

A.D. MDXL, published by J. Tanner (1744); reprinted with additions by J. Nasmith (Cambridge, 1787). Includes notes of recorded registers, for Tanner's correspondence about which see Oxford, Bodl., Tanner 343. **Cited as** (*T*).

SIR WILLIAM DUGDALE, *Monasticon Anglicanum*; a new edition enriched . . . by J. Caley, H. Ellis and the Rev. B. Bandinel. 6 vols. in 8 pts. (1817–30; reprinted, 1846). Notices recorded registers, sometimes with lists of contents. Extracts are mainly reprinted from the original edition above, and much of the added material is derived from Tanner's *Notitia Monastica*. **Cited as** *Mon. Angl.*

(SIR T.) P(HILLIPPS) & (SIR F.) M(ADDEN), 'List of Monastic Cartularies at present existing, or which are known to have existed since the Dissolution of Religious Houses', *Coll. Top. et Genealogica* i (1834), 73–9, 197–208, 399–404; ii (1835), 102–14, 400. Lists English and Welsh cartularies. Marred by many misprints.

(SIR) T. P(HILLIPPS), *Index to Cartularies now or formerly existing since the Dissolution of Monasteries* (Middlehill, 1839). A revision of the preceding, with added lists of Scottish, Irish and secular cartularies. **Cited as** (*P*).

(W. B. D. D. TURNBULL), *Fragmenta Scoto-Monastica. Memoir of what has already been done, and what materials exist towards the formation of a Scotish* (sic) *Monasticon . . . By a Delver in Antiquity* (Edinburgh, 1842). Notices Scottish cartularies.

R. SIMS, *Manual for the Genealogist, Topographer and Legal Professor* (revised edition, 1888), 14–29. A list of English, Welsh, Scottish, Irish and secular cartularies in public libraries. Based mainly on Phillipps's list, with some supplementary material.

H. A. DOUBLEDAY & W. A. PAGE, *Guide to the Victoria History of the Counties of England* (1903 ?), 49–120 ('Records arranged under Counties'). Includes many references to cartularies taken mainly, and somewhat uncritically, from one or other of the preceding.

W. HOLTZMANN, *Papsturkunden in England*, 3 vols. (Abhandlungen der Gesellschaft der Wissenschaften zu Göttingen, phil.-hist. Klasse, neue Folge xxv, dritte Folge xiv–xv, xxxiii, 1930–52). Lists, by collections, with brief descriptive notes, large numbers of cartularies in English libraries and archives.

W. A. PANTIN, 'English Monastic Letter-Books', *Historical Essays in honour of James Tait*, ed. J. G. Edwards, V. H. Galbraith, E. F. Jacob (Manchester, 1933), 201–22. Lists, with valuable discussion, extant examples of this class of register.

I. G. P(HILIP), 'Short List of Chartularies of Religious Houses in the Bodleian Library', *Bodl. Libr. Quart.* viii (1935–8), 263–8.

J. C. DICKINSON, *The Origins of the Augustinian Canons and their Introduction into England* (1950), 286–9, lists surviving English Augustinian cartularies and their transcripts.

H. M. COLVIN, *The White Canons in England* (Oxford, 1951), 377–88, notices cartularies and other registers of English Praemonstratensian houses.

ARRANGEMENT OF THE CATALOGUE

The catalogue is arranged, like most of its predecessors, in alphabetical order of the houses, people or estates for whom the cartularies which it records were made, and is in two parts:

I. Cartularies of religious houses
    A. England and Wales
    B. Scotland
II. Secular cartularies

In the spelling of place-names, modernised versions are normally used, as given in Bartholomew's *Survey Gazetteer of the British Isles* (9th edition, 1950). The entries for each house etc. are in chronological order of MSS., with inventories, cartularies of obedientiaries etc. and registers other than cartularies placed under separate sub-heads. Dates of foundation of religious houses are taken from D. Knowles & R. N. Hadcock, *Medieval Religious Houses: England and Wales* (Longmans, 1953), as corrected in *The English Historical Review* lxxii (1957), 60–87, and from D. E. Easson, *Medieval Religious Houses: Scotland* (Longmans, 1957), except when the contents of cartularies have made the adoption of an earlier alternative seem more appropriate.

Location and Ownership of MSS. The present location and ownership of all MSS. are normally given. In cases where the legal ownership of cartularies in private hands is obscured by the existence of family trusts, settlements etc., it has sometimes been necessary to name putative owners or *de facto* custodians. A conspectus of the distribution of MSS. is given by Index I, which is for practical convenience divided into two parts: (A) Corporate Bodies and Public Institutions, arranged in alphabetical order of the places where they are situated; (B) Private individuals in alphabetical order of titles or surnames. Untraced MSS. have been treated with caution, in view of the number of 'ghosts' which have found their way into previous lists, and references to them have as a rule been included only when their identity and nature are considered to be adequately attested.

Dating of MSS. Cartularies have been dated with reference to their original compilation, and additions to this are so described. Dating 'aft(er)' a given year is based on evidence of contents.

Script and Decoration. Charter-hand, written one column to the page, is to be assumed unless otherwise stated. Coloured decoration is noticed when present.

Scope and Arrangement of Contents. Obvious limitations and the inclusion of royal, papal or episcopal material are explicitly noticed. Material other than copies of charters and deeds, if too fragmentary or varied to be itemised, is described as 'misc(ellaneous)'. Chronological scope, unless otherwise indicated, is to be inferred from the date of a cartulary's compilation and that of the foundation of the house to which it belongs. The original arrangement of MSS. is described, and any subsequent disturbances of this are mentioned.

Transcripts or photostat copies of cartularies are as a rule noted only when they are in public collections, and short extracts only when they are also a source of information about them. The listing of microfilm copies proved impracticable.

Bibliography. Editions, discussions and descriptions of MSS. are cited, but the relevant catalogues of libraries are referred to only for special reasons. Discrepancies between statements made in the catalogue and those contained in other works referred to normally imply intentional correction. Publications of short extracts, single documents etc. have as a rule been ignored. Unless otherwise stated, London is to be assumed as the place of publication of all printed works mentioned, except periodicals and publications of learned societies.

Bindings are noticed only when they are of special interest or provide an indication of the date when a composite cartulary was put together.

Foliation etc. Vellum or parchment is to be assumed unless paper is specified. The most recent foliation of MSS. has been used, and the existence of earlier ones noted only for special reasons, e.g. to indicate loss or addition of leaves. Where MSS. have remained unfoliated, approximations have been necessary.

F(ormer) O(wnership). Attributions are based in most cases on the internal evidence of MSS. or of sale- and other catalogues in which they appear. The source of unconfirmed attributions is given. Where the modern shelf-marks of MSS. incorporate the names of former owners (e.g. Cotton, Harley, Fairfax, Tanner), these are not normally repeated. In the case of privately owned MSS., the names of direct ancestors of the present owners have also usually been omitted unless they have special interest or relevance. So far as possible, the individuals and families named under this head are identified in Index II; they are described in the catalogue with corresponding brevity.

ABBREVIATIONS

The expanded forms of references to MSS. etc. are given in Index I(A)

BM.   British Museum, Bloomsbury, London W.C.1.

Bodl.   Bodleian Library, Oxford.

(D)   Sir William Dugdale's MS. list of cartularies, see p. xvi above.

D. & C.   Dean and Chapter.

FO: Former owner(s).

HMC.   Historical Manuscripts Commission.

Mon. Angl.   Sir William Dugdale, *Monasticon Anglicanum*, ed. J. Caley, H. Ellis and the Rev. B. Bandinel, 6 vols. in 8 pts. (1817–30).

NLS.   National Library of Scotland, Edinburgh.

NLW.   National Library of Wales, Aberystwyth.

(P)   Sir Thomas Phillipps's list of cartularies, see p. xvii above.

PRO.   Public Record Office, Chancery Lane, London W.C.2.

R.O.   Record Office.

(T)   Bishop Thomas Tanner, *Notitia Monastica*, see p. xvi above.

U.L.   University Library.

Part One

CARTULARIES OF RELIGIOUS HOUSES

A. ENGLAND AND WALES
B. SCOTLAND

A. ENGLAND AND WALES

ABBOTSBURY co. Dors.
Ben. Abbey *f. c.* 1044
1. **Untraced.** Cartulary *penes* Sir John Strangways, 17th cent. (*D*). Subsequently reported in the archives of the 3rd earl of Ilchester, see *Coll. Top. et Genealogica* ii (1835), 400. Not found by the 6th earl at Melbury, 1953.

ABERCONWAY co. Carnarvon
Cist. Abbey *f.* (at Rhedynog-Felen) 1186
No cartulary recorded.
¶ *Other registers etc.*
2. **BM., Harley 3725**, fos. 40v–65. Chronicle of the abbey, 14th cent., incorporating copies of a few royal charters *passim.* Ed. Sir H. Ellis, 'Register & Chronicle of ... Aberconway', *Camden Miscellany* i (Camden Soc. xxxix, 1847), 1–23.

ABINGDON co. Berks
Ben. Abbey *f.* 675
3. **BM., Cotton Claud. C. ix**, fos. 105–203. History of the abbey, in two books, compiled apparently before 1170 and introducing copies of numerous royal, papal and other charters, A.D. 687–*temp.* Hen. II; followed (fos. 177v–186) by misc. additions *temp.* Ric. I–Hen. III and (fos. 187–202) extracts from Domesday, lists of rents, fees, bounds etc., also with additions. A 12th–13th cent. MS. written in double columns with rubrics, illuminated initials at the beginning of each book of the History and red, blue or green ones, sometimes decorated, elsewhere. Ed. (mainly from No. 4) J. Stevenson, *Chronicon Monasterii de Abingdon*, 2 vols. (Rolls ser., 1858); see also F. M. Stenton, *The Early History of the Abbey of Abingdon*, (Reading, 1913).
Fos. 98. $12\frac{1}{8} \times 8\frac{1}{2}$ in. Extracts, early 17th cent., in Bodl., Twyne 22, either from this or No. 4, describe it as in the hands of T. Allen and formerly of 'Dominus de Fenton baro.'.
4. **BM., Cotton Claud. B. vi.** A late 13th cent. revision and amplification of

No. 3, written in double columns with rubrics, red and blue initials etc. and a number of portrait miniatures of royal grantors. Imperf. at the beginning and wants a few other leaves *passim.* Followed (fos. 178–202) by a treatise on the obedientiaries of the abbey. Stevenson, *op. cit.* Stenton, *op. cit.*
Fos. 202. $12\frac{3}{4} \times 8\frac{1}{2}$ in. *FO:* cf. No. 3.
5. **Oxford, Bodl., Lyell 15.** Gen. cartulary, *c.* 1300, with rubrics and red and blue decorated initials. Arranged in five *Particulae* by grantors (papal, royal, archiepiscopal and episcopal, the abbots, private), with a sixth added at the end (fos. 145–208) containing copies of misc. 14th cent. pleas, inquisitions and charters. A contemp. Table of *Particulae ii–v*, incomplete at the beginning, is at fos. 1–6. Further additions, to 1498, have been made *passim.* For extracts in Bodl., Twyne 22, see H. E. Salter, 'A lost Cartulary of Abingdon Abbey', *Berks, Bucks. & Oxon Arch. J.* xxiv (1918), 28–34.
Fos. iii + 209. $12\frac{3}{4} \times 8\frac{1}{2}$ in. *FO:* Sir H. Norreys *al.* Norris, 1st baron of Rycote, 1594 (see Abingdon Corporation, Verney Deed 85, where fo. 69 is copied); E. Wray (*T*); the Earls of Abingdon (see the early 19th cent. note in the PRO., Round Room, copy of Tanner's *Notitia Monastica* (1787)); the Aubrey, afterw. Aubrey-Fletcher fam., barts., Dorton House; J. P. R. Lyell, 1934.
6. **Chatsworth Libr.**, co. Derby (Trustees of the Chatsworth Settlement). Register, mid-14th cent., of deeds and other documents, apparently rel. the abbey's spiritual and temporal rights, revenues etc. Written without decoration in several hands, with leaves left blank at the ends of quires etc. *passim.* The contents include copies of: (*a*) papal and episcopal constitutions etc., beginning imperfectly, fos. 1–10; (*b*) charters etc. rel. churches, tithes, pensions etc., fos. 13–58; (*c*) rentals of the *Coquinarius* and *Infirmarius* for Oxford, 1349, fos. 70v–1, 144v–5; (*d*) royal charters etc., *temp.* Hen. I–Edw. III, incl. Henry

2

III's confirmations of Magna Carta etc.,
fos. 123–7; (e) misc. additions incl. (fo. 165v)
a statement, 15th cent., of the abbot's responsibility for meeting expenses of litigation etc., fos. 146 ff.

Fos. 167 (medieval foliation in plummet,
13–174). 11 × 7¼ in. *FO:* the Dukes of
Devonshire.

7. **BM., Cotton Julius C. ii,** fos. 295–
308. Fragm. of a late 15th cent. register
containing copies of deeds, *temp.* Edw.
I–IV, rel. lands in Nuneham Courtenay
etc. acquired, according to a deleted contemp. heading (fo. 295), 18 Edw. IV
(1478–9).

Fos. 14 (mainly consecutive). 11½ × 8¼ in.
Paper.

ABINGDON co. Berks
Fraternity & Guild of the Holy Cross
incorp. 1441
8. **Abingdon, Christ's Hospital,**
Muniments. Gen. cartulary, 15th cent.
(aft. 1450), with blue and red initials,
titles etc. on the opening leaves and additions, 1482–1560, on blank leaves at the
beginning and end. The material, which is
arranged and numbered in sections,
apparently by grantors, includes copies of
royal charters, pleas, inquisitions and other
miscellanea.

Fos. 224. 9 × 6¾ in.

ACONBURY co. Heref.
Aug. Priory (Canonesses) *f.* (for sisters
of the order of St. John) *temp.* John.
9. **PRO., Exch., Augm. Off.** (Misc.
Bks. 55). Cartulary, late 13th cent., containing copies of a royal confirmation,
1266, and 94 private deeds, followed (fo.
79) by a rental, 1283, etc. A 15th cent.
Kalendar and Table have been added at the
beginning (pp. 1–16). *PRO. Deputy
Keeper's Eighth Report,* App. ii, 135–9
(abstract).

Fos. 9 + 85 (post-medieval pagination,
1–194). 6⅝ × 5⅜ in.
¶ *Other registers etc.*
10. **PRO., Exch., K.R.** (Transcripts of
Deeds and Charters, E.132/11). Roll of
charters, 13th cent.

ALNWICK co. Northumb.
Carmelite House at Hulne by *f.* 1240–2
11. **BM., Harley 3897.** Cartulary (fos.
1–41), late 14th cent. (aft. 1368), with

rubrics, red initials etc., and additions (fos.
33 ff.) to *temp.* Hen. VI. Contains copies of
about 25 royal, papal and other charters;
with a Table at fo. 1. Bound (fos. 41* ff.)
with contemp. lists of books and vestments, for the former of which see *Cat.
Veteres Librorum Dunelm.* (Surtees Soc. vii,
1838), 128–35.

Fos. iii + 59. 7 × 4½ in. *FO:* Ld. Wm.
Howard; J. Warburton.

ALVINGHAM co. Linc.
Gilb. Priory *f.* 1148–54
12. **Oxford, Bodl., Laud misc. 642.**
Gen. cartulary, written mainly in 13th
cent. book-hand with spaces for initials
and titles, and arranged topographically in
sections. The opening sections (fos. 1–32,
papal, episcopal and royal charters,
'Alvingham'), written in charter-hand,
aft. 1266, with rubrics and red initials, are
possibly of later date than the remainder.
Contemp. Table, with pressmarks, fos.
42v–54. Additions, down to the 14th cent.,
between the sections *passim.* H. O. Coxe,
Cat. MSS. Bibl. Bodl. ii (i) (Oxford, 1853),
463–5, lists the places etc.

Fos. 169 (contemp. pagination in red, by
sections). 13¼ × 10 in.

ANKERWYKE co. Bucks.
Ben. Priory (Nuns) *f. c.* 1160
13. **Untraced.** Fragm. ('about 2 sheets
in vellum') of a cartulary *penes* Philip
Harcourt Esq. of Ankerwyke, 9 July 1732;
see Bodl., Hearne's Diaries 136 (*SC.*
15259), p. 76, ed. H. E. Salter, *Remarks &
Collections of Thomas Hearne* xi (Oxford
Hist. Soc. lxxii, 1921), 78.

ANNESLEY co. Nott.
Parish church
v. No. 289.

ASHBY, CANONS Co. Northt.
v. Canons Ashby.

ASHRIDGE co. Bucks.
Coll. of Bonshommes *f.* 1283
No cartulary identified.
¶ *Other registers etc.*
14. **San Marino, Huntington Libr.**
(EL. 9. H. 15). Kalendar, martyrology,
constitutions, etc., 14th cent., incl. a
few copies of charters (fos. 105-6, 110).

S. de Ricci & W. J. Wilson, *Census of Medieval & Renaissance MSS. in the U.S.A. & Canada* i (New York, 1935), 130. H. J. Todd, *Hist. Coll. Bonhommes at Ashridge* (1823), 11 ff. *FO:* the Egerton fam., earls and dukes of Bridgewater, earls of Ellesmere.

ATHELNEY co. Som.
Ben. Abbey *f.* 888
15.   **Untraced.** Cartulary *penes* Sir Wm. Wyndham, bart., Orchard Wyndham, 1735. Calendared, from a transcript by the Rev. G. Harbin (Phillipps MSS. 4810–11: owned, 1957, by David Rogers Esq., c/o The Bodleian Libr., Oxford), by E. H. Bates, *Two Cartularies ... of Muchelney and Athelney* (Somerset Record Soc. xiv, 1899), 115–201.

AXHOLME co. Linc.
   v. EPWORTH.

AYLESFORD co. Kent
Carmelite friary *f.* 1241–2
16.   **Untraced.** 'Leiger-book' lent, 17th cent., by Sir J. Sedley, bart., of Aylesford, to R. Twysden. For the latter's extracts in the former Phillipps MS. 8130, pp. 495 ff., see W. Holtzmann, *Papsturkunden in England* iii (Göttingen, 1952), 77, and Sotheby's sale-cat., 25 June 1935, lot 357.

BADDESLEY, NORTH co. Southt.
Preceptory of Knts. of St. John *f.* (at Godsfield) bef. 1167
   v. also ST. JOHN OF JERUSALEM.
17.   **The Duke of Portland** (Welbeck MS. I. D. 1), deposited in the British Museum (MSS. Loans No. 29/57). Cartulary 'renewed' 1397–8 by W. Hulles, preceptor (cf. No. 952), whose arms appear at fos. 1, 6. Blue initials decorated with red, blue paragraphs and misc. additions at the end. Contains copies of private etc. deeds arranged topographically and numbered consecutively, with a contemp. Table at fos. 1–5. Extracts, 1739, by the Rev. G. Harbin are in BM., Harley 6603, fos. 72–127.
   Fos. 57 (unnumbered). $13\frac{1}{2} \times 9\frac{1}{2}$ in.

BARDNEY co. Linc.
Ben. Abbey *f.* 1087
18.   **BM., Cotton Vesp. E. xx.** Gen. cartulary, 13th cent. (aft. 1269). Arranged mainly topographically with sections of general, incl. papal, episcopal and royal, charters at the beginning (fos. 8–75) and a few misc. additions, incl. a 14th cent. index (fo. 4), on blank and added leaves *passim* and at the end (fos. 267v ff.). A transcript, 20th cent., and rotographs of fos. 29–279, are in Lincolnshire Archives Office (Foster Libr.). *Mon. Angl.* i, 626 (*l*), prints a summary list of contents.
   Fos. 292. $10 \times 7\frac{1}{4}$ in. *FO:* John Bell; Sir W. Thorold, knt. (*D*); Sir E. Walker.

BARLINGS co. Linc.
Praem. Abbey *f.* 1154
19.   **BM., Cotton Faust. B. i,** fos. 30–179. Gen. cartulary, late 13th cent. (*temp.* Edw. I), with rubrics, red paragraphs etc. Contains copies of private and some episcopal etc. charters arranged topographically, followed (fos. 93v ff.) by misc. 13th–14th cent. additions on added leaves etc. Imperf. at the beginning. *Mon. Angl.* vi, 915 (*b*), lists place-names.
   Fos. 150 (wants leaves *passim*). 10×7 in. (cropped). *FO:* E. Heyward.

BARNWELL co. Cambr.
Aug. Priory *f.* (at Cambridge) 1092
   No cartulary recorded.
❡ *Other registers etc.*
20.   **BM., Harley 3601.** 'Liber Memorandorum'. A collection, 1295–6 etc., of misc. evidences and some historical and other material in eight bks., incl. copies of a few royal and other charters etc. *passim.* Ed. J. W. Clark, *Liber Memorandorum ... de Bernewelle* (Cambridge, 1907), and (bk. *viii*) *The Observances ... of ... Barnwell* (Cambridge, 1897). *FO:* R. Hagar *al.* Haggard; Sir R. St. George; Sir H. St. George.
21.   **Oxford, Bodl., Gough Cambr. 1** (*SC.* 17751). Register of rents and fines payable to the priory, 1277–1370. *FO:* Dr. R. Farmer.

BATH & WELLS, See of *f.* 909
   For the registers (which include no cartularies) in the Bishop's Registry at Wells, see H. T. Riley, *HMC. First Report* (1870), App., 92–3. The 'small folio volume in very old limp vellum' (p. 93) was restored, *c.* 1919, to the Dean & Chapter, see No. 1005 below.

¶ *Inventory*

22.   The Marquess of Bath, Longleat
(MS. 39, fos. ccxxx–i). Inventory of royal
and papal charters found, *c.* 1300, in the
Treasury at Wells; included among addi-
tions to a cartulary of Glastonbury Abbey
(No. 434 below).

BATH   co. Som.
Ben. Cath. Priory   *f.* (as an Abbey) 676

23.   Cambridge, C.C.C., MS. 111,
pp. 55–131. Cartulary of royal and episcopal charters to the abbey, 9th–12th cent.,
written in mid-12th cent. book-hand (*temp.*
Hen. II?) with rubrics etc. and large red,
blue, green and buff initials (illuminated,
p. 57). A few misc. 13th cent. additions
have been made on end leaves etc. Pp. 53–4
of the MS. appear not to form part of the
cartulary. Ed. W. Hunt, *Two Chartularies
of . . . Bath* (Somerset Record Soc. vii,
1893), pt. i. M. R. James, *Cat. MSS.
C.C.C.* i (Cambridge, 1912), 236 ff., lists
the contents.
    Fos. 40. 12 × 8½ in. *FO:* Archbp. M.
Parker.
24.   BM., Egerton 3316, fos. 14–111.
Cartulary, 14th cent. (*temp.* Edw. III), with
occasional pen-wash drawings of the heads
of grantors and (fos. 14–22) red and blue
initials. Arranged roughly by grantors
(royal, 11th–14th cent., episcopal, private)
and gives only abstracts etc. of the less
important documents, duplicates etc.
Bound in an early 16th cent. stamped
binding (cf. No. 25) with statutes, 1445, of
Winchester Cath. Priory (fos. 1–9) and
Acts of the Provincial Chapter of the
Benedictine Order at Northampton, 1450
(fos. 10–13, paper).
    Fos. 98 (111 in the MS.). 13 × 9 in. *FO:*
Sir T. Phillipps, 1827 (MS. 3518); Sir L.
Harmsworth, 1919.
¶ *Other registers etc.*
25.   London, Lincoln's Inn, MS. 185.
Register of grants, leases etc. by the
priory, *c.* 1200–*temp.* Edw. III etc., incl.
copies of some royal writs and other misc.
material. Calendared by Hunt, *op. cit.*, pt.
ii. Stamped binding similar to that of No.
24.
26.   BM., Harley 3970. Register of
grants, leases etc. by the priory, *temp.* W.
Holleway, prior 1525–39. Hunt, *op. cit.*,
pp. lxxii–lxxiv.

27.   The Marquess of Bath, Longleat.
'The Red Book of Bath.' A misc. volume,
without charters. A. J. Horwood, *HMC.
Third Report* (1872), App., 182. *FO:* T.
Guidott.

BATTLE   co. Suss.
Ben Abbey   *f.* 1067
28.   London, Lincoln's Inn, MS. 87.
Gen. cartulary, 13th cent. (aft. 1234), with
rubrics etc. and red and green decorated
initials. Arranged topographically in sections by counties, with the copies of royal,
papal and episcopal etc. charters placed at
the beginning, and misc. 13th–14th cent.
additions (incl. a later 13th cent. Table, fos.
1–2) *passim* and on 28 added leaves of
smaller format at the end.
    Fos. 98 (numbered, 17th cent., 1–102;
wants 18, 39, 40, 63). 11¼ × 7¾ in. *FO:* Sir
M. Hale.
29.   San Marino, Huntington Libr.
(Battle Abbey Papers, vol. 29). Cartulary,
late 13th cent., with rubrics, in two parts:
(1) fos. 13 ff., with red and blue decorated
initials, copies of royal, papal and episcopal
charters down to 1286; (2) fos. 100 ff.,
without coloured initials, abstracts of deeds
arranged and numbered by places, with
numerous additions on blank and added
leaves *passim.* Each part is preceded by an
alphabetical Table in the hand of (2), and
the whole is corrected in a small 14th cent.
hand down to fo. 130. An 18th cent. transcript by D. Casley (formerly Phillipps MS.
9930, vol. 1) is *ib.*, vol. 31; and others by
W. Hayley, 1762, are in BM., Add. 6348,
fos. 2–83 and 6344, fos. 22–110. *Descriptive
Catalogue of the . . . Muniments of Battle
Abbey etc. on sale by Thomas Thorpe* (1835),
pp. 1–2.
    Fos. 246 (numbered, 1–219, from fo. 13).
10 × 7 in. *FO:* Anthony Browne, 1st
viscount Montagu and his successors; Sir
T. Webster, bart., and his successors; T.
Thorpe, bookseller, 1835; Sir T. Phillipps
(MS. 9928).
30.   R. G. H. M. Kirkwood Esq.,
Kidnams Farm, Whitminster. Two Quires
(*vii* and *viii*) of an early 15th cent. cartulary
containing copies of 107 private deeds etc.
rel. Cranbrook etc., co. Kent, with a few
misc. additions at the end. A typewritten
calendar is in National Register of Archives
Report No. 0651 (Kirkwood).

Fos. 26 (unnumbered). 11×8 in. *FO:* the Hendley and Kirkwood fams., Gore Court.

¶ *Sacristarius*

31. **San Marino, Huntington Libr.** (Battle Abbey Papers, vol. 30). Cartulary, 1408–10, of lands assigned to the sacrist, made by John Waller, sacrist. Written with red and blue initials, sometimes decorated, and some rubrication, and arranged topographically with later additions. An 18th cent. transcript by D. Cayley is *ib.,* vol. 32 (formerly Phillipps MS. 9930, vol. 2), of which an abstract by W. Hayley, 1762, is in BM. Add. 6348, fos. 84–165. Thorpe's *Descriptive Catalogue,* p. 2. *Mon. Angl.* iii, 236 (*t*), 'vol. ii'.

Pp. 270. $10\frac{1}{2} \times 7\frac{3}{4}$ in. *FO:* as No. 29 (Phillipps MS. 9929).

¶ *Other registers etc.*

32. **BM., Cotton Domit. A. ii,** fos. 8–130. 'Liber de situ ecclesie Belli et de possessionibus sibi a Rege Willo. et ab aliis quibuslibet datis.' A 13th cent. account in narrative form.

33. **BM., Campbell Ch. xvi, 11, 12.** Parts of two early 14th cent. rolls of deeds rel. Wye and Pluckley, co. Kent.

34. **BM., Harley 3586,** fos. 2–66. Misc. 14th cent. register, mainly of records of legal proceedings, forms of instruments, presentations to livings, manumissions and other *acta* of the abbey. *Mon. Angl.* iii, 237 (*a*).

35. **Wye College,** co. Kent (Muniments). Register, 16th cent., on paper, of pleas and abstracts of charters rel. the abbey's lands in Wye etc., made apparently after the Dissolution. *FO:* the earls of Winchilsea and Nottingham.

36. **PRO., Exch., Augm. Off.** (Misc. Bks. 18, 56, 57, 488). Misc. terriers, rentals, custumals etc., 13th–15th cent. *PRO. Deputy Keeper's Eighth Report,* App. ii, 139–46.

37. **Ditto** (Misc. Bk. 493). A small collection of original late 14th cent. final concords, notes of pleas, writs etc., bound as a volume.

BAYHAM co. Suss.
Praem. Abbey *f.* (from Brockley, *f.* bef. 1182, and Otham, *f.* 1180–7) 1199–1208

38. **BM., Cotton Otho A. ii.** Gen. cartulary, 13th cent. (*c.* 1245 ?), written in book-hand with rubrics etc. and occasional red initials. Arranged in sections mainly topographically (papal charters, fos. 6–9; royal and episcopal documents, fos. 48–51; compositions and fines, fos. 60–4; leases by the abbey, fos. 66 ff.) with numerous misc. additions at the beginning (fos. 1–5), end (fos. 68 ff.) and elsewhere *passim.* The whole severely damaged by fire, 1731, and the leaves now mounted. Extracts, 1627, for Sir E. Dering, are in BM., Stowe 924, fos. 48–87 and Add 6037, fos. 75–121; others, taken from these *c.* 1800, are in Cambridge U.L., Add. 4156.

Fos. 79 (originally 90; wants 1–8, 38, 40–1). $8\frac{1}{4} \times 5\frac{1}{2}$ in. (shrunk).

BEAUCHIEF co. Derby
Praem. Abbey *f.* 1173–6

39. **Aberystwyth, NLW., Gwysaney 15.** Gen. cartulary, early 15th cent., with rubrics, red initials etc. Contains copies of private deeds arranged mainly by grantors, one royal *Inspeximus* and, at the beginning, Pope Lucius III's privileges to the Praemonstratensian Order (1183). An 18th cent. transcript is in Coll. of Arms, S. Pegge's MS. Collections, vol. 8. Used by S. Pegge, *Hist Account of Beauchief Abbey* (1801), vii–x etc. Noticed by G. R. Potter (who has an edition in preparation), 'The Cartulary of Beauchief Abbey', *Derbyshire Arch. J.,* New ser. xii (1938), 160–2.

Fos. 114 (leaves excised aft. fos. 53, 83). $8\frac{7}{8} \times 5\frac{7}{8}$ in. *FO:* Robert Davies, 17th–18th cent.

BEAULIEU co. Southt.
Cist. Abbey *f.* (at Faringdon) 1203

40. **The Duke of Portland** (Welbeck MSS.), deposited in the British Museum (MSS. Loans No. 29/330). Gen. cartulary, 13th cent. (*temp.* Hen. III), with rubrics and in some sections red initials. Arranged in nine parts or sections (1, copies of seven royal charters; 2–9, each prefaced by a Table, topographical), with additions on blank and added leaves between the sections and at the end. Extracts, *c.* 1739, by the Rev. G. Harbin are in BM., Harley 6603, fos 128–201.

Fos. 158. $8\frac{1}{2} \times 6$ in. Trial signatures, 16th–17th cent., of Humfry English, Walter Venables and David Cotmore.

41. **BM., Cotton Nero A. xii,** fos. 1–154. Cartulary (fos. 5–80), mid-14th cent.,

with rubrics and red initials, of documents rel. the abbey's rights, privileges etc. in the manor of Faringdon and its members, incl. copies of royal, papal and other charters etc. Preceded (fos. 1–4) by a Table and followed (fos. 81–154) by a custumary. *Mon. Angl.* v, 681 (*h*) lists the contents.

Fos. 154. 5 × 3½ in.

BEAUVALE co. Nott.
Carthus. Priory *f.* 1343
42.　**BM., Add. 6060.** Gen. cartulary, *c.* 1486, with rubrics and elaborate uncompleted coloured initials, made by Prior N. Warter. Arranged in sections, each with its own Table or space left for one, mainly topographically (fos. 10–28, copies of the foundation, incl. some royal, charters; fos. 77v–91, 104–22, papal charters; fos. 92–103, appropriations etc. of churches, incl. episcopal charters; other royal charters *passim*). T. L. Cursham, *Gentleman's Magazine* lxxxiv (1) (1814), 108 (a note).

Fos. 122 (1–9, binding leaves). 12¼ × 8¾ in. Signature 'J. Watkinson', fo. 5v. Given to the Rev. T. L. Cursham by W. Stretton, 1814.

BEC, Abbey of in Normandy
v. OGBOURNE.

BELVOIR co. Linc.
Ben. Priory *f.* 1076–88
43.　**The Duke of Rutland,** Belvoir Castle (Add. MS. 98). Fragms. of a late 13th cent. cartulary with some rubricated headings, red initials and additions. Arranged topographically. Pp. 27–58 are noticed by J. H. Round, *HMC. Rutland* iv (1905), 173 ('Fragment of a Belvoir Cartulary'); the remainder, since added from 'drawer 6' (*ib.*, 92) etc., contains copies of deeds rel. Barkston, Stathern, Redmile, Granby, Tallington etc. with one or two papal charters and (pp. 63–77) a rental and other misc. material.

Fos. 26 (15th cent. pagination 27–46, 51–2, 57–8, 63–91, omitting 66). 11½ × 7½ in.
44.　**Ditto** (Add. MS. 105). Gen. cartulary, early 15th cent. (*temp.* Hen. IV), with large rubricated initials, some heraldic and other decoration, and misc. additions at the end (fos. 101 ff.). Arranged topographically in alphabetical order of places,

with copies of the general royal, papal, episcopal etc. charters grouped at the beginning, and of others under the appropriate topographical heads *passim*. Round, *op. cit.*, 105–71 (calendar).

Fos. 112. 19 × 14 in.

BERMONDSEY co. Surr.
Clun. Abbey *f.* (as a priory) 1089
45.　**Untraced.** Gen. cartulary made, 1363, by W. de Preston, from which extracts down to fo. 277 are in BM., Harley 4757, fos. 2–15 and Cotton Claud. A. viii, fos. 115–22. Owned, 16th cent., by Robert Trappis, lord of the manor of Bermondsey. Possibly identical with the volume listed, 1621, as MS. 231 in Sir Robert Cotton's library (BM., Harley 6018, fo. 104; cf. fo. 148, 'a long book old bound in folio') and subsequently, *c.* 1655, in that of John Selden (Bodl., Selden supra 111, fo. 7).
❡ *Other registers etc.*
46.　**BM., Harley 231.** Annals, 1042–1432. Ed. H. R. Luard, *Annales Monastici* iii (Rolls ser., 1866), 423–87. Extracts, 1648, are in Bodl., Dodsworth 55 (*SC.* 4197), fos. 97 ff. *FO:* Ld. Wm. Howard, 1590; Sir S. D'Ewes.

BEVERLEY co. York
Minster (Coll. Church) *f.* 7th cent.
47.　**Oxford, Univ. Coll. MS. 82,** deposited in the Bodleian Libr. Cartulary (of the vicars?), late 15th cent. (aft. 1462), with occasional elaborate pen-drawn initials (pp. 7, 18) and page-headings in black. Arranged: (1) Statutes etc., pp. 1–5; (2) general charters of liberties etc., pp. 7–24; (3) *Obitus et Compositiones*, pp. 33–56 (25–32, blank); (4) by places, pp. 57–134. A Table at p. 6 shows a number of sections containing custumaries, statutes, inventories and copies of other misc. documents to be wanting. H. O. Coxe, *Cat. MSS. Oxon.* i (Oxford, 1852), *ad loc.*, lists the contents.

Fos. 67 (paginated, 1–134). 13¾ × 10⅜ in.
48.　**Washington, Libr. of Congress, MS. Ac. 1093** (item 12 (F)). Cartulary, late 15th cent. (bef. 1478?), of the Rolleston chantry refounded, 1450, at the altar of St. Katherine by R. Rolleston, provost. Rubrics, red initials and some additions. Arranged mainly by properties, with a

preface and copy of the *ordinacio cantarie* at fos. IV–9, and a rental at fos. 77V–8. Medieval binding. A 19th cent. abstract is in BM., Add 24469, fos. 8–14.

Fos. 80. 11 × 7½ in. *FO:* the Rev. J. Coltman; Sir T. Phillipps (MS. 11915).

49. **H. L. Bradfer-Lawrence Esq.,** F.S.A., Sharow End, Ripon. Folcard's Life and Miracles of St. John of Beverley etc., followed (fos. 60 ff.) by copies of selected royal, papal and episcopal privileges to the Minster down to 1380, the earlier of which (fos. 60–9) are described as translations 'de anglico in latinum' made by Alveredus, sacrist. A late 14th cent. MS., written in double columns with illuminated initials etc. Medieval binding. Transcripts, 16th cent., are in BM., Harley 560 and Cotton Otho C. xvi, fos. 65–102. Sotheby's sale-cat., 6 Feb. 1861, lot 61 (description).

Fos. 90 (lacks a leaf at the beginning and four others at the end). 14⅝ × 10¼ in. *FO:* W. Wray, 1586; Sir John and (or) Sir Henry Savile, 16th–17th cent.; Sir T. Phillipps (MS. 23875).

¶ *Other registers etc.*

50. **London, Soc. of Antiquaries, MS. 81.** Chapter Act Book, 1286–1347. Ed. A. F. Leach, *Memorials of Beverley Minster,* 2 vols. (Surtees Soc. xcviii, cviii, 1898–1903). FO: J. Topham.

51. **Beverley Minster,** 'The Provost's Book'. Rental of the provostry, 1417, with copies of court-rolls and other misc. documents, incl. a few charters, rel. the rights etc. of the same. Leach, *op. cit.* ii, 305–39. Extracts are in Bodl., Dodsworth 26 (*SC.* 4168), fos. 103–45.

52. **BM., Harley 4292.** Sanctuary Book, 1478–1540 etc. Ed. J. Raine, *Sanctuarium Dunelmense et . . . Beverlacense* (Surtees Soc. v, 1837).

BICKNACRE (*al.* **WOODHAM FERRERS**) co. Essex
Aug. Priory *f.* 1175

53. **Untraced.** 'Cartularium . . . penes dominum Barrington, 1723' (*T*), i.e. John, 1st viscount Barrington, d. 1734.

BIDDLESDEN co. Bucks.
Cist. Abbey *f.* 1147

54. **BM., Harley 4714.** Gen. cartulary, 16th cent. (*temp.* Hen. VIII), with bold titles in black, uncompleted red page-

headings and red, blue and green decorated initials etc. Contains copies of deeds (incl. royal, episcopal etc. charters) arranged and numbered topographically in sections, with two or three additions at the end (fos. 353 ff.). *Mon. Angl.* v, 365 (*γ*) lists the places etc.

Fos. 363. 15½ × 11½ in. *FO:* George Villiers, 2nd duke of Buckingham, 1640 (*D*).

BILLESWICK co. Brist.
v. BRISTOL.

BILSINGTON co. Kent
Aug. Priory *f.* 1253

55. **BM., Add. 37018.** Gen. cartulary (fos. 1–41), *c.* 1300, with red paragraphs etc. and a few additions at the end (fos. 35V ff.). Contains copies and abstracts of charters (the royal, papal, episcopal and baronial material being grouped mainly towards the beginning), and is followed (fos. 42–78) by a 15th cent. survey and rental etc. Ed. N. Neilson, *The Cartulary & Terrier of . . . Bilsington, Kent* (1928).

Fos. 78. 10¼ × 6½ in. Descended with the manor of Bilsington to the Halliday fam., Linton.

BINHAM co. Norf.
Ben. Priory *f.* bef. 1093

56. **BM., Cotton Claud. D. xiii.** Gen. register of evidences, mid-14th cent., with rubrics, red initials etc. and occasional additions *passim* and at the end (fos. 194V ff.). Contains copies of deeds, rentals, surveys and other material, arranged mainly topographically with sections of papal, royal and episcopal charters at fos. 26–48, after that for Binham. An 18th cent. transcript is in the possession of the Earl of Dalhousie, Brechin Castle. *Mon. Angl.* iii, 343 (*k*) (partial list of contents).

Fos. 208. 12 × 8¼ in. *FO:* the Paston fam., *c.* 1627–8? (Bodl., James 23 (*SC.* 3860), p. 104); R. Dodsworth (*D*); Sir T. Widdrington (*D*); Sir J. Legard, bart.

BLACKBOROUGH co. Norf.
Ben. Priory (Nuns) *f.* (for monks) 1150

57. **BM., Egerton 3137.** Gen. cartulary, late 14th cent. (aft. 1370). Contains copies of deeds arranged and numbered topo-

graphically in sections with a contemp. Table at fos. 7–29v and copies of a few royal, episcopal etc. charters included *passim*. Extracts, 18th cent., are in Bodl., Gough Norf. 24 (*SC.* 18079), fos. 10–48 (*FO:* T. Martin). A 20th cent. transcript and photostats are with the Norfolk & Norwich Arch. Soc. *Mon. Angl.* iv, 205 (*o*) lists the places etc. A. J. Collins, 'The Blackborough Chartulary and the Library of Sir Henry Spelman', *Brit. Mus. Quart.* xi (1936–7), 63–5, describes the history of the MS.

Fos. iv + 222 (contemp. roman foliation by sections). 13¼ × 9⅜ in. *FO:* Sir H. Spelman, 1594; Charles Spelman; Cox Macro; Hudson Gurney.

BLYTH co. Nott.
Ben. Priory *f.* 1088
58. **BM., Harley 3759.** Cartulary (fos. 52 ff.), late 13th cent. (*c.* 1285?), with rubrics etc., containing copies of private and other deeds, incl. four royal writs, episcopal charters etc. Contemp. Table, fos. 47–50. Continued (fos. 123v ff.) in a succession of contemp. and later 13th–14th cent. hands and preceded (fos. 1–46) by added rentals and memoranda, incl. copies of a few further deeds. *Mon. Angl.* iv, 622 (*a*) (partial list of contents).

Fos. 153. 11 × 7½ in. *FO:* Sir Gervase Clifton, bart.
59. **Untraced.** Roll *penes* Wm. Saunderson of Blyth, 1629, containing copies of 219 charters, some of them royal. Extracts are in Bodl., Dodsworth 152 (*SC.* 5093), fos. 128–43 and 155 (*SC.* 5096), fo. 139; BM., Lansdowne 326, fo. 85v.

BLYTHBURGH co. Suff.
Aug. Priory *f.* bef. 1135
60. **BM., Add. 40725.** Gen. cartulary, late 14th cent., with red initials and occasional additions *passim*. Arranged topographically in rough alphabetical order of places, with the royal, papal and episcopal charters etc. entered under the appropriate topographical heads. H. C. Maxwell Lyte, *HMC. Tenth Report*, App. iv (1885), 451–7 (abstract). *BM.Cat. Add. MSS.* 1921–1925, 144–5 (description).

Fos. i + 60. 10½ × 7⅞ in. *FO:* the Rev. T. Smythe Hill, 1885; F. A. Crisp.

BOLTON co. York
Aug. Priory *f.* (at Embsay) 1120
61. **Untraced.** Cartulary *penes* Wm. Ingilby of Ripley, 1638. Extracts down to fo. 162 in Bodl., Dodsworth 144 (*SC.* 5085), fos. 1–77, suggest a topographical arrangement. The material copied is mainly 12th–13th cent. but includes one charter of *temp.* Hen. VI.

BOSTON co. Linc.
Fraternity or Guild of Corpus Christi
f. 1335
No cartulary recorded.
Other registers etc.
62. **BM., Harley 4795.** Register of admissions, obits etc., 15th cent., with additions to 1543.

BOXGROVE co. Suss.
Ben. Priory *f.* aft. 1105
63. **BM., Cotton Claud. A. vi,** fos. 4–155. Gen. cartulary, 13th cent. (aft. 1235), with uncompleted red initials and numeration of the entries. Arranged in two parts: (1) fos. 19 ff., charters of the founder and his descendants (De la Haye, St. John), imperf. at the beginning; (2) fos. 49 ff., other (incl. episcopal etc.) charters, arranged by grantors. Misc. additions at the end of each section and *passim* include a later 13th cent. Table (fos. 14–16, 18v, partly duplicated at fo. 1), a rental of 1253 (fos. 5–13), a section of grants, leases etc. by the priory (fos. 139–55), and copies of one or two royal charters. *Mon. Angl.* iv, 643 (*c*) (partial list of contents).

Fos. 152 (17th cent. foliation, 1–150). 9¾ × 6 in.

BOXLEY co. Kent
Cist. Abbey *f.* 1143
No cartulary recorded.
Inventories
64. **PRO., Exch., K.R.** (Eccl. Docs., E.135/22/13). Inventories, mid-14th cent., of charters rel. the abbey's possessions in various places.

Roll of 2 membrs. 22½ × 7¾ in. (imperf.).

BRACKLEY co. Northt.
Hosp. of SS. James & John *f. c.* 1150
65. **Oxford, Magdalen Coll., MS. Lat. 273** (formerly Muniments, Arch. C. ii. 3. 11). Gen. cartulary, late 13th cent. (*temp.*

Edw. I), with uncompleted rubrication etc. Arranged apparently by grantors with the copies of papal, episcopal etc. charters at the beginning. Lacks at least one quire at the end.

Fos. 84. $9\frac{1}{8} \times 6\frac{3}{4}$ in.

BRADENSTOKE   co. Wilts
Aug. Priory   *f.* bef. 1140
66.   **BM., Cotton Vit. A. xi,** fos. 38–208. Gen. cartulary written in a series of 14th cent. hands (*temp.* Edw. III ?). Arranged mainly topographically, with copies of royal charters, charters of the earls of Salisbury, and fines, at the end (fos. 189 ff.); of *Munimenta ecclesiarum,* incl. papal and episcopal charters, at fos. 142–8; and of other episcopal charters *passim. Mon. Angl.* vi, 337 (*i*), lists the places.

Fos. 171 (imperf. at the beginning). $8\frac{3}{4} \times 6\frac{1}{2}$ in. (damaged by fire, 1731, and the leaves now mounted).
67.   **BM., Stowe 925.** Gen. cartulary written, 14th–15th cent., by brother 'T. de M.', apparently as a revision of No. 66, than the latter part of which it is only slightly, if at all, later. Red and blue initials, numeration of the entries etc. Arranged mainly topographically, by counties, in 106 numbered sections (*i Munimenta ecclesiarum,* incl. copies of papal, episcopal etc. charters; *ciiii* fines, *cv* royal, *cvi* earls of Salisbury), with a contemp. Table at fos. 2–24, a *taxatio* at fos. 24v–25 and misc. additions (fos. 182 ff.). *BM. Cat. Stowe MSS.* i, 611 (description).

Fos. 195. $12\frac{1}{2} \times 8\frac{1}{4}$ in. *FO:* T. Astle.

BRADSOLE   co. Kent
v. ST. RADEGUND'S.

BRADWELL   co. Bucks.
Ben. Priory   *f. c.* 1155
68.   **PRO., Special Collections** (Rentals & Surveys, SC. 11/75). Abstracts, 16th cent., made perhaps at the priory's dissolution, of 86 original charters and a number of others 'per regestrum cuiusdam libri in papiro conscriptum', with copies of rentals, *temp.* Hen. VI, etc.

Roll of 7 membrs. *c.* 16 ft. × $10\frac{1}{2}$ in.

BRECON   co. Brecon
Ben. Priory   *f. c.* 1110
R. W. Banks, 'Cartularium Prioratus S. Johannis Evang. de Brecon', *Arch. Cam-*

brensis, Fourth ser. xiii (1882), 275-308 & xiv (1883), 18-311 *passim,* prints 18th cent. copies of charters, from an unspecified source, in Bodl. Carte 108 (*SC.* 10853).
69.   **Untraced.** 'Liber Prioratus' *penes* Evan Seys, late 17th cent. Extracts down to fo. 107 by M. Hutton are in BM., Harley 6976, fos. 6–26 and others are in BM., Lansdowne 958, fos. 141–3.
70.   **Untraced.** 'Registrum antiquum . . . MS. penes Gulielmum Brewster M.D. Herefordiae', d. 1715 (*T*). Perhaps identical with No. 69.

BREEDON   co. Leic.
Aug. Priory   *f.* bef. 1122
71.   **Manchester, Rylands Libr., Lat. MS. 222.** Cartulary (fos. 28–70), 13th cent., with rubrics etc. and a contemp. index at fos. 17–25v *passim.* Preceded and followed by misc. additions, which have also been made on blank leaves etc. throughout, and incl. copies of a few royal charters. Fos. 5–16, misbound, should follow fo. 27. J. Nichols, *Hist. Leicester* iii, pt. 2 (1804), 695–701, prints an almost complete analysis. An unpublished edition by R. A. McKinley (M.A. thesis, 1950) is in Manchester U.L.

Fos. iv + 77 (13th cent. foliation, i–xlviii, of fos. 28–70). $11\frac{5}{8} \times 8\frac{1}{2}$ in. *FO:* the Shirley fam., barts. and earls Ferrers; Sir T. Phillipps (MS. 21710).

BRETTON, MONK   co. York
v. MONK BRETTON.

BRICETT   co. Suff.
Aug. Priory   *f.* 1114–19
72.   **Cambridge, King's Coll.,** Muniments (B. 121). Copies, 13th cent. (aft. 1243), of about 65 private deeds, arranged roughly topographically with a few additions of *temp.* Edw. I.

Roll of 3 membrs. (apparently lacks a 4th at the head). *c.* 70 × 10 in.

BRIDLINGTON   co. York
Aug. Priory   *f.* bef. 1113–14
73.   **BM., Add. 40008.** Gen. cartulary, early 14th cent., written in book-hand, in double columns, with rubrics, red and blue initials etc. Arranged mainly topographically (fos. 159v–62, *Confirmaciones* (earls of Lincoln and royal); 163, *Libertates* (royal); 323v–7, *Confirmaciones ecclesiarum* (episcopal etc.); 328–31, *Privilegia* (papal etc.)),

with a contemp. index at fo. 2v, followed by copies of three charters of *Inspeximus* of Edward II, and additions on blank leaves etc. *passim*. W. T. Lancaster, *Chartulary of . . . Bridlington* (Leeds, 1912), prints an abstract. *BM. Cat. Add. MSS.* 1916–1920, 285–6.

Fos. iv + 355. 15 × 9¼ in. Annotated by R. Gascoigne (d. 1663), antiquary. *FO:* Sir J. Bellingham, 1627 (?) ; the Ingilby fam., Ripley, bef. 1719.

74. **Untraced.** Cartulary *penes* Sir R. Mauleverer, 2nd bart. (d. 1675), of Allerton Mauleverer (*D*).

75. **Untraced.** 'Registrum penes Walterum Clavell arm', early 18th cent. (*T*).

BRINKBURN   co. Northumb.
Aug. Priory   *f. c.* 1135
76.   **BM., Stowe 926.** Gen. cartulary, 14th cent. (aft. 1349), with rubrics and blue initials etc. decorated with red. Arranged in eight *Capitula*, apparently by grantors (*viii* royal, *vii* incl. a few episcopal charters). Additions, fos. 93v ff., include copies of two papal charters. Fos. 3–5, 103–6 (fly-leaves) contain an 18th cent. Table. Ed. Wm. Page, *The Chartulary of Brinkburn Priory* (Surtees Soc. xc for 1892, 1893). *BM. Cat. Stowe MSS.* i, 611–12.

Fos. 106 (incl. 11 insertions; wants the first leaf of the text and several others aft. fo. 78). 8¼ × 5 in. *FO:* Ld. Wm. Howard, 1630 (*D*); T. Astle.

BRISTOL   co. Brist.
Aug. Abbey of St. Augustine   *f.* 1142
77.   **Trustees of the Berkeley Estates,** Berkeley Castle (Muniments). Gen. cartulary, late 13th cent., with red, blue or green initials, sometimes decorated, and partial rubrication. Arranged mainly topographically in sections (fos. 17–43, by grantors incl. copies of royal charters), with additions at the beginning (fos. 1–16) and *passim*. A. J. Horwood, *HMC. Fourth Report* (1874), App., 364–5 (description).

Fos. ii + 221. 9⅝ × 6¾ in. *FO:* the Berkeley fam., barons and earls of Berkeley, baron Segrave, earl and barons Fitzhardinge.

BRISTOL   co. Brist.
St. Mark's *al.* Gaunt's Hosp., Billeswick   *f.* bef. 1229
78.   **Bristol R.O.** Gen. cartulary, late

3—M.C.

15th cent., with red and blue decorated initials and some additions. Arranged mainly topographically with a section of general, incl. royal, episcopal etc., charters at the beginning (fos. 1–38). Transcripts, 18th cent., are in Bodl., Top. Glouc. c. 9 and Taunton, Somerset Arch. Soc. Libr. (Braikenbridge Collections). A 20th cent. transcript taken from the latter is in Gloucester Public Libr. (Hockaday Abstracts). W. Barrett, *Hist. Bristol* (Bristol, 1789), 358 ff. prints a partial calendar. An edition for the Bristol Record Soc. is in preparation. Wm. H. Robinson Ltd., *Catalogue No.* 81 (1950), item 52 (plate).

Fos. 240. 11 × 8 in. *FO:* R. Haynes; Sir T. Phillipps (MS. 1084).

BROMHOLM   co. Norf.
Clun. Priory   *f. c.* 1113
79.   **Cambridge U.L., Mm. 2. 20.** Gen. cartulary, 14th cent. (aft. 1344), with uncompleted rubrication, some pen-work decoration of capitals and a few 15th cent. additions at the end. Arranged roughly topographically, with the copies of royal and papal charters grouped at the beginning. *Cambr. U.L. Cat. MSS.* iv, 144–73, lists the contents.

Fos. 91. 14 × 9 in. *FO:* Bp. J. Moore.

80.   **Untraced.** 'Leiger-book' (?) *penes* Mr. Paston of Pauntley, co. Glouc., 8 Feb. 1727, from which an extract rel. the Paston fam. is printed by T. Hearne, *A. de Domerham* (Oxford, 1727), lviii; cf. *Mon. Angl.* v, 62. Hearne's diary, however, leaves room for doubt as to the precise nature of his source, cf. H. E. Salter, *Remarks and Collections of Thomas Hearne* ix (Oxford Hist. Soc. lxv, 1914), 267–9.

BROOKE   co. Rutl.
Aug. Priory   *f.* bef. 1153
81.   **PRO., Exch., K.R.** (Eccl. Docs., E.135/2/9). Bifolium (non-consecutive leaves) from a 15th–16th cent. cartulary, with marginal titles and headings. Contains copies of about 12 undated private deeds rel. Belton and Martinsthorpe, co. Rutl., of which two, for the latter, concern grants to the sacrist.

Fos. 2. 11¾ × 8¼ in.

BRUISYARD   co. Suff.
Franciscan Abbey (Nuns)   *f.* 1364–7
82.   **Untraced.** 'A chartulary of this

abbey, in English, for the use of the lady abbess and sisters, MS. in folio, in the library of Sir John Rous bart. of Henham hall in Suffolk' (*T*). Reported still to be at Henham Hall, 1836 (*P*). Not known to the 4th earl of Stradbroke, 1954, nor traced among books deposited by him at Ham House.

BRUTON co. Som.
Aug. Priory and (1511) Abbey *f. c.* 1142
83.   **The Earl of Ilchester**, Melbury. The latter part of a late 13th cent. gen. cartulary (*temp.* Edw. I), with rubrics and red and blue paragraphs against each entry. Arranged topographically with copies of royal, papal and episcopal charters included *passim* and additions, 14th–15th cent., at fos. 102–3, 116–29 etc. Inserted at the beginning is a transcript, 1840, of the Rev. G. Harbin's extracts, 1719, from the first part of the volume, which was then still present (Phillipps MS. 4808: owned, 1957, by David Rogers Esq., c/o the Bodleian Library, Oxford). Medieval binding. Calendared in *Two Cartularies of . . . Bruton and . . . Montacute*, ed. members of the Council (Somerset Record Soc. viii, 1894), 1–104 etc.
Fos. ii + 59 (numbered 73–129). $11\frac{5}{8} \times 7\frac{1}{2}$ in. *FO:* Ld. Berkeley of Stratton, 1719; the Earls of Ilchester, bef. 1839.

BUCKENHAM co. Norf.
Aug. Priory *f. c.* 1146
No cartulary recorded.
❡ *Other registers etc.*
84.   **Untraced.** Register, late 15th cent. (*temp.* Edw. IV), listed as no. 4466 in the sale-cat. (1773) of T. Martin of Palgrave. Perhaps identical with the 'Compotus Prioratus de Bokenham' listed as Folio MS. 243 in the earlier sale-cat. of his MSS. (Lynn, 1772).

BUCKFAST co. Devon
Cist. Abbey *f.* 1136
85.   **Buckfast Abbey Libr.** Leaves from an early 14th cent. cartulary (aft. 1313), with a few additions, incl. perambulations of Dartmoor etc., at the end. Contains copies of about 60 charters arranged and numbered topographically, each leaf being headed in red *Tertia Pars*. The material relates to Buckfastleigh, Hone and

vicinity. Ed., with a facsimile page, F. C. Hingeston-Randolph, *Reg. J. de Grandisson, Bishop of Exeter* pt. iii (1899), 1563–1610.
Fos. 23 (contemp. foliation, iii–vi, ix–xxiiii, cxlii–cxliiii; later foliation, 61–4, 67–84 etc.). $10\frac{1}{4} \times 7\frac{1}{4}$ in. *FO:* Mr. Winslow Jones, *c.* 1890 (from Pearse, waste-paper merchant, Exeter); acquired, again from Pearse, 1932.
❡ *Other registers etc.*
86.   **BM., Add. 37640.** Extracts, 17th cent., from a leiger-book of the abbey and other sources rel. the manors of South Brent and Churchstow (grants by the abbots etc., 1240–1402; court-rolls, 1331–1607). *FO:* the Elliott fam., South Brent.

BUCKLAND co. Som.
Preceptory & Nunnery of the Order of St. John *f.* (for Aug. canons) *c.* 1166
v. also ST. JOHN OF JERUSALEM.
87.   **Taunton, Somerset Arch. Soc. Libr.** Gen. cartulary, mid-15th cent. (aft. 1423), with uncompleted rubrication. Arranged mainly topographically and incl. copies of a few royal, papal and episcopal charters *passim*. Calendared by F. W. Weaver, *Cartulary of Buckland Priory* (Somerset Record Soc. xxv, 1909), who describes the medieval binding, p. xvii.
Fos. 78 (perhaps lacking a few leaves at the beginning and end). $16 \times 11\frac{1}{4}$ in. *FO:* J. Brooking-Rowe.

BULLINGTON co. Linc.
Gilb. Priory *f.* 1148–54
88.   **Untraced.** Cartulary, lacking fos. 13–14, *penes* R. Metham Esq. of Bullington, 1642. The foundation charter is copied in Bodl., Dodsworth 95 (*SC.* 5036), fo. 91.

BURSCOUGH co. Lanc.
Aug. Priory *f. c.* 1190
89.   **PRO., Duchy of Lanc.** (Misc. Bks. 6). Gen. cartulary, late 14th cent. (*c.* 1390–1400), arranged in two parts: (1) fos. 1–62, with rubrics and red initials, copies of private and a few monastic charters arranged topographically in sections (*Registra*); (2) fos. 63–110, copies of papal, ecclesiastical etc. charters. Added memoranda at the end include a 15th–16th

cent. note of 13 royal charters *cum sigillis largis* and 3 papal bulls not copied elsewhere in the volume.

Fos. 6 + 110 (numbered) + 4. $9\frac{1}{8} \times 6\frac{1}{4}$ in.

BURTON LAZARS   co. Leic.
Hosp. of the BVM & St. Lazarus
                   f. 1138–62
v. also HOLBORN.
90.   **BM., Cotton Nero C. xii,** fos. 2–119. Gen. cartulary, 1404, made for W. de Lynton, master. Arranged topographically in sections, with a few later additions, and incl. copies of occasional royal and papal charters *passim*. Extracts, 1644, are in BM., Lansdowne 207E, fos. 69–74. J. Nichols, *Hist. Leicester* ii, pt. 1 (1795), 273–5 and App., 128–32, notices the contents etc.

Fos. 118 (post-medieval pagination, 1–250; lacks a leaf aft. fo. 99). $12\frac{1}{2} \times 8\frac{1}{2}$ in. *FO:* Christopher, baron Hatton, 1644; Sir Wm. Dugdale (?).

BURTON-UPON-TRENT   co. Staff.
Ben. Abbey   f. 1002–4
91.   **The Marquess of Anglesey,** deposited in the British Museum (MSS. Loans No. 30). Gen. cartulary, 13th cent. (c. 1230–41) with additions. The original compilation (fos. 8–73 *passim*), written in double columns with rubrics and red, blue or occasionally green initials etc., is arranged in sections partly according to the status of grantors (foundation and royal; papal, episcopal and capitular; knights and free tenants, chronologically by abbots) and partly (fos. 49 ff.) according to types of document (*Carte Sigillate*, final concords). Additions and insertions, mainly 13th–14th cent., between the sections *passim* and at the end, include (all 13th cent.): (*a*) two Tables, fos. 1–7; (*b*) a Survey of the abbey's lands *temp.* Hen. I, fos. 28–36; (*c*) a supplement of material *temp.* L. de St. Edward, abbot 1229–60, partly duplicating material entered elsewhere and preceded by an uncompleted Table, fos. 75–97. Late medieval binding. G. Wrottesley, 'The Burton Chartulary', Wm. Salt Arch. Soc., *Coll. Hist. Staffordshire* v, pt. 1 (1884), 1–101 (abstract).

Fos. ii + 157 (13th–14th cent. foliation, i–lxxxvii from fo. 8, supplemented by a 15th cent. numeration of leaves subsequently added). $11 \times 7\frac{3}{4}$ in.

92.   **The Marquess of Anglesey,** deposited in Burton-upon-Trent Museum and Art Gallery. Part of a gen. (?) cartulary, 13th cent. (aft. 1262), written in double columns in a hand somewhat similar to that of the Survey inserted in No. 91, with red initials, uncompleted rubrics etc. and some additions *passim*. Arranged in sections, partly according to the status of grantors (royal, earls, archdeacons) and partly according to types of document (ordinations and compositions, incl. some episcopal charters; assignments of revenues by the abbot to the *Coquina, Camera* etc.; *Carte Sigillate*, arranged topographically). Includes material not entered in No. 91.

Fos. 42 (later medieval foliation, 12–54, 57; lacks material at the beginning and end). $10\frac{1}{2} \times 7\frac{1}{2}$ in.

¶ *Other registers etc.*
93.   **Aberystwyth, NLW., Peniarth 390.** Treatises on dictamen, Glanville 'de legibus Angliae' etc., with misc. formulary and other material, 13th–14th cent., incl. copies of Anglo-Saxon and other charters etc. to Burton Abbey. A. J. Horwood, *HMC. Second Report* (1871), App., 105. Used by W. de G. Birch, *Cartularium Saxonicum*, 3 vols. (1885–93). *FO:* R. Vaughan (Hengwrt MS. 150); the Wynne fam., Peniarth, 1859.
94.   **Lord Middleton,** deposited in Nottingham U.L. Register compiled, 1474–92, by Abbot T. Field, containing copies of inquisitions rel. tithes etc. and of some other misc. documents, 15th cent. etc. W. H. Stevenson, *HMC. Middleton MSS.* (1911), xii, 247–68 (calendar).

BURY ST. EDMUNDS   co. Suff.
Ben. Abbey   f. 1020
For accounts of the abbey's registers see *Mon. Angl.* iii, 117–31; M. R. James, *On the Abbey of St. Edmund at Bury* (Cambr. Antiq. Soc., 1895), 95–9 and *Engl. Hist. Rev.* xli (1926), 259–60; D. C. Douglas, *Feudal Documents from the Abbey of Bury St. Edmunds* (London, 1932), xix–xxvii, who also prints a number of 11th and 12th cent. charters. Extracts, 17th cent., by Sir Simonds D'Ewes (who is cited below as *D'E*) are in BM., Harley 294, 298, 312, 639.
95.   **BM., Harley 230,** fos. 176–87. Quire from a 13th cent. cartulary, with

rubrics, containing copies of fines, *temp.* John–Hen. III, followed by misc. additions, incl. lists of lands etc., in a number of contemp. or slightly later hands. At the foot of the first leaf a later hand has written 'Quaternus inventus per Rog(eru)m (?) de Hunt pertinens Abbath(ie) '. Bound at the end of the 'Reg. T. de Totingtone' (fos. 191), a composite register of documents and other misc. material rel. the abbacies of T. de Totington, 1301–12, and R. de Draughton, 1312–35, incl. (fos. 8–53) a formulary. *Mon. Angl.* iii, 118 (*a*).

Fos. 12 (Medieval foliation, 148–59). 9 × 7 in. *FO:* Sir E. Peyton (?) (*T*).

96.   **BM., Add. 14847.** 'Reg. Album', compiled apparently *temp.* J. de Northwold, abbot 1279–1301, with additions mainly of *temp.* Edw. I down to the 15th cent. Written in a rather square, heavy hand with red initials, rubrics, paragraphs and underlinings, and contains copies of papal bulls (fos. 3–14, 84–6 etc.) and royal charters (fos. 27–53), both from the earliest times; an account of Anglo-Saxon benefactions to the abbey, incl. texts of some wills and further royal charters (fos. 15–20v); an inventory of deeds headed 'Haec sunt . . . carte quae continentur in Registro quod Willus (de Hoo ?) sacrista fecit scribi et in registro quondam Willi de Beccles (see No. 108 below) et in veteri registro posito in vestiario' (fos. 21v–25); and copies of other misc. charters, lists of fees, pleas, manumissions etc., mainly *temp.* J. de Northwold. Much of the material is repeated in No. 117. W. Holtzmann, *Papsturkunden in England* i (Göttingen, 1936), 160–1, lists the bulls.

Fos. 96. 14¼ × 9 in. *FO:* R. B(acon), 16th cent.; Sir E. Bacon, 1633 (*D' E*); Sir E. Bacon, 1725; bought of E. Wodehouse, 1844.

97.   **BM., Harley 743.** 'Reg. J. de Lakynghethe' (d. 1381), 14th cent. (*temp.* Edw. III). Written mainly as a single compilation in sections, of which some have red headings etc., and contains a misc. collection of evidences formed to make good the destruction, 1327, of the abbots' registers 'praedonibus et igne', see fo. 3v. They consist mainly of terriers, lists of fees, extracts from official records etc., but include: (*a*) a list, in alphabetical order of places and subjects, of evidences to be found in other registers, fos. 4–51; (*b*) copies of some royal charters, 11th cent.— *temp.* Edw. III, fos. 54–74; (*c*) fines rel. fees, 8–9 Ric. I, fos. 133–9. *Mon. Angl.* iii, 121 (*a*).

Fos. 280. 12½ × 8 in. *FO:* Sir E. Bacon, 1645 (*D' E*); Bp. E. Stillingfleet (*T*).

98.   **Bury St. Edmunds, Bury & W. Suffolk R.O.** (ETI/2/1/1). Copies, 14th cent. (*temp.* Edw. III), of royal and papal charters to the Liberty of St. Edmund.

Roll of 3 membrs. 84 × 7 in. Presented, 1952, by the Marchioness of Bristol.

99–104.   A SERIES OF 15TH CENT. REGISTERS of the evidences of single manors, made *temp.* Abbot Curteys (1429–46). The first page of each has a pen-decorated initial and sometimes a border, occasionally with colour wash, see the facsimile in J. L. Fisher, 'The Harlow Cartulary', *Trans. Essex Arch. Soc.* xxii (1939), 239–70. Other capitals are sometimes touched with yellow. Each contains copies of the relevant charters (incl. royal and papal privileges), extents, rentals etc., opening with the phrase '(Culford) contulit Sco. Edmundo (Thirketel Dreing inclitus)'. 16 × 10½ in. etc. As follows:—

99.   **Oxford, Bodl., Gough Suff. 23** (*SC.* 18232). Coney Weston. Lacks the preliminary charter material. Fos. 62.

100.   **BM., Add. 42055.** Culford. *BM. Cat. Add. MSS.* 1926–1930, *ad loc.* (description). Fos. 56.

101.   **BM., Add. 34689.** Fornham. Fos. 54. *FO:* J. White, 1851; bought of E. Peacock, 1894.

102.   **Cambridge U.L., Add. 6874.** Harlow. J. L. Fisher, *l.c.*, describes and summarises the contents. Fos. 83 (incomplete at the end). *FO:* R. B. Wheler; Sir T. Phillipps (MS. 23628).

103.   **BM., Add. 45951.** Palgrave. Fos. 58. Presented, 1944, by E. C. Baynham.

104.   **BM., Add. 14850.** Redgrave, Wortham etc., fos. 1–84; Rickinghall, fos. 85–143. A note written with his foot by Christopher Wells, 1559, on the front flyleaf. *FO:* Sir N. Bacon, 1572; bought of E. Wodehouse, 1844.

¶ *Inventories*

105.   **BM., Harley 1005,** fos. 223–72. Inventory or syllabus of charters, mid-13th cent., arranged under the headings *Regum, Privilegia, Celeraria, Sacristia, de Camera,*

Elemosinar., *de Hospitali*, *Pitanciaria*, *de Domo Hospitum*, *de Infirmaria*, *Abbatia*, with numbered topographical subdivisions. Written with red initials etc. on quires numbered *i–viii* and bound with misc. rentals, notes of tithes etc. and (fos. 127–92) the chronicle of Jocelin de Brakelond, in a register known as the 'Liber Albus'. *Mon. Angl.* iii, 122 (*a*).

Fos. 50 (281 in the MS.). 9 × 5½ in. *FO:* Sir E. Bacon, 1633 (*P*); Bp. E. Stillingfleet (*T*).

106.   **BM., Harley 638**, fos. 119–38. Inventory, *c.* 1260, similar in arrangement to the preceding, written in double columns (fos. 119–20 in three columns) with spaces for initials and occasional red headings. Incorporated in a composite register of pleas, surveys, misc. charters (royal licences to alienate, grants by the abbots etc.) and other 13th–15th cent. documents, which was perhaps put together in the 15th cent., when the Table (fos. 3–12) was made, being subsequently entitled 'Reg. Werketone' (*D'E*). *Mon. Angl.* iii, 119 (*a*).

Fos. 20 (270 in the MS.). 12½ × 9½ in. *FO:* J. Mallowes, 1635 (*D'E*); Sir S. D'Ewes.

107.   **Destroyed.** 'Index imperfectus chartarum de terris', contained in the former Cotton MS. Vit. D. xv, art. 3, which was burnt in 1731. T. Smith, *Cat. Bibl. Cotton.* (Oxford, 1696), *ad loc.*

¶ *Cellerarius*

108.   **PRO., Duchy of Lanc.** (Misc. Bks. 5). Cartulary of the cellarer's lands begun 1265–6, *temp.* H. de Hospitali and W. de Beccles, cellarers. The original compilation (fos. 10–96), written in double columns with uncompleted rubrication and spaces for initials, and arranged topographically, is augmented by numerous misc. additions (pleas, rentals etc.) *passim*, down to *temp.* Edw. III.

Fos. iii + 149 (later medieval foliation, with many unnumbered insertions). 13¼ × 8⅝ in. *FO:* 'Mr. Stywarde' (Augustine Steward?), 1543; 'L.W.', 1588.

109.   **Cambridge U.L., Gg. 4. 4.** Vol. i of a 15th cent. register of evidences rel. the cellarer's lands (*temp.* Abbot Curteys (?), 1429–46), written in double columns with decorated initials and paragraphs (red and blue in some sections, touched with red and yellow in others), and arranged in

rough alphabetical order of places. Contains copies of charters, rentals, extents etc. for Barton Magna–Dunwich, incl. some royal and papal documents. Wants sections *passim*. *Cambr. U.L. Cat. MSS.* iii, 88–144, lists the contents.

Fos. 302 (contemp. foliation, up to 416). 13½ × 10 in. *FO:* J. Cradock; Bp. J. Moore.

110.   **Cambridge U.L., Add. 4220.** Vol. ii (cf. No. 109). Similar material for Hilgay–Wainfleet. Wants sections *passim*, cf. Nos. 111–13. A. J. Horwood. *HMC. Third Report* (1872), App., 240.

Fos. 196 (contemp. foliation, up to 523). 13½ × 9 in. *FO:* Sir T. Hanmer (*P*); Sir H. Bunbury, bart., 1832 (*P*).

111.   **BM., Add. 31970**, fos. 1–69. Detached sections of No. 110 (fos. 193–254, 278–89, in the medieval foliation). Material for Hinderclay and Rickinghall.

Fos. 69. 13½ × 9¼ in. Purchased of J. J. Johnson, 1882.

112.   **BM., Add. 36910.** A further detached section from No. 110 (fos. 404–45 in the medieval foliation). Material for Southery.

Fos. 42. 13½ × 9¾ in. *FO:* the Aston fam., Aston Hall.

113.   **Untraced.** A further detached section from No. 110 (fos. 486–513 in the medieval foliation). Material for Whepstead.

Fos. 27 (?). (*c.* 13½ × 9½ in.). *FO:* C. Ord; Sir T. Phillipps (MS. 3794).

¶ *Hostilarius*

114.   **BM., Cotton Claud. A. xii**, fos. 84–195. 'Reg. Hostilarie . . . factum . . . per fratrem Andream Astone', 1426, with decorated initials and paragraphs similar to those of No. 116 and occasional additions. Contains copies of deeds, leases and rentals rel. the hostiller's lands with other misc., incl. literary, material. *Mon. Angl.* iii, 117 (*b*). T. Arnold, *Memorials of St. Edmund's Abbey* ii (Rolls ser., 1892), 327–54 and iii (1896), 77–174, prints fos. 84–155, 193–5.

Fos. 112 (contemp. foliation, 9–119). 9⅝ × 6½ in. *FO:* J. Holt.

¶ *Infirmarius*

115.   **BM., Lansdowne 416.** 'Reg. T. Ikworth', 1425, with decorated initials and occasional additions. Contains copies of deeds and rentals rel. the infirmarer's lands, arranged in alphabetical order of places,

the section for Bury (fos. 5–38) being sub-divided by streets and some sections un-completed. *Mon. Angl.* iii, 128 (*a*).

Fos. 87. 12¼ × 8½ in. *FO:* C. Batteley, 1698; James West, 1763.

¶ *Pitanciarius*

116.   **BM., Harley 27.** Register, *c.* 1430, with decoration similar to that of No. 114 and some later additions, containing copies of deeds, rentals and other memoranda rel. the pittancer's lands, arranged in alpha-betical order of places and subjects. Apparently a revision of an earlier register, see fo. 65, and later entitled 'Reg. Croftis' (*D'E*). *Mon. Angl.* iii, 117 (*c*).

Fos. 3 + 177. 11 × 7½ in. *FO:* T. Eden, Ll.D. (*P*); Sir S. D'Ewes.

¶ *Sacristarius*

117.   **Cambridge U.L., Ff. 2. 33.** Car-tulary, 13th–14th cent. (*temp.* R. de Den-ham, sacrist), in two parts: (1) fos. 1–90, copies, in a small charter hand with red underlinings and touching of letters, and occasional small red and blue capitals, of royal and papal privileges to the abbey and other general benefactions, much of the material being repeated in No. 96; (2) fos. 91–160, copies, in a square hand with red touching of letters and spaces for rubrics, of deeds etc. rel. the sacrist's lands, arranged by hundreds, with additions *passim* incl., aft. fo. 139v, further royal grants and privil-eges. Fos. 150–5 contain an added rental. *Cambr. U.L. Cat. MSS.* ii, 357–402.

Fos. vii + 160 (medieval foliation, 1–148). 13 × 9¼ in. *FO:* J. Cradock; Bp. J. Moore.

¶ *Vestiarius*

118.   **Cambridge U.L., Mm. 4. 19.** 'Nigrum Registrum de Vestiario', late 12th cent., with additions down to the 14th cent. Register of papal and royal privileges and other grants, documents etc. rel. the abbey's possessions and liberties, incl. fees, fines etc. The original compila-tion (fos. 52–146, with red and blue decor-ated initials), incl., as fos. 132–43, the feudal book of Abbot Baldwin, is preceded and followed by eight sections of additions grouped roughly chronologically. *Cambr. U.L. Cat. MSS.* iv, 222–65.

Fos. vi + 241. 11⅝ × 8 in. *FO:* Sir E. Bacon, 1633 (*D'E*); J. Cradock; Bp. J. Moore.

119.   **Cambridge U.L., Ee. 3. 60.**

'Reg. W. Pynchebeck' *al.* 'Reg. (Album) Vestiarii', begun 1333. Misc. register of pleas, fees, surveys (1286–7) etc., written in double columns with some rubrication, red underlinings etc. Includes a section of papal bulls (fos. 1–22) and copies of some royal and other charters *passim.* Ed. Lord Francis Hervey, *The Pinchbeck Register,* 2 vols. (Brighton, 1925).

Fos. iv + 332. 11⅜ × 7¼ in. *FO:* Sir E. Bacon, 1633 (*D'E*); J. Cradock; Bp. J. Moore.

120.   **Cambridge U.L., Ff. 2. 29.** 'Reg. Rubeum Vestiarii', vol. i. The first part of a 15th cent. register (*temp.* Hen. VI) of extracts rel. the liberties and jurisdiction of the abbey, taken largely, it would appear, from official records and incl. notes of pleas, royal grants and privileges, writs, allowances of fines etc. Red underlining of headings, touching of capitals etc. *Cambr. U.L. Cat. MSS.* ii, 347–54.

Fos. ii + 96. 12 × 9 in. Alienated from the abbey and restored, 1462, by John Brough-ton of Toddington, co. Bedf., who had it of a stationer in London (fo. 96v). *FO:* J. Cradock; Bp. J. Moore.

121.   **Cambridge U.L., Ff. 4. 35.** 'Reg. Rubeum Vestiarii', vol. ii (cf. No. 120).

Fos. 54. 12 × 9 in. *FO:* as No. 120.

¶ *Other registers etc.*

For BM., Harley 230 ('Reg. T. de Totingtone'), see No. 95 above; for BM., Harley 1005 ('Liber Albus'), see No. 105; and for BM., Harley 638 ('Reg. Werke-tone'), see No. 106.

122.   **BM., Harley 76.** Gospel book, 11th cent., with copies of charters of Cnut, Alexander II and William I written on the end leaves (fos. 138–41).

123.   **Cambridge U.L., Add. 6006.** 'Liber de Consuetudinibus', 13th cent., incl. copies of two or three charters (for which see D. C. Douglas, *op. cit.,* cxxxiin., 141) etc. and (fos. 81–104v) the *Kalendarium* of Abbot Samson. The latter is edited, and the MS. described, by R. H. C. Davis, *The Kalendar of Abbot Samson* (Camden Third ser. lxxxiv, 1954), ix–xi etc. *FO:* the 1st marquess Cornwallis; A. Page; J. Gage; Sir T. Rookwood Gage; J. Toovey; Prince Duleep Singh.

124.   **BM., Harley 645.** A composite 13th–15th cent. register of pleas, rentals, taxations, fees and similar material, incl.

copies of a few charters of the abbots and other persons, mainly *temp.* Edw. I–III. Later entitled 'Reg. Kempe' (*D'E*). *Mon. Angl.* iii, 120 (*a*). *FO:* J. Mallowes, 1635; Sir S. D'Ewes.

125.   **BM., Cotton Vit. F. xii,** fos. 195–272. Register of pleas etc., mainly 1–2 Edw. III. Damaged by fire, 1731.

126.   **BM., Harley 3977.** Register of custumaries, 14th cent. *Mon. Angl.* iii, 124 (*b*). *FO:* (Sir ?) N(icholas ?) B(acon ?).

127.   **BM., Add. 14849.** 'Liber Monachorum S(an)c(t)i Edmundi'. Register of extents of the abbot's lands, 1357 etc., followed by 24 leaves of a register *temp.* W. de Bernham, abbot 1335–61, with later additions. *FO:* 'Ambros Jermyn'; Sir R. Bacon; bought of E. Wodehouse, 1844.

128.   **BM., Cotton Tib. B. ix.** 'Reg. W. Cratfield & W. Exeter', 14th–15th cent.

129.   **BM., Add. 14848.** 'Reg. Curteys' (abbot 1429–46), vol. i. J. A. Herbert in Lord Francis Hervey, *The Pinchbeck Register* ii (Brighton, 1925), 301–54. *FO:* R. Bacon; Sir E. Bacon, 1747 (T. Martin); bought of E. Wodehouse, 1844.

130.   **BM., Add. 7096.** 'Reg. Curteys', vol. ii. *Mon. Angl.* iii, 129–30. *FO:* T. Gooche; H. Spelman; J. Nowel; Cox Macro; C. Ord.

131.   **Douai, Bibl. publ., MS. 553.** 'Registrum Coquinarii', *c.* 1424, compiled by A. Aston and written in the same hand as No. 114. Contains a list of benefactors followed by rules of the *Officium Coquinarii* etc. C. Dehaisnes, *Cat. gén. MSS. des Départements* vi (1878), Douai, 347–9. *FO:* Robert Woode; John Smith of London; the English Benedictine monastery at Douai.

132.   **BM., Harley 58.** Rental of the sacrist for the town of Bury, 1433 (*temp.* J. de Cranewys, sacrist). *Mon. Angl.* iii, 124 (*a*).

133.   **Cambridge, Jesus Coll., MS. 18.** Formulary etc., 15th cent.

134.   **BM., Harley 308.** 'Reg. Reeve' *al.* 'Melford'. Leases, manumissions etc., 9–31 Hen. VIII. *Mon. Angl.* iii, 125–7. *FO:* 'R. B(acon), (1)57(1)'.

BURY ST. EDMUNDS   co. Suff.
Hosp. of St. John E., *al.* 'Domus Dei'   *f.* (as a dependency of the Abbey), 1248–56

135.   **BM., Arundel 1.** Cartulary (fos. 1–29), 15th cent. (aft. 1425), with red decoration of initials, red and blue paragraphs etc. Contains copies of private etc. deeds and one or two surveys, rentals etc. Ten paper leaves of similar date at the end (fos. 30–9), headed 'Munimenta pro Dontonhalle', duplicate part of the material.

Fos. vii + 39. 13 × 9⅜ in. *FO:* Thomas Howard, 2nd earl of Arundel; presented by Henry Howard, 6th duke of Norfolk, to the Royal Society, 1678.

BURY ST. EDMUNDS   co. Suff.
Hosp. of St. Saviour   *f. c.* 1184
136.   **Untraced.** Cartulary 'commencing in the year 1290 and ending 1490, with an index'.

Quarto. *FO:* C. Ord (sale-cat. 1829, lot 563); Sir T. Phillipps (MS. 3792).

BUSHMEAD   co. Bedf.
Aug. Priory   *f. c.* 1195
137.   **Untraced.** Cartulary *penes* Arthur Trevor of the Inner Temple, 1640. Extracts from fos. 17–63 are printed in *Mon. Angl.* vi, 280–4.
138.   **W. R. Wade-Gery Esq.,** deposited at Bedford, Bedfordshire R.O. (D.D. GY, 9/2). Gen. cartulary, *c.* 1348, with rubrics and blue initials decorated with red. Arranged topographically by counties and places, with *Privilegia* (papal and episcopal) at the beginning, preceded by a contemp. Table on three preliminary leaves (fos. iii–vi), and with a few misc. additions at the end (fos. 83v ff.) etc. Ed. G. H. Fowler & J. Godber, *The Cartulary of Bushmead Priory* (Bedfordshire Hist. Record Soc. xxii, 1945).

Fos. vi + 87 (wants single leaves aft. fos. 55, 81). 12⅛ × 8⅛ in. *FO:* Anthony Cokett; W. Gery, *c.* 1552.

BUTLEY   co. Suff.
Aug. Priory   *f.* 1171
139.   **Untraced.** 'Kalendare evidentiarum . . . penes Rob. Hawes de Framlingham in com. Suff. gen. 1715' (*T*). Perhaps the second of the two registers which subsequently belonged to T. Martin and (1779) to J. Ives, see BM., Add. 5489, fo. 107 and No. 140 following.

¶ *Other registers etc.*

140.   **Untraced.** 'Chronicon sive cartu-larium . . . quod incipit . . . anno 1509 et desinit anno 1536' (*T*). Ed. (from a partial 18th cent. transcript in Bodl., Tanner 90, fos. 24–67) A. G. Dickens, *The Register or Chronicle of Butley Priory, Suffolk*, 1510–1535 (Winchester, 1951).

Fos. 72. Folio. Paper. *FO:* P. Le Neve; T. Martin; J. Ives.

BYLAND   co. York
Cist. Abbey   *f.* 1177

141.   **Oxford, Bodl., Dodsworth 76** (*SC.* 5018), fo. 146. Copies, late 13th cent., of 15 charters, with part of a 16th, mainly rel. Denby. Some have press-marks. W. H. Turner & H. O. Coxe, *Cal. Charters and Rolls . . . in the Bodl. Libr.* (Oxford, 1878), 688–9.

Roll of 1 membr. $12\frac{1}{4} \times 7$ in.

142.   **BM., Egerton 2823.** Part of a gen. cartulary, early 15th cent. (*temp.* Hen. IV), with rubrics, red and blue initials etc. Arranged in alphabetical order of places (Ampleforth–Scarborough) with a few sub-ject headings intermixed, incl. *Libertates* (royal etc.), *Mowbray scrinium, Magnatum baculus.* Transcripts and extracts, 17th–18th cent., from missing leaves are in Bodl., Dodsworth 63 (*SC.* 5005), fos. 9–78 and Top. Yorks. d. 11, fos. 255–78v etc.

Fos. 118 (post-medieval foliation, 74–224; lacks leaves *passim*). $15\frac{1}{2} \times 10\frac{3}{4}$ in. *FO:* Brian Fairfax (*T*); J. Rushworth, 1647; T. Belasyse, earl of Fauconberg, 1698 (*T*); Sir T. Frankland, bart. (*T*); Sir T. Phillipps (MS. 13843, 'ex bibl. C. D. arm.').

CADBURY, NORTH   co. Som.
Secular Coll.   *f.* 1423
No cartulary recorded.

¶ *Other registers etc.*

143.   **Durham U.L., Mickleton & Spearman 57.** Statutes given by John Stafford, 1428. Notarially attested. *FO:* the Mickleton and Spearman fams., 17th–18th cent.; the Rev. G. Wasey; Bp. Shute Barrington; the Bp. Cosin library, Dur-ham, 1817.

CAMBRIDGE   co. Cambr.
Hosp. of St. John E.   *f.* 1200
v. also No. 155 below.

144.   **Cambridge, St. John's Coll.,** Muniments. Cartulary, *c.* 1250 (?), with

some additions *passim*, containing copies of private deeds arranged by places. Fos. 8–9, 81–8, 89–90 are inserted rentals of later date. Roll-stamped binding by N. Spierwick of Cambridge, 1520–5.

Fos. ii+90 (wants leaves at the begin-ning and aft. fo. 9). $10\frac{3}{4} \times 7\frac{1}{2}$ in.

CAMBRIDGE   co. Cambr.
King's Coll.   *f.* 1441

145.   **Cambridge, King's Coll.,** Muni-ments (M. 9). Register, *c.* 1450, containing copies of papal confirmations of the col-lege's privileges, documents rel. the hand-ing over of nine bulls to Eton College for safe custody etc.

Fos. 21. $16 \times 11\frac{1}{2}$ in.

146.   **Ditto,** 'The Oak Cartulary'. A similar 15th cent. register containing copies of : (1) royal privileges to the college 1438–53, with a Table, fos. 5–55; (2) episcopal etc. privileges 1446–9, fos. 55v–65; (3) in-quisitions, extents etc., fos. 68–75. Original binding, oak boards.

Fos. 77. $16 \times 10\frac{3}{4}$ in.

147.   **Ditto,** 'Kalendarium Rotuli'. Copy, late 15th cent., with blue paragraphs decorated with red, of No. 146, pt. 1.

Roll of i+19 membrs. 47 ft. (approx.) × $11\frac{1}{2}$ in.

148.   **Ditto** (Box E). Abstracts, 15th cent., of royal letters patent and Acts of Parliament rel. the college, *temp.* Hen. VI. Somewhat roughly written. Limp vellum wrapper.

Fos. 53. $12\frac{1}{4} \times 9$ in.

¶ *Inventory*

149.   **Ditto,** 'Manuscript Inventory', fos. 13–26. Inventory 15th cent. (*temp.* Hen. VI), of royal letters patent to the college, 1441–57, with notes of their storage places, seals etc. and summaries of their contents. Included in a collection of similar invent-ories of the college's possessions.

Fos. 14 (82 in the MS.). 18×12 in.

¶ *Other registers etc.*

150.   **Ditto,** 'Reg. R. Wodelarke'. Leases of the college manors etc., 1446–54 etc.

CAMBRIDGE   co. Cambr.
Michael House   *f.* 1324
For notices of the cartularies see R. Willis & J. W. Clark, *Architectural History of . . . Cambridge* ii (1886), 669–70; H. T.

Riley, *HMC. First Report* (1870), App., 82–3; A. E. Stamp, *Michaelhouse* (Cambridge, 1924).

151. **Cambridge, Trinity Coll.**, Muniments (Box 29 B). Quire from a 14th cent. cartulary (*temp.* Edw. III) with spaces for initials and titles. Contains copies of deeds, incl. some royal licences to alienate, rel. Cheadle, co. Staff., and Cambridge.

Fos. 8. 12⅛ × 6¼ in.

152. **Ditto**, 'The Ottringham or Michael House Black Book'. Register of evidences rel. the college's lands etc., traditionally begun by J. Ottringham, master 1427–33. Written in several 15th cent. hands with red underlining of the titles etc. on the earlier leaves and some later additions. Contains copies of charters (incl. some royal and episcopal documents), rentals etc. arranged by places, preceded by a contemp. Table. The opening section for Cambridge includes statutes, lists of benefactors etc.

Fos. v + 89. 14½ × 9½ in.

CAMBRIDGE co. Cambr.
Pembroke Coll. *f.* 1347

153. **Cambridge, Pembroke Coll.**, Muniments, 'Registrum Magnum I'. Cartulary, *c.* 1390–1400, arranged in sections by places, with some repetition of headings, and incl. copies of royal and episcopal documents *passim*. Misc. additions throughout include inventories and (at the end) a 16th cent. index. 15th cent. stamped binding. H. T. Riley, *HMC. First Report* (1870), App., 70–2.

Fos. 112. 15¾ × 11¼ in. Paper.

CAMBRIDGE co. Cambr.
St. Catharine's Coll. *f.* 1473

154. **Cambridge, St. Catharine's Coll.**, Muniments (xl/18). 'Memoriale . . . de perquisicionibus factis per Magistrum Robertum Wodelarke . . . de diversis terris et tenementis in villa Cantebrigie', 1465. Register of the founder's property, written in his own hand and incl. copies of a number of deeds. A typescript copy is in Cambridge U.L. H. T. Riley, *HMC. Fourth Report* (1874), App., 421–2. W. H. S. Jones, *Hist. St. Catharine's Coll.* (Cambridge, 1936), 364 etc.

Fos. 54. 11¾ × 8 in. Paper.

CAMBRIDGE co. Cambr.
St. John's Coll. *f.* 1511

155. **Cambridge, St. John's Coll.**, Muniments. Cartulary, 16th cent. (aft. 1519), with some additions, 1529–30, at the end. Contains copies of royal, papal etc. charters rel. the college's foundation, and some similar 13th–14th cent. material rel. the hospitals of St. John the Evangelist, Cambridge (cf. No. 144), and St. Mary, Ospringe (cf. No. 736), preceded (pp. 1–24) by a copy of the Will of the foundress. C. H. Cooper, *Memoir of Margaret Countess of Richmond & Derby* (Cambridge, 1874), 129–78 (calendar).

Fos. 118 (19th cent. pagination, 1–236). 14½ × 11 in.

CAMPSEY ASH co. Suff.
Aug. Priory (Nuns) *f. c.* 1195
No cartulary recorded.
¶ *Other registers etc.*

156. **PRO., Exch., T.R.** (Misc. Bks. 112). Copies, 16th cent., of statutes etc. rel. the establishment of a perpetual chantry in the priory, 1390, with a few related confirmations etc. Fos. 14. Paper.

CANONS ASHBY co. Northt.
Aug. Priory *f.* 1147–51

157. **BM., Egerton 3033.** Gen. cartulary, 13th cent. (*temp.* Edw. I), with spaces for initials and rubrics in some sections, and additions down to the 15th cent. *passim*. Arranged topographically, with the fines grouped at fos. 98–9 and copies of a few episcopal indulgences at the end. Copies of some other episcopal etc. documents are included *passim*. Extracts, 18th cent., by J. Bridges are in Bodl. Top. Northt. c. 19 (*SC.* 16635), pp. 283 ff. *BM. Cat. Add. MSS.* 1921–1925, 304–5 and references there cited. A. J. Horwood, *HMC. Third Report* (1872), App., 274 (list of places etc.)

Fos. v + 122. 9 × 5½ in. *FO*: G. Orlebar, 1647, and his descendants at Hinwick.

CANONSLEIGH co. Devon
Aug. Abbey (Canonesses) *f.* (as a priory for canons) 1161–73

158. **BM., Harley 3660.** Gen. cartulary, 14th cent. (aft. 1321–2), with a few later additions. Arranged topographically in sections with a Table at fos. 2–16 which, like the titles throughout, is in French, and

incl. copies of royal and occasional episcopal charters *passim*. Followed (fos. 141–78) by Surveys, 1323. G. Oliver, *Mon. Exon.* (1846), 229n. etc. *Mon. Angl.* vi, 333 (t).

Fos. 179. $10\frac{3}{4} \times 7\frac{1}{4}$ in.

CANTERBURY, See of *f.* 597
The cartularies are discussed by Kathleen Major, *Acta Stephani Langton* (Canterbury & York Soc. l., 1950), 158–9; A. J. Collins, 'The Documents of the Great Charter of 1215', *Proc. Brit. Academy* xxxiv (1948), 237–43 *passim*.

159.   **London, Lambeth Palace, MS. 1212.** Composite cartulary of muniments of or rel. to the See, written in a number of 13th and 14th cent. hands. Arranged mainly by grantors and types of grant etc., with a contemp. Table at the beginning, and incl. sections of early royal and papal charters, misc. memoranda 'transcripta de veteri libro Cant.' etc. Pp. 186–225 are rubricated, with red and blue decorated initials. M. R. James, *Cat. Lambeth MSS.* (Cambridge, 1932), 828–34 (description). W. Holtzmann, *Papsturkunden in England* i (Göttingen, 1930), 197–9 (notes on the collation etc.).

Fos. iv + 201 (17th cent. pagination, 1–431). $12\frac{1}{2} \times 9$ in. *FO:* John, Ld. Lumley; Sir R. Twysden (?); Sir W. Twysden, 1681.

160.   **Oxford, Bodl., Tanner 223.** Register of royal, papal and some other charters, 16th cent. (*temp.* Hen. VIII), with uncompleted marginal rubrication. The material is apparently copied, in revised sequence, from No. 159. D. M. Barratt, 'The Library of John Selden and its later history', *Bodl. Libr. Record* iii (1950–1), 137 (a note).

Fos. 186 (paginated, 1–364). $15\frac{5}{8} \times 13$ in. *FO:* John Selden (?); Sir M. Hale (?); Archbp. W. Sancroft ('out of Cheshire').

¶ *Inventory*

161.   **PRO., Exch., T.R.** (Misc. Bks. 137). Inventory, 1330, of charters in the Archbishop's treasury, written in double columns without decoration. Arranged by *Vasa* in two parts: (1) 'Capitula Cartarum Regiarum' etc. (Will. II–Edw. II, *Vasa* i–xi), pp. 3–6; (2) 'Carte aliorum quam regum' (*Vasa* xii–xxxii), pp. 8–16. Ed. Irene J. Churchill, 'Table of Canterbury

Archbishopric Charters', *Camden Miscellany* xv (Camden Third ser. xli, 1929).

Fos. 8 (post-medieval pagination, 1–16). $11 \times 7\frac{1}{2}$ in.

¶ *Other registers etc.*

162.   **BM., Cotton Cleop. E. i,** fos. 16–55. Register, 12th cent., of papal and other privileges of the See, followed by copies of professions of obedience to the Archbishop by suffragan bishops and Kentish abbots. Made apparently in 1120, with additions to 1163, as a source book of evidences rel. the See's supremacy over York. H. Boehmer, 'Die Fälschungen Erzbischof Lanfranks von Canterbury', *Studien zur Gesch. der Theologie und der Kirche* viii, ed. N. Bonwetsch & R. Seeberg (Leipzig, 1902), Heft 1, 8 ff. (analysis) etc. *New Palaeographical Soc.*, First ser., pls. 60–2 (description).

CANTERBURY co. Kent
Christ Church (Ben. Cath. Priory) *f.* 997
The registers are listed by R. A. L. Smith, *Canterbury Cathedral Priory* (Cambridge, 1943), 222–4. For those at Canterbury see G. R. Brigstocke Sheppard, *HMC Eighth Report*, pt. i (1881), App., 315–55 and *Ninth Report*, pt. i (1883), App., 72–129, whose account is supplemented and amended by R. L. Poole, *HMC. Various Collections* i (1901), 208–11, and W. Holtzmann, *Papsturkunden in England* ii (Göttingen, 1936), 8–25.

163.   **Cambridge, C.C.C., MS. 189,** fos. 195–201 + 1. Quire (from a cartulary ?) containing notes and copies, 12th cent., with spaces for initials and titles, of about 70 royal and other grants, privileges etc., A.D. 616–early 12th cent., arranged chronologically. The verso of the last leaf (a fragm.) is blank. Bound up at the end of W. Thorne's chronicle etc., with which it is printed by R. Twysden, *Historiae Anglicanae Scriptores* X (1652), 2207–26. Cf. No. 163A.

Fos. 8. $11 \times 7\frac{1}{2}$ in. *FO:* T. Twyne; Archbp. M. Parker.

163A.   **Canterbury, D. & C.,** Muniments, 'Reg. P', fos. 11–29. A similar collection of early charters to that in No. 163, early 13th cent., with spaces for initials. Much of the material is also repeated in Lambeth Palace MS. 1212 (No. 159 above), pp. 304 ff. Incorporated in a composite

13th–14th cent. register which was originally the first part of 'Reg. O' (cf. No. 166 below).

Fos. 19 (ii + 89 in the MS.). 7½ × 5 in. (shrunk and mutilated by fire, 1670, in the cathedral audit office, and the leaves now mounted).

164. **Ditto**, 'Reg. H.', fos. 25–34, 47. Eleven leaves from an early 13th cent. cartulary, with rubrics and capitals touched with red. Contains copies of about 80 private, ecclesiastical and monastic charters rel. various places. Incorporated in a misc. composite register, *c.* 1200–15th cent., of rentals, extents, *acta* of the priory 1355–73, etc.

Fos. 11 (231 in the MS.). 12 × 9 in.

165. **Ditto**, 'Reg. I', fos. 5–123. 'Liber Adriani Pape' (fo. 106). Cartulary, late 13th cent., of papal, royal, episcopal and a few other charters, down to 1271. Rubrics and initials touched with red. A contemp. Table and the first 17 folios are misbound at the end (fos. 102–23).

Fos. 119. 10 × 7 in.

166. **Ditto**, 'Reg. O', fos. 155–91. Copies, late 13th cent., of papal bulls, royal charters, writs etc., with some rubrication and touching of initials with red, and one or two deeds rel. Halstow added at the end. Incorporated in a composite 13th–14th cent. register, mainly of rentals and other misc. memoranda (cf. No. 163A).

Fos. 47 (*c.* 200 in the MS.). 7½ × 5½ in. (damaged by fire, 1670, and the leaves now mounted at the fore-edges and foot).

167. **BM., Add. 6159**, fos. 5–17, 279–88. Copies, late 13th cent., of royal, papal, archiepiscopal etc. privileges. The first section has blue initials decorated with red, red underlining of headings etc., and the second has pen-decorated initials with grotesques drawn in the lower margins. Holtzmann, *op. cit.* ii, 21–2, connects the papal documents with those in No. 165. Incorporated in a composite 13th–14th cent. register of custumals, rentals, extents etc.

Fos. 23 (288 in the MS.). 11 × 8 in. *FO:* T. Jordan; presented by G. H. W. Beaumont, 1819.

168. **Canterbury, D. & C.**, Muniments, 'Reg E.' Gen. cartulary, late 13th cent. (aft. 1290), with rubrics, red page-headings etc., red and blue decorated initials, and a few additions *passim*. Arranged mainly topographically with sections of royal (French and English) and episcopal charters, compositions and *carte de Feretro et de altaribus* at the beginning. An elaborate contemp. Table at fos. 1–33, carrying the medieval foliation down to 'ccccxxvii', shows a section of fines to be wanting. Among other missing leaves, fos. cliii–cliiii in the same foliation are **BM., Add. 25109** (*FO:* Sir E. Dering). Abstracts for Sir E. Dering, 1630, are in BM., Add. 6037, fos. 1–74; Stowe 924, fos. 88–183. The leaves from another register, formerly bound at the end of the volume, are now *ib.*, 'Reg. T', fos. 1–42.

Fos. 402 (medieval foliation, i–ccccviii). 16 × 11 in.

169–172. **Ditto**, 'Reg. A–D'. Gen. cartulary, late 13th–15th cent., the original compilation being a contemp. copy of No. 168 and written in similar format, apparently as a single vol., with early 14th cent. additions in blank spaces etc. *passim*. After the addition of substantial 15th cent. sections of supplementary material down to *c.* 1430, which are written in a rather large hand with rubrics and blue initials decorated with red, the whole was apparently divided and to some extent rearranged in four vols., each 16 × 11 in., as follows:—(169) 'Reg. A'. Copies of papal bulls (added), royal charters and charters rel. Canterbury. Four further leaves are preserved separately *ib.*, among the fragms. of registers. Extracts by Sir E. Dering are in BM., Add. 5506, fos. 62–90. Fos. ii + 412;—(170) 'Reg. C'. Manors in Kent. Fos. 293;—(171) 'Reg. D'. Manors in Kent, ctd. Fos. 224;—(172) 'Reg. B'. Manors outside Kent. Fos. 442.

173. **Cambridge, St. John's Coll., MS. N. 6**. Fragm. of an early 14th cent. register with rubrics, red and blue decorated initials etc., containing copies of 12th–13th cent. papal etc. privileges to the see and church (fos. 1–5) and to the prior and convent (fos. 6–12). M. R. James, *Cat. MSS. St. John's Coll.* (Cambridge, 1913), 281–2.

Fos. 12 + 1 (foliated in red, x–xxi). 10½ × 7¾ in.

¶ *Inventories*

174. **Canterbury, D. & C.**, Muniments, 'Reg. I', fos. 452–77. Repertorium,

early 14th cent., of papal bulls, royal charters and other misc. documents, arranged by places of storage and incl. (fos. 452–5) a 'Kalendar(ium) de memorand(is) et de diversis transcript(is) content(is) in diversis libris H (enrici de Eastreia) prioris'. Written apparently as a separate *libellus*, and the original order of the leaves disturbed.

Fos. 26. $9\frac{5}{8} \times 5\frac{1}{2}$ in.

175.   **PRO., Exch., T.R.** (Misc. Bks. 138). Inventory, late 15th cent., of royal, papal, episcopal and other charters, arranged and numbered by *Ciste*.

Fos. 21. $11\frac{3}{4} \times 4$ in. Paper.

¶ *Elemosinarius*

176.   **London, Lambeth Palace** (Carte Misc. xiii, pt. i, art. 15). Fragms. of an early 14th cent. cartulary of the almoner, written in book-hand with rubrics etc. and uncompleted red and blue initials. Comprises sections of: (1) private deeds rel. Farningham and Meopham, fos. i–vi; (2) papal, episcopal and other charters etc. rel. churches etc., fos. vii–xii (ix^v, xii^v blank); with two or three later additions.

Fos. 12 (modern foliation, i–xii). $13\frac{1}{2} \times 9\frac{1}{4}$ in. (cropped ?).

¶ *Other registers etc.*

For other registers at Canterbury, see *HMC.*, *ll. cc.*

177.   **London, Lambeth Palace, MS. 771.** Gospel-book ('Macdurnan Gospels'), 9th cent., with copies of Anglo-Saxon charters added, 10th–11th cent., at the end of St. Matthew's and St. Mark's Gospels. **BM. Cotton Tib. B. iv**, fo. 87, a detached leaf, contains further similar copies. M. R. James, *Cat. Lambeth MSS.* (Cambridge, 1932), 843–5. N. R. Ker, *Cat. MSS. containing Anglo-Saxon* (Oxford, 1957), no. 284. *FO:* Archbp. M. Parker; F. Howel.

178.   **BM., Cotton Tib. A. ii; Faust. B. vi**, pt. i, fos. 95, 98–100; **Claud. A. iii**, fos. 2–7, 7*. Gospel-book ('Aethelstan's Gospels'), 10th cent., with contemp. copies of 11th–12th cent. papal documents and pre-conquest charters in Latin and Old English added on the fly-leaves. N. R. Ker, *op. cit.*, no. 185.

179.   **BM., Royal 1 D. ix.** Gospel-book, early 11th cent., with a copy of a charter etc. of Cnut, *c.* 1017, added on blank leaves after St. Matthew's Gospel. N. R.

Ker, *op. cit.*, no. 247. *FO:* John, Ld. Lumley.

180.   **Oxford, St. John's Coll., MS. 194.** Gospel-book, 11th cent., with copies of two charters of King Aethelred in Latin and Anglo-Saxon (979 & n.d.) added, 13th cent., on the fly-leaf. *FO:* Henry Price.

181.   **Cambridge U.L., Ee. 5. 31.** Register, *temp.* H. de Eastry, prior 1285–1331. *Cambr. U.L. Cat. MSS.* ii, 190–250. *FO:* Bp. J. Moore.

182.   **BM., Cotton Galba E. iv**, fos. 1–186. 'Memoriale multorum Henrici (de Eastreia) prioris', early 14th cent., with a few additions. Uniform with No. 168 above and contains copies of misc. material rel. the priory's rights, possessions etc., incl. inventories and a few royal and other charters. *FO:* John Twyne (father & son).

183.   **BM., Cotton Cleop. C. vii**, fos. 2–59. Register of statutes etc., 13th–14th cent. etc.

184.   **BM., Add. 6160.** Register of extents, taxations etc., 14th cent., incl. copies of some royal charters of liberties etc. *FO:* T. Jordan; presented by G. H. W. Beaumont, 1819.

185.   **Cambridge, Trinity Coll., MS. O. 9. 26.** Register of statutes etc., 14th cent. etc. *FO:* R. Gale.

186.   **BM., Harley 1006.** Register of extents, rentals etc., 14th–15th cent.

187.   **BM., Arundel 68.** Composite 14th–15th cent. register containing admissions to fraternity, obits etc. and a martyrology. *FO:* Ld. Wm. Howard; presented by Henry Howard, 6th duke of Norfolk, to the Royal Society, 1678.

188.   **Oxford, Bodl., Tanner 165.** Register of Prior W. de Molash, from 1427. *FO:* W. Bowyer, 1566; Bp. T. White, 1685; Archbp. W. Sancroft.

189.   **Cambridge, C.C.C., MS. 298**, pt. ii. Collectanea, 16th cent., incl. (pp. 61–85) notes rel. the acquisition of manors and churches. M. R. James, *Cat. MSS. C.C.C.* ii (Cambridge, 1912), 80–6. *FO:* Archbp. T. Cranmer; Archbp. M. Parker.

CANTERBURY   co. Kent
Ben. Abbey of St. Augustine   *f.* 598–605
190.   **BM., Harley 337**, fos. 1–11. Fragm. of a late 12th cent. register, written in book-hand with plain red and green initials. Contains copies of misc. papal and

imperial privileges etc., for the most part not relating directly to St. Augustine's. The verso of fo. 11, which has been used for scribblings, was perhaps originally the last leaf of the compilation. W. Holtzmann, *Papsturkunden in England* i (Göttingen, 1930), 120–1, lists the contents.

Fos. 11. $9\frac{1}{2} \times 6\frac{1}{4}$ in. *FO:* Sir E. Dering (?).

191. BM., Cotton Vit. A. ii, fos. 6–19. Fragm. of another late 12th cent. register, written in a rather more rounded bookhand with red or occasionally green headings and red, green and blue initials, sometimes decorated. Contains copies of royal and papal privileges, with marginal notes in the hand of the text and occasional representations of *bullae*. Holtzmann, *l.c.*, 91, lists the contents.

Fos. 14. *c.* 9×7 in. (shrunk and damaged by fire, 1731, and the leaves now mounted).

192. BM., Cotton Julius D. ii. A composite 13th–14th cent. register comprising: (1) the Rule of St. Benedict (fos. 24–39), followed without break (fos. 39v–133v) by a cartulary of papal, royal and archiepiscopal privileges etc., fines, compositions and some other charters, interspersed with the titles, in red, of many more; written apparently towards the middle of the 13th cent. with rubrics, red and blue decorated initials etc. and additions *passim*. Preceded (fos. 1–23) by lists of kings, popes, annals etc. and followed (fos. 134–72v) by rentals, a *forma brevium* and other misc. material. Stated by Holtzmann, *l.c.*, 69–74, to be the source of the texts used in the latter part of Thomas of Elmham's history of the abbey (No. 198). See also No. 200 below;—(2) a misc. 13th–14th register (fos. 173–264) of pleas, deeds and other memoranda, *temp.* Edw. I–II etc., incl. copies of some royal and papal privileges. An abstract of both parts by Sir E. Dering, 1628, is in BM., Stowe 924, fos. 184–244.

Fos. 266. $7\frac{1}{4} \times 5\frac{1}{4}$ in.

193. BM., Cotton Claud. D. x, fos. 9–319. The 'Red Book', 13th–14th cent. (*temp.* Edw. I). Gen. cartulary with rubrics and red page-headings, red and blue decorated initials (of which many are uncompleted), and an illuminated border to the first leaf. Arranged in sections partly by obedientiaries (*Sacristia, Infirmaria, Vestiaria, Redditus Beatae Mariae, Cameraria*,

with topographical subdivisions) and partly by places, with sections of papal and royal privileges at the beginning, and additions *passim*.

Fos. 310 (lacks about 14 leaves *passim*). $13\frac{1}{2} \times 10$ in. *FO:* John Twyne (father & son).

194. BM., Cotton Faust. A. i. The 'Black Book', late 13th cent., with rubrics and later additions and insertions, comprising: (1) fos. 3–237, misc. rentals, custumals, writs etc., incl. copies of a few deeds; (2) fos. 238–385, a cartulary of 12th–13th cent. deeds, incl. some royal and episcopal documents, rel. various small properties acquired after the Norman conquest. Ed. G. J. Turner & H. E. Salter, *The Black Book of St. Augustine, Canterbury*, 2 vols. (1915–24).

Fos. 385. $8\frac{5}{8} \times 6\frac{1}{4}$ in.

195. PRO., Exch., K.R. (Misc. Bks. i. 27). Cartulary (imperf. at the beginning) written in a succession of 13th and 14th cent. hands. Contains memoranda of early grants and copies of papal, royal and episcopal charters, compositions, inquisitions and some private deeds, down to 1323, arranged roughly chronologically. Followed (fos. 194–227) by Annals from the Nativity down to 1324, with additions down to 1332, and (fos. 230–2) added copies of deeds, *temp.* Edw. III. Holtzmann, *l.c.*, 44–6.

Fos. 233 (medieval foliation, 4–237). $8\frac{3}{8} \times 5\frac{3}{4}$ in.

196. Canterbury, D. & C., lit. MS. E. 19. Composite misc. 13th–14th cent. register of documents rel. the abbey's possessions incl. (fos. 1–31) a cartulary, 1311, of deeds (incl. some early royal grants) and other evidences rel. the manor of Minster in Sheppey. C. E. Woodruff, *Cat. MSS. Ch. Ch. Canterbury* (Canterbury, 1911), 37–9. G. R. Brigstocke Sheppard, *HMC. Ninth Report*, pt. i (1883), App., 128.

Fos. 31 (215 in the MS.). $10\frac{3}{4} \times 7$ in. *FO:* R. Farmer, 1784 (from a London bookstall).

197. BM., Cotton Vit. D. x. Fragm. of an early 14th cent. register with rubrics and red and blue decorated initials, containing copies of 12th–13th cent. papal privileges etc.

Fos. 7. 7×6 in. (shrunk and damaged by fire, 1731, and the leaves now mounted).

198.   **Cambridge, Trinity Hall, MS. I.** Thomas of Elmham, 'Historia Abbatiae S. Augustini', early 15th cent., incorporating a series of transcripts and facsimiles of early royal and papal privileges to the abbey down to 1191, continuous aft. fo. 78. Incomplete at the end. Elaborately written in double columns with rubrics, red page-headings and red and blue initials, and incl. a diagram of the *Ciclus solaris* (fo. 12), a map of Thanet (fo. 42v) and a view of the altar and shrines of St. Augustine's (fo. 77). Preceded (fos. 1–11) by tables of popes, archbishops, kings and abbots down to 1417. Ed. C. Hardwick (Rolls ser., 1858). M. R. James, *Cat. MSS. Trinity Hall* (Cambridge, 1907), 1–4. F. Taylor, 'A Note on Rolls Series 8', *Bull. Rylands Libr.* xx (1936), 379–82. See also No. 192 above.

Fos. 116. 21¾ × 14¾ in. Presented by Robert Hare.

❡ *Inventories*

199.   **Cambridge, C.C.C., MS. 301.** A 14th cent. collection of misc. historical material, tracts on husbandry etc., incl. a list (pp. 180–1) of the abbey's *privilegia*, among some memoranda (pp. 177–221) rel. its possessions. A vellum strip attached to p. 1 is inscribed, 14th cent., 'Liber fratris Stephani de Hakynton de librario Sci. Aug. Cant.' M. R. James, *Cat. MSS. C.C.C.* ii (Cambridge, 1912), 88–91.

Pp. 221. 10½ × 6 in. *FO:* Archbp. M. Parker.

❡ *Other registers etc.*

199A.   **Cambridge, C.C.C., MS. 286.** Gospel-book, 6th cent., with 10th cent. copies of two Anglo-Saxon grants to the Abbey (844–64 ?, 989–1006) written in blank spaces between St. Matthew's and St. Mark's Gospels. N. R. Ker, *Cat. MSS. containing Anglo-Saxon* (Oxford, 1957), no. 55. *FO:* Archbp. M. Parker.

200.   **BM., Add. 46352.** Composite 13th cent. register (now bound in some disorder), containing copies of misc. documents and memoranda, incl. papal bulls, pleas, compositions, letters etc. Appears once to have formed the central part (fos. ccxxvi–cccxli etc. in a later medieval foliation) of No. 192 above. A title at fo. 94, perhaps the original first leaf of the whole compilation, reads 'Matricula de camera abbatis Sci. Augustini Cant.', to which another hand has added the words 'D. Th-(omae Fyndone) abbatis' (1283–1309).

Fos. vii + 155. 7¼ × 5½ in. *FO:* John Twyne (father & son); Sir E. Dering; Sir T. Phillipps (MS. 1085).

201.   **London, Lambeth Palace, MS. 1213.** Misc. register of statutes, pleas etc., 13th–14th cent. Inscribed (fo. ii), 14th cent., 'Est liber fratris Willelmi de Byholte'. *FO:* Archbp. M. Parker; R. Twysden.

202.   **BM., Arundel 310.** Misc. register of statutes and other material rel. the abbey's possessions, *c.* 1330 ('de adquisicione fratris Willelmi de Byholt', fo. 8v). *FO:* Ld. Wm. Howard; presented by Henry Howard, 6th duke of Norfolk, to the Royal Society, 1678.

203.   **Untraced.** A 'Reg. Byholt', apparently distinct from Nos. 201 & 202, *penes* Heneage Finch of Ravenstone, co. Bucks., 1646. Extracts are in BM., Harley 312, fos. 27–9; 294, fos. 231v–7v.

204.   **BM., Cotton Tib. A. ix,** fos. 107–80. Lives of the abbots, 14th cent., incl. some copies, extracts etc. of papal and other charters *passim*, down to 1340. Holtzmann, *l.c.*, 75–6. T. D. Hardy, *Cat. Hist. Great Britain* iii (Rolls ser., 1871), 125 (no. 225).

205.   **Destroyed.** Register of leases, presentations etc., 1434–91, which was formerly Cotton MS. Otho B. xv and was burnt in 1731. T. Smith, *Cat. Bibl. Cotton.* (Oxford, 1696), *ad loc.* *FO:* T. Allen ? (cf. N. R. Ker, *Bodl., Libr. Record* ii (1941–9), 212–13), in which case extracts are in Bodl., James 8 (*SC.* 3845), pp. 164–71.

206.   **Canterbury, D. & C., lit. MS. E. 23.** 'Registrum dompni Willielmi Sellyng, precentoris', 1521–2. Mainly leases. Woodruff, *op. cit.*, 39.

CANTERBURY   co. Kent
Aug. Priory of St. Gregory   *f.* bef. 1087
207.   **Cambridge U.L., Ll. 2. 15.** Gen. cartulary, 13th cent. (aft. *c.* 1240), written in double columns with rubrics and red initials. Contains copies of episcopal and papal followed by private charters, with some additions of material down to 1265 *passim*, mainly towards the end. Ed. Audrey M. Woodcock, *Cartulary of the Priory of St. Gregory, Canterbury* (Camden Third ser. lxxxviii, 1956).

Fos. 63 (post-medieval foliation, 1–68; wants 3–6 and leaves aft. fos. 11, 63). $11\frac{1}{4} \times 8\frac{1}{4}$ in. *FO:* Bp. J. Moore.

CANTERBURY co. Kent
Ben. Priory of St. Sepulchre (Nuns)
                          f. c. 1100
208.   **BM., Add. 5516,** fos. 9–12. Four leaves from a 15th cent. cartulary or register containing copies of 10 misc. deeds, all apparently 13th cent., with the opening words of an 11th (unfinished).
Fos. 4. $8 \times 5\frac{3}{4}$ in. (cropped). Paper. *FO:* E. Hasted.

CANTERBURY co. Kent
Eastbridge Hosp. *f. c.* 1170
No cartulary recorded.
¶ *Other registers etc.*
209.   **Oxford, Bodl., Top. Kent c. 2** (*SC.* 29292). Copies, late 16th cent., of about 76 charters etc. rel. property in Blean, Harbledown, Westgate etc. *FO:* the Towneley fam.

CANTERBURY co. Kent
Hosp. of St. James 'extra muros'
v. THANINGTON.

CANTERBURY co. Kent
Hosp. of St. Laurence *f.* 1137
No. 212 is described by C. E. Woodruff, 'The Register and Chartulary of St. Laurence, Canterbury', *Arch. Cantiana,* l (1938), 33–49.
210.   **Oxford, Bodl., Top. Kent d. 3.** Composite register of title-deeds, written at various dates, mainly in the latter part of the 14th cent. Preceded by copies of the statutes and foundation etc. charters (late 13th cent., with rubrics and red initials), some papal bulls, a terrier, rental and other similar misc. material.
Fos. ii + 50 (wants leaves *passim,* incl. eight (a quire) aft. fo. 28). $9 \times 6\frac{3}{4}$ in. *FO:* W. Shaw Mason; the Dukes of Newcastle, Clumber.
211.   **Cambridge U.L., Add. 6845.** Register, early 15th cent., similar in content and arrangement to No. 210, of which it is apparently a revision. Rubrics etc. and (fos. 4–9) red and blue initials.
Fos. 44. $10\frac{1}{4} \times 5\frac{1}{2}$ in. *FO:* W Shaw Mason; Sir T. Phillipps (MS. 6960).

212.   **Canterbury, D. & C., lit. MS. C. 20.** A third similar register, 15th cent.
Fos. 60. $11\frac{1}{4} \times 7\frac{3}{4}$ in. *FO:* W. Kingsley, 1667.

CARISBROOKE I. of Wight
Ben. Priory *f. c.* 1156
v. also No. 891 below.
213.   **BM., Egerton 3667.** 'The Black Book'. Gen. cartulary, 13th cent. (*temp.* Hen. III), with rubrics and red initials. Arranged by grantors (foundation and royal, episcopal and archidiaconal, papal, knights and lay) with misc. continuations (fos. 60 ff.), down to the 15th cent., and a contemp. Table of fos. 17–75 at fos. 12–15. Fos. 1–10 are fly-leaves. A transcript, 1573–4, by Francis Harris and John Potinger, is in the possession of the Earl of Yarborough, Brocklesby Park (Worsley MS. 12). An English version, 1600, by John Kingeswell, is in London, Soc. of Antiquaries MS. 254, fos. 1–100. Extracts by Wm. Camden, 1575 (who, in the *Britannia* i (ed. Gough, 1789), 124, says it was shown to him by R. Glover), and similar but fewer ones for R. St. George, 1607 (which may be the source of those printed in *Mon. Angl.* vi, 1040 ff.), are in BM., Lansdowne 229, fos. 116v–18v; 259, fos. 73–5. Used by Sir R. Worsley, *Hist. Isle of Wight* (1781), 63n. etc.
Fos. iii + 102. $8\frac{3}{4} \times 6\frac{3}{4}$ in. At fo. 2 a note that 'Sir John Oglander of ye Isle of Wyght hath reade most of this booke— 1646'. *FO:* Sir R. Worsley, bart., 1781; Sir T. Phillipps, 1845 (MS. 11532).

CARMARTHEN co. Carmarth.
Aug. Priory *f.* bef. 1148
214.   **Untraced.** Cartulary of which a 17th cent. transcript (pp. 207, $11 \times 8\frac{1}{4}$ in.) is in Aberystwyth, NLW., Peniarth 401 (Hengwrt 440). In the latter, the material is mainly 13th–14th cent. (down to *temp.* Ric. II) with a few later items at the end, and is arranged roughly chronologically, incl. copies of royal, episcopal and private charters, pleas, inquisitions and other misc. documents. Abstracts and indexes, 19th cent., are in *ib.,* NLW. MS. 3787 (Floyd 147). Ed. (from the transcript) Sir T. Phillipps, *Cartularium . . . de Caermarthen* (Cheltenham, 1865).

CARROW co. Norf.
v. NORWICH.

CASTLE ACRE co. Norf.
Clun. Priory *f.* 1089
215. **BM., Harley 2110.** Gen. cartulary, 13th cent. (*c.* 1250–60?), with marginal rubrics, small red and green initials, and some additions *passim*. Arranged mainly topographically with a section of charters of the earls of Warenne at the beginning (fos. 1–7) and others of royal and episcopal charters, and fines, at the end (fos. 112 ff.). *Mon. Angl.* v, 46 (*e*) lists the contents. H. H. E. Craster, *Bull. Inst. Hist. Research* iii (1925–6), 71 and C. E. Wright, 'Two Aelfric Fragments', *Medium Aevum* vii (1938), 50–5, describe the MS.'s history, fly-leaves etc.

Fos. 152 (incl. some inserted deeds etc.). $12\frac{1}{2} \times 8\frac{1}{2}$ in. *FO:* the King's Remembrancer's office, 1638; R. Dodsworth; Sir T. Widdrington; Sir S. D'Ewes, 1644; Randle Holme II.

¶ *Other registers etc.*
216. **Untraced.** Register of rentals, on vellum. *FO:* T. Martin (sale-cat., Lynn, 1772, Folio MSS. 9); J. Ives (sale-cat., 1777, lot 408; bought by 'Peart').

CASTLE HEDINGHAM co. Essex
Ben. Priory (Nuns) *f.* bef. 1191
217. **Untraced.** Register *penes* Wm. Pierpoint Esq., 17th cent., from which four charters rel. the foundation are printed in *Mon. Angl.* iv, 437–8.

CASTLE HYMEL co. Northt.
v. FINESHADE.

CERNE co. Dors.
Ben. Abbey *f.* 987
No cartulary recorded.
¶ *Other registers etc.*
218. **Cambridge U.L., Ll. 1. 10,** fos. i–xxvi. Quires etc., apparently from more than one register, containing 13th and 14th cent. copies of letters of the abbots and other misc. material, incl. a few royal and episcopal documents. Bound up at the beginning of the 'Book of Cerne', a 9th cent. collection of Passion narratives, prayers and hymns. Ed. B. F. Lock, 'The Cartulary of Cerne Abbey', *Proc. Dorset*

Nat. Hist. & Antiq. Field Club xxviii (1907), 65–95; xxix (1908), 195–223. *FO:* Bp. J. Moore.

CHACOMBE co. Northt.
Aug. Priory *f. temp.* Hen. II
No cartulary recorded.
¶ *Other registers etc.*
219. **PRO., Exch., Augm. Off.** (Misc. Bks. 378). Rental and survey, 14th cent.

CHALGRAVE co. Bedf.
Chantry in the Parish Church *f.* 1406
220. **PRO., Exch., Augm. Off.** (Misc. Bks. 149). Cartulary, early 15th cent., rel. the foundation etc. of a chantry for the souls of Sir Nigel Loring (d. 1386) and R. Braybrooke, bp. of London (d. 1404); written in book-hand with small pen-decorated initials (coloured, fo. 3), red and blue paragraphs, and one or two additions at the end. Contains copies of royal, papal, episcopal and other documents, 13th–15th cent., some concerning the appropriation to the chantry of Offley church, co. Hertf.

Fos. 39 (incl. 8 fly- and other blank leaves). $10\frac{5}{8} \times 7\frac{1}{4}$ in.

CHATTERIS co. Cambr.
Ben. Abbey (Nuns) *f.* 1006–16
221. **BM., Cotton Julius A. i,** fos. 71–188. Gen. cartulary made, 15th cent. (aft. 1427), by Abbess Agnes Ashfield and Henry Bubworth *al.* Buckworth (d. 1456), vicar of Chatteris. Rubrics etc. and black pen-decorated initials. Arranged topographically (fos. 172–80, miscellaneous) with the copies of papal, royal and episcopal charters inserted in the appropriate places. Misc. additions at fos. 151v–4, 180 ff., include (fo. 186) an index of places. *Mon. Angl.* ii, 615 (*i*) (incomplete list of contents).

Fos. 118 (earlier post-medieval foliation, 69–186). $8 \times 5\frac{1}{2}$ in. (edges damaged by fire, 1731, and the leaves now mounted).

CHERTSEY co. Surr.
Ben. Abbey *f.* 666
222. **BM., Cotton Vit. A. xiii,** fos. 20–82. Cartulary, 13th cent., of the foundation and royal, papal etc. grants to the abbey down to 1260, written in double

columns in book-hand with uncompleted rubrication, one illuminated initial at the beginning and spaces for other initials throughout. Opens (fos. 20–49) with a narrative from A.D. 666 incorporating copies of charters and continues with sections of further royal (fos. 50–69) and papal (fos. 69v–77) charters, followed (fos. 79–82) by grants and memoranda rel. the assignment of rents to obedientiaries. *Mon. Angl.* i, 425 (*o*), 426–34 (partial list of contents and extracts).

Fos. 63 (earlier post-medieval foliation, 19–81). 8¼ × 6 in. (edges damaged by fire, 1731, and the leaves now mounted). *FO:* A. Agard (see BM., Harley 6018, fo. 162).

223. **BM., Lansdowne 435.** Register, mid 14th cent., with coloured initials and a few additions, of deeds and other memoranda, incl. copies of some royal and episcopal documents, rel. additions to, and the administration of, the abbey's property, *temp.* J. de Rotherwick, abbot 1307–46. Contains material for the years 1307–44 etc., arranged annalistically. Noticed in *Mon. Angl.* i, 424 etc.

Fos. 235 (incl. 6 added paper fly-leaves). 12½ × 9½ in. *FO:* H. Powle; John, Ld. Somers; Sir J. Jekyll; James West.

224. **Lord Clifford of Chudleigh,** Lawell House, Chudleigh. Similar to No. 223, containing largely identical material for the years 1313–45 etc., with some additions (fos. 142 ff.). Noticed, with extracts, by G. Oliver, 'Register of Chertsey Abbey', *Coll. Top. et Genealogica* iv (1837), 164–8; A. Way, 'Notices of a Register . . . in the possession of . . . Lord Clifford', *Archaeological J.* xix (1862), 350–6.

Fos. 153 (misbound, and lacks some leaves). 10⅞ × 6⅞ in.

225. **PRO., Exch., K.R.** (Misc. Bks. i. 25). Gen. cartulary, 1432 etc., with uncompleted titles and long explanatory notes etc. in red, spaces for initials, and misc. additions *passim* and at the end. Opens with a section of papal, royal, ecclesiastical and other general charters etc., and is arranged thereafter topographically. Includes a coloured map of the abbey's lands (fo. ccxxii) and some rentals. Ed. *Chertsey Cartularies*, 3 vols. (Surrey Record Soc. xii, 1915–33, in progress).

Fos. 402 (contemp. foliation, viii–cccxciiii; lacks a few further leaves *passim*).

4—M.C.

19 × 13 in. *FO:* Mrs. Coggs of Egham, 17th cent.; delivered into the Exchequer by Sir H. Spiller, 1637.

¶ *Other registers etc.*

226. **BM., Lansdowne 434.** Extracts from court-rolls etc., 1327–47, rel. changes in the tenure of the abbey's lands, messuages etc., incl. copies of a few deeds rel. Egham. Elsie Toms, *Chertsey Abbey Court-Rolls Abstract* (Surrey Record Soc. xxi, 1937–54).

227. **Untraced.** Leiger-Book *penes* John Minterne of Thorpe, co. Surr., 1653, from which copies of leases etc. by the abbey, *temp.* Hen. VII–VIII, in Ash, co. Surr., are extracted in Winchester College Muniments (Ashe 3; pp. 20, large folio).

CHESTER co. Chest.
Ben. Abbey *f.* 1093

J. Tait, *The Chartulary or Register of the Abbey of St. Werburgh, Chester*, 2 vols. (Chetham Soc., New ser. lxxix, lxxxii, 1920–3), edits No. 229 with additions from other sources and discusses the other cartularies, vol. i, pp. xxvii–xxxv.

228. **BM., Harley 2071,** fos. 38–9. Bifolium from a late 13th cent. cartulary, written in double columns with rubrics. Contains copies of deeds rel. Neston and Goostrey, co. Chest., lettered serially *d–q* in the margin.

Fos. 2. 11⅝ × 8⅝ in. *FO:* Randle Holme.

229. **BM., Harley 1965.** Cartulary, early 14th cent. (aft. 1310), written in double columns with rubrics and a few additions (fos. 44v–6 etc.). Contains abstracts of charters arranged partly topographically and partly according to subject matter, with those of the earls of Chester, kings, popes and bishops at the beginning. A contemp. Table (fos. 2–3) is arranged by pressmarks (*distinctiones*). Ed. Tait, *op. cit.*

Fos. 46. 12½ × 9 in. *FO:* H. Birkenhed; Randle Holme.

230. **BM., Harley 2062.** An early 14th cent. copy of No. 229, written as far as fo. 16 in book-hand and thereafter, without break, in a small charter-hand, with rubrics and red initials. Lacks the Table, but incorporates in the main text the additions at the end of its exemplar.

Fos. 30 (lacks two or three leaves *passim*). 14½ × 10⅜ in. *FO:* Thomas Case (?); Randle Holme.

231. **Manchester, Rylands Libr., Lat.**

MS. 460. 'Copia diversarum cartarum de terris et tenementis que tenentur libere de monasterio Sancte Werburge Cestrie': a 16th cent. register of charters and other misc. late 15th–16th cent. material, incl. presentations, grants of advowsons and annuities etc.

Fos. 75. $15\frac{3}{4} \times 11$ in. Paper. *FO:* Sir M. Hale, 17th cent.; J. Fairhurst.

¶ *Other registers etc.*

232.   **Windsor, St. George's Chapel,** Muniments (xi. E. 5). Illuminated *Inspeximus*, 1280, by G. de Badlesmere, justiciary of Chester, of sixteen charters of the earls of Chester etc., 1100–1265. Printed by Tait, *op. cit.* i, 85–6 etc.

233.   **BM., Harley 2148.** Register of pleas etc., *temp.* Edw. I etc. *FO:* Randle Holme.

CHESTER   co. Chest.
Fraternity of St. Anne in the Coll. Church of St. John

234.   **BM., Harley 2061.** Parts of a 15th cent. cartulary (aft. 1420), containing copies of deeds (mainly 14th–15th cent.) rel. the city of Chester, arranged in sections by streets. Calendared by J. H. E. Bennett, 'Chartulary of the Hospital of St. Anne, Chester', *The Cheshire Sheaf*, Third ser. xxxvi (1948 for 1941), 1–65 *passim*.

Fos. 26 (contemp. roman foliation by sections and post-medieval arabic foliation, both imperf.; wants at least 34 leaves at the beginning and others *passim* and at the end). $14\frac{3}{4} \times 10\frac{3}{4}$ in. *FO:* Randle Holme.

CHICHESTER, See of   *f.* (at Selsey) c. 681
The cartularies of the See and Dean & Chapter at Chichester are described by R. L. Poole, *HMC. Various Collections* i (1901), 177–204 and W. D. Peckham, *The Chartulary of the High Church of Chichester* (Sussex Record Soc. xlvi, 1946 for 1942–3), who calendars No. 248 with the charter material from the other registers.

235.   **Chichester, Diocesan R.O.,** 'Liber B' *al.* 'Vol. XVIII' (Ep. vi/1/2). Cartulary made for W. Reade, bp. 1368–85, with red underlinings of headings etc., and misc. additions incl. (fos. 5–10) a 16th cent. Table. Arranged in sections by manors etc. with copies of royal, incl.

Anglo-Saxon, charters at the beginning (fos. 16–38).

Fos. 143. $10 \times 6\frac{1}{2}$ in.

236.   **Ditto,** 'Liber A' *al.* 'Vol. XVII' (Ep. vi/1/1). Fragm. of a misc. register of evidences rel. the bishop's lands (mainly feodaries, scutages, pleas, inquisitions etc.), made for Bp. Reade by W. atte Hulle, *clericus compotorum suorum*, and in similar format to No. 235. Includes (fos. 23–38, or 168–9, 1–13, 178, in a contemp. arabic foliation) copies of a series of Anglo-Saxon, Norman and later royal charters etc. to the See, now incomplete. Fo. 4 contains the beginning of a contemp. Table.

Fos. 43 (bound in disorder). $10\frac{1}{2} \times 7$ in.

237.   **Ditto,** 'Liber P' *al.* 'Vol. VII' (Ep. vi/1/5). A similar misc. register made for Bp. Reade, incl. (fos. 161–202) a cartulary of the bishop's manors which refers back, for the royal and some other charters, to fos. 7–29 and 168–82 *passim*, in the medieval foliation, of No. 236.

Fos. 212 + ii. $10\frac{1}{2} \times 6\frac{3}{4}$ in.

238.   **Ditto,** 'Liber E' *al.* 'Reg. W. Reade' (Ep. vi/1/4). Misc. register of statutes, writs, ordinations, taxations etc. made for Bp. Reade. More elaborately written than Nos. 235–7, with blue initials decorated with red, red underlinings of headings etc. Includes, with other scattered charter material, copies of: (*a*) royal charters etc. to the See, *temp.* Hen. III–Edw. III, fos. 157–64v; (*b*) 12th cent. papal bulls, fos. 174–7. A 16th cent. transcript is *ib.*, Cap. i/12/1. A Table, down to fo. 229, is in **Bodl. Ashmole 1146** (formerly 'Liber D', containing constitutions), which is the first half (pts. *i* & *ii*) of the same compilation, cf. W. D. Peckham, *Sussex Notes & Queries* ii (1928–9), 105–8.

Fos. 139 (numbered 137–275). $10 \times 7\frac{1}{2}$ in.

239.   **Ditto,** 'Chapter Book CL. 9' (Cap. i/16/1). Cartulary, 16th cent., of estates acquired by R. Sherborne, bp. 1508–36, for the endowment of his foundations. Arranged topographically with a Table on five unnumbered preliminary leaves and contemp. additions at the end (fos. cxxii ff.). Antecedent title-deeds are not included.

Fos. 5 + 142 (numbered i–cxlii). $13\frac{3}{4} \times 9\frac{1}{2}$ in. Paper.

¶ *Other registers etc.*

For further registers at Chichester see also Poole and Peckham, *ll. cc.*

240. **Ditto,** 'Liber C' (Ep. vi/1/3). Feodary, rental, custumary etc., late 14th cent., incl. copies of a few misc. charters and other documents *passim*.

241–247. ORDINATIONS of Bp. Sherborne's foundations (cf. No. 239), early 16th cent. Partly printed in *Statutes and Constitutions of the Cathedral Church of Chichester*, ed. F. G. Bennett, R. H. Codrington, C. Deedes (Chichester, 1904); see also C. E. Welch, 'Bishop Sherburne . . . and his "Donations"', *Notes & Queries* cic (1954), 191–3. Seven copies, as follows:—

241–2. **Oxford, New Coll., MSS. 313, 313A** (two copies, one deposited in the Bodleian Libr.). H. O. Coxe, *Cat. MSS. Oxon.* i (Oxford, 1852), *ad loc.*, lists the contents.

243. **Winchester College,** Muniments (Chest ii, no. 168).

244–7. **Chichester, Diocesan R.O.,** 'Sherborne's Foundations' *al.* 'Vol. III' (Cap. i/14/1), 'Liber Q' (Cap. i/14/2), 'Sherborne's *Ordinationes*' (Cap. i/14/3), 'Sherborne's Donations' (Cap. i/14/5). Four copies.

CHICHESTER co. Suss.
Cath. Church *f.* (at Selsey) *c.* 681
Bibliography as for the See.

248. **Chichester, Diocesan R.O.,** 'Liber Y' (Ep. vi/1/6). Gen. cartulary. The original compilation, written apparently *c.* 1250–60 with rubrics etc. and spaces for small initials, and arranged partly by grantors etc. (royal incl. Anglo-Saxon, papal, episcopal, magnates) and partly according to subject (compositions, grants to and leases by the Dean & Chapter, grants to the altar of the Virgin, *Carte Anniversariorum* etc.) is preceded, followed and interspersed with 13th–14th cent. additions. Fos. 1–60, 226–49, are added 14th–16th cent. quires of misc. contents, incl. (fos. 3–43) a 16th cent. Table. See also No. 251 below. Ed. Peckham, *op. cit.*

Fos. 246. 10¼ × 7½ in. Formerly stated to belong to the Dean & Chapter.

249. **Untraced.** 'Magnus Liber Evidentiarum' *al.* 'The Leiger Book', probably destroyed, 17th cent., in the Civil Wars. Cartulary, early 14th cent., 'in a very great folio with a wooden cover bound over with leather of a murrey colour and with two clasps', containing upwards of 400 pages, written mainly in the hand of John Stilman. Partial 18th cent. Tables, copied from a 17th cent. one now lost, are in Chichester, Diocesan R.O., 'Statute Book B' (Cap. i/1/2), fos. 24–6 and 'Dr. Hayley's Book' (Cap. i/12/3), pp. 238–57. Extracts, 16th cent., are in *ib.*, John Swayne's Book' *al.* 'Liber K' (Cap. i/12/2), pp. 167–324.

¶ *Other registers etc.*
For other registers at Chichester see Poole and Peckham, *ll. cc.*

250. **Oxford, Univ. Coll. MS. 148,** deposited in the Bodleian Libr. 'Dean Croucher's Book'. See No. 251 following.

CHICHESTER co. Suss.
Hosp. of St. Mary *f.* 1172

251. **Oxford, Univ. Coll. MS. 148** (deposited in the Bodleian Libr.), fos. 57–70. Cartulary, 13th cent. (aft. 1252), identical in execution with the original compilation of No. 248, with which it is perhaps to be associated. Opens with the heading, 'Sequuntur alique carte de domo beate Marie Cic. et praecipue de decimis', and contains copies of 82 charters. Bound up in a misc. register, incl. some liturgical etc. material, put together between 1426 and 1447 by Dean J. Croucher, who was also warden of the hospital. A transcript, 1725, formerly in the Cathedral library, is now in Chichester Diocesan R.O. (Cap. i/1/1). A. Ballard, *Sussex Arch. Coll.* li (1908), 37–64 (calendar). W. D. Peckham, *ib.* lxxxiv (1944–5), 11–32 (description of the whole MS., with further bibliography).

Fos. 14 (119 in the MS.). 9¾ × 7 in. *FO:* G. Langbaine.

CHRISTCHURCH (*al.* TWYNHAM)
co. Southt.
Aug. Priory *f.* bef. 1066

252. **BM., Cotton Tib. D. vi.** 'Speculum Prioris'. Gen. cartulary, 1372, with red and blue initials etc., occasionally illuminated, and misc. additions *passim*. Now bound in two parts. Arranged mainly topographically by counties, with sections of papal, royal, episcopal and other general charters and of deeds rel. the various *Officia* at the beginning, preceded (pt. i, fos. 1–12) by a preface and contemp. Table; and with others of miscellaneous

material, incl. charters, pleas, rentals etc., at the end (pt. ii, fos. 30 ff.). The whole damaged by fire, 1731, and the leaves now mounted, with some loss of marginalia etc.

Fos. 161 + 150 (18th cent. foliation, 1–323). 12½ × 8½ in. Trial signatures of John and Roger Tichbourne, 16th cent., on the end flyleaf (pt. ii, fo. 148v).

⁋ *Other registers etc.*

253. **PRO., Exch., K.R.** (Transcripts of Deeds and Charters, E. 132/17). Roll of misc. evidences, 13th–14th cent.

CIRENCESTER   co. Glouc.
Aug. Abbey   *f.* bef. 1066

An edition of Nos. 255–6 is in preparation by C. D. Ross.

254. **The Marquess of Bath,** Longleat (MS. 38 (b)). Fragm. of a late 12th cent. cartulary, written in double columns with rubrics and alternate red and pale blue initials. Contains copies of 27 royal, archiepiscopal and other ecclesiastical etc. charters, with about 13 additions down to *temp.* Hen. III incl. copies of some 12th cent. papal bulls. Calendared by W. St. Clair Baddeley, *Hist. Cirencester* (Cirencester, 1924), 111–17.

Fos. 7. 11½ × 7¼ in.

255. **Lady Vestey,** Stowell Park, Northleach. 'Registrum A'. Gen. cartulary, 13th cent. (aft. 1249), written mainly in double columns with rubrics etc., red initials sometimes alternated with blue, and substantial misc. additions *passim* and at the end (fos. 167 ff.). Arranged mainly topographically, with sections of royal and papal charters and of fines at the beginning, preceded (fos. 1–7) by a contemp. Table, and incl. copies of some episcopal charters *passim.*

Fos. v + 201 (medieval foliation, 1–182, from fo. 8; other post-medieval foliations and pagination). 12½ × 8½ in. *FO:* Sir Wm. Master, d. 1662 (if one of the '2 fair books' ascribed to him in Bodl., Dugdale 48 (*SC.* 6536), fo. 56v); John Prynne (?), by whom there are extensive annotations; Sir T. Phillipps (MS. 6692), by gift of W. Prowse.

256. **Ditto.** 'Registrum B'. Gen. cartulary, late 14th cent. (aft. 1360), with largely uncompleted rubrication etc., spaces for initials, and a few misc. additions *passim* and at the end. Arranged mainly

topographically, with sections of royal and papal charters at the beginning, and incl. copies of some episcopal charters *passim.*

Fos. ii + 252. 13 × 8 in. *FO:* as No. 255.

⁋ *Other registers etc.*

257. **Oxford, Bodl., Rawlinson B. 326.** Register of presentations, grants of corrodies etc., 1421–1539. *FO:* R. Parsons, D.C.L.; W. Clavell.

258. **Untraced.** Leiger book (containing terriers, rentals etc. ?), 'in the possession of one Mr. Willoughby dwellinge nigh Gloucester and after in the hands or custody of Mr. Birde, towne Clark of Gloucester', from which extracts, 16th cent., are in Winchester Coll. Muniments (Millborne Port, unnumbered rolled paper book).

259. **Untraced.** 'Registrum penes dom. Hen. Pool de Saperton, postea penes dom. Rob. Atkyns (i.e. Sir R. Atkyns, chief baron of the Exchequer, who bought Sapperton in 1660), et nunc penes Ed. Cartaret arm.' (*T*).

CIRENCESTER   co. Glouc.
Chapel of St. Mary in the Parish Church

260. **Oxford, Bodl., Dugdale 42** (*SC.* 6530). 'Registrum diversarum cartarum ... factum per Willelmum Brome et Willelmum Dodyngton custodes capelle, 1460'. Copies of deeds, 1258–1427, followed (fos. 18 ff.) by a rental, 1459, and inventory of ornaments.

Fos. iii + 25. 12 × 8 in.

CLARE   co. Suff.
Ben. Priory   *f.* 1090

v. STOKE BY CLARE.

CLARE   co. Suff.
House of Aug. Friars Hermit   *f.* 1248

261. **BM., Harley 4835.** Cartulary, 14th cent. (*temp.* Ric. II), of private deeds rel. Clare etc., with a copy of one royal charter (1364) at the beginning. The entries are lettered serially throughout. Fos. 58–9 should follow fo. 6. A 19th cent. transcript is in BM., Add. 8188, fos. 55–84 and extracts, 1638, are in BM., Harley 294, fo. 174; 639, fos. 94–7.

Fos. 69 (excl. blank leaves). 11 × 8⅜ in. Paper. *FO:* G. Barnardiston, 1638; E. Johnston (*T*).

CLEEVE co. Som.
Cist. Abbey *f.* 1198
262. **Untraced.** 'Registrum . . . penes
Wadham Windham justit. ad plac. A.D.
1662' (*T*), i.e. Sir Wadham Wyndham of
Norrington and St. Edmund's Coll., Salisbury (d. 1668). Extracts down to fo. 115 in
Mon. Angl. v, 732-3, cite it as in the hands,
1677, of his elder brother Sir Hugh Wyndham, judge (d. 1684).

CLERKENWELL co. Middx.
Ben. or Aug. Priory (Nuns) *f. c.* 1144
263. **BM., Cotton Faust. B. ii,** fos. 6-
116. Gen. cartulary, mid-13th cent., with
rubrics and red and blue initials. Arranged
in two parts with misc. additions at the end
of each: (1) fos. 6-60, copies of royal
charters (English and Scottish), followed
by deeds rel. estates outside London
arranged topographically; (2) fos. 61 ff.,
copies of deeds rel. properties in London.
Ed. W. O. Hassall, *The Cartulary of St.
Mary, Clerkenwell* (Camden Third ser.
lxxi, 1949).
Fos. 111. 9¾ × 6½ in. (cropped). *FO:*
John Stow.

CLERKENWELL co. Middx.
Hosp. of St. John of Jerusalem *f. c.* 1144
v. ST. JOHN OF JERUSALEM.

COCKERSAND co. Lanc.
Praem. Abbey *f.* (as a hosp.) bef. 1184
264. **BM., Add. 37769.** Gen. cartulary
written, 1268, by R. de Lacheford, with
red page-headings etc. Contains sections of
papal and royal charters copied in full, followed by abstracts of deeds arranged topographically, with a few misc. additions
passim. A transcript, 1661, for C. Towneley,
is in BM., Add. 32099. Ed. W. Farrer, *The
Chartulary of Cockersand Abbey,* 7 vols.
(Chetham Soc. xxxviii-xl, xliii, lvi-vii,
lxiv, 1898-1909). *BM. Cat. Add. MSS.*
1906-1910, 129-30.
Fos. iii + 164. 11¾ × 8 in. *FO:* the Dalton
fam., Thurnham; Sir T. R. Gage, bart.,
1861; Sir T. Brooke, bart.
265. **The Hon. Mrs. H. Hornyold-
Strickland,** Sizergh Castle. Part of a roll
of charters. The recto contains late 13th
cent. abstracts, perhaps contemp. with No.
264, of 35 deeds etc. arranged topographic-

ally. On the verso there are misc. 14th and
15th cent. additions, incl. a list of places
which shows the whole to be now probably not more than one-third of its
original length. A. J. Horwood, *HMC.
Fifth Report* (1876), App., 332, names the
places and grantors.
Roll of 2 membrs. 44 × 8¼ in. (mutilated
at the foot).

COGGESHALL co. Essex
Cist. Abbey *f.* 1140
266. **Untraced.** Cartulary or cartularies
(apparently more than one vol.) from
which extracts, 16th cent., are in BM.,
Cotton Tib. E. ix, fos. 49-57 (mutilated by
fire, 1731).

COLCHESTER co. Essex
Ben. Abbey *f.* 1095
267. **Colchester, Borough Muniments.** Gen. cartulary, late 13th cent.
(*temp.* Hen. III), compiled by John de
Hadleigh and written in double columns
with rubrics, red and blue decorated initials, and additions *passim.* Arranged in
four books, following the order of the
muniments (*i* royal, papal, episcopal etc.
charters; *ii* & *iii* private deeds etc.; *iv
Cirographa conventualium ecclesiarum*), with
some further subdivision into sections
and an elaborate Table at the beginning.
An 18th cent. abstract by P. Morant is in
BM., Stowe 837 (*FO:* T. Astle). Ed. S. A.
Moore, *Cartularium . . . de Colecestria,* 2
vols. (Roxburghe Club, 1897). *Trans.
Essex Arch. Soc.,* New ser. xvi (1923), 217-8
(an anonymous note).
Fos. *c.* 155 + i. 14½ × 10½ in. *FO:* John
Lucas, 1548, and his descendants in the
baronies of Lucas of Shenfield and Lucas
of Crudwell, latterly at Wrest Park (MS.
56): hence cited as of the Earls and Duke of
Kent; the Marchioness Grey; Philip Yorke,
2nd earl of Hardwicke; Earl de Grey; Earl
Cowper.
⁋ *Pitanciarius*
268. **BM., Arundel 145.** Cartulary,
late 15th cent., of lands assigned to the
pittancer, preceded (fos. 1-10) by a rental,
1478.
Fos. 45 (contemp. foliation, 1-43, from
fo. 11). 11½ × 8¼ in. Presented by Henry
Howard, 6th duke of Norfolk, to the Royal
Society, 1678.

¶ *Other registers etc.*
269. **Colchester, Borough Muniments.** Register of extents, leases, quitclaims, rentals, inquisitions, pleas etc., early 14th cent. (*temp.* Edw. II) with additions. Calendared by J. L. Fisher, 'The Leger Book of St. John's Abbey, Colchester', *Trans. Essex Arch. Soc.*, New ser. xxiv (1951), 77–127. FO :as No. 267 (Wrest Park MS. 57).

COLD NORTON co. Oxon
Aug. Priory *f.* 1148–58
No cartulary recorded.
¶ *Other registers etc.*
270. 'Registra, cartas, computos etc., in pyxide intra thesaurarium coll. Aenei Nasi Oxon. cui titulus Prioratus de Coldnorton' (*T*). For material now at Brasenose Coll., Oxford, see A. J. Butler, 'The College Estates' and I. S. Leadam, 'The Early Years of the College', *BNC. Quatercentenary Monogrs.* i & ii (Oxford Hist. Soc. lii, liii, 1909), monogrs. vi (pp. 6 ff.), ix (pp. 54 ff.).

COLNE, EARLS co. Essex
Ben. Priory *f.* 1111
Extracts, 16th cent., from apparently at least two cartularies (one described as 'Liber Maior'), are in BM., Cotton Tib. E. ix, fos. 5–17 and Vesp. B. xv, fos. 59–70. Neither appears to correspond to No. 271.
271. **Colne Priory Estate Archives,** deposited at Chelmsford, Essex R.O. (D/DPr. 149). Gen. cartulary, 12th–13th cent., written in a small book-hand with rubrics and red, green and black decorated initials, contemp. additions at the end (fos. 33–5), and a 15th cent. copy of the foundation charter added at fos. 1–2. Arranged according to the status of grantors (royal, episcopal, baronial and private). An 18th cent. transcript is in BM., Add. 5860, fos. 110–33v. A photostat copy is BM., MS. Facsimiles 472. Ed. J. L. Fisher, *Cartularium Prioratus de Colne* (Essex Arch. Soc. Occasional Publns. i, 1946). *Mon. Angl.* iv, 97 (*h*) lists the contents etc.
Fos. 35. 7½ × 5⅜ in. *FO:* R. Andrews of Colne ('nuper in ruinis prioratus repertum' (*T*)), 1719; the Wale, Holgate, Carwardine and Probert fams.
272. **BM., Stowe 841,** fos. 52–3. Two leaves from a mid-14th cent. cartulary (the outer bifolium of a quire), with rubrics and spaces for initials. Headed *Carte Comitum* and contain copies of grants by the de Veres, earls of Oxford etc.
Fos. 2. 10¾ × 7⅝ in. *FO:* the Rev. P. Morant.

COMBE co. Warw.
Cist. Abbey *f.* 1150
273. **BM., Cotton Vit. D. xviii.** Cartulary, 13th cent., with rubrics, red decoration of initials etc. Arranged topographically, with some additions on blank leaves etc. *passim*, and a few entries subsequently deleted in red. Damaged by fire, 1731, and now consists of fragms. only of some leaves. Extracts, 17th cent., are in Bodl., Dugdale 12 (*SC.* 6502), pp. 111–72; BM., Harley 294, fos. 183–3*.
Fos. 82 (before the fire 163, numbered 50–212). Small Quarto (?).
274. **BM., Cotton Vit. A. i,** fos. 32–172. Cartulary, 1255, written by R. de Wlvrechestun (Wolston) with rubrics etc. and some misc. additions *passim*. Arranged topographically in sections, with a list of places at fo. 36v and a title-page misbound as fo. 142. Damaged by fire, 1731, and the leaves now mounted. *Mon. Angl.* v, 583 (*q*), lists the heads of sections.
Fos. 141. 9¼ × 7 in. (shrunk).

CONWAY co. Carnarvon
v. ABERCONWAY.

COTHAM, NUN co. Linc.
v. NUN COTHAM.

COVENTRY co. Warw.
Ben. Cath. Priory *f.* (as an abbey) 1043
Joan C. Lancaster, 'The Coventry Forged Charters: a Reconsideration', *Bull. Inst. Hist. Research* xxvii (1954), 113 ff., discusses the cartularies *passim*.
275. **Major A. M. H. Gregory-Hood, M.C.,** deposited at Stratford-upon-Avon, Shakespeare Birthplace Libr. ('Gregory Leiger-Book', pp. 19–46). A rubricated 14th cent. quire with spaces for initials and touching of letters with red, containing copies of early royal, papal (Alexander II) and other (Earl Leofric) charters to the house, followed apparently by misc. additions. From p. 33 the leaves, which are bound up with a cartulary of Stoneleigh Abbey (No. 936) in a 16th cent. register of

the Gregory family (No. 1249), are almost entirely illegible through damp.

Fos. 14. $7\frac{1}{2} \times 5\frac{7}{8}$ in. Descended in the Gregory, afterw. Gregory-Hood, fam., Stivichall and Loxley Hall.

276.　**PRO., Exch., K.R.** (Misc. Bks. i. 21). Register, early 15th cent., of 14th–15th cent. rentals, extents, inquisitions etc., incl. (fos. 75–130) copies of a number of royal, foundation and other charters, the majority (fos. 85 ff.) apparently rel. grants subsequent to the enactment of the Statute of Mortmain, 1279. A late 16th cent. transcript of the first part, incl. copies of one or two charters, is in BM., Lansdowne 400 (*FO:* Humfry Burton, town clerk of Coventry, 17th cent.), for which see *Mon. Angl.* iii, 185.

Fos. 271. $13\frac{1}{2} \times 9\frac{3}{4}$ in. The words 'Civitas Coventr.' written on the front fly-leaf.

277.　**Destroyed** (by fire, 1879, at Birmingham Reference Libr.). 'A thin quarto volume,' apparently containing copies of royal charters, pleas etc., mainly *temp.* Edw. I–III. *Mon. Angl.* iii, 185 (*a*).

Fos. 25. Quarto. *FO:* F. Douce (part of Bodl., Douce 139); T. Sharp; W. Staunton.

278.　**Ditto.** Cartulary, apparently arranged topographically, incl. copies of documents down to *temp.* Hen. VI. *Mon. Angl.* iii, 184 (*l*).

Fos. 126. *FO:* T. Sharp; W. Staunton.

279.　**Untraced.** 'Registrum imperfectum . . . in archivis civitatis Coventriae' (*T*). Not now known to exist in Coventry City Archives: possibly to be identified with, or with extracts from, one of the preceding.

279A.　**Untraced.** Roll in the possession, late 16th cent., of Wm. Walters of the Temple, from which the foundation, early royal, papal, episcopal and capitular charters etc., down to *temp.* Edw. III and for the most part rel. the priory's churches, are copied in BM., Add. 32100, fos. 114–22.

COXFORD　co. Norf.
Aug. Priory　　f. (at E. Rudham) *c.* 1140

280.　**Norwich, Diocesan Registry.** Gen. cartulary, late 13th cent. (aft. 1288), with rubrics, red paragraphs etc. and additions, mainly 14th cent., down to 1485 *passim*. Arranged topographically and incl. copies of royal, papal and episcopal chart-

ers. Calendared by H. W. Saunders, 'A History of Coxford Priory', *Norfolk Archaeology* xvii (1910), 355 ff., from a transcript (1886) by A. Jessopp, now Norwich Public Libr. MS. 3201.

Fos. 62 (numbered 1–64; wants 41–2). $14\frac{1}{4} \times 11$ in. *FO:* the Townshend fam., viscounts & marquesses Townshend (*T*); A. Jessopp, D.D. (?); the Rev. M. P. M. Mclean.

281.　**BM., Add. 47784.** Gen. cartulary, *c.* 1400 etc., with rubrics and red initials. Mainly a revision of the preceding but incl. copies of some 70 additional charters etc. rel. Hillington, Lynn, Tittleshall etc., and lacking some other material. Contemp. index of places, fo. 1. G. R. C. Davis, 'A Lost Chartulary of Coxford Priory', *Brit. Mus. Quart.* xviii (1953), 70–1 (descriptive note).

Fos. iii+93 (contemp. foliation, i–cxviii, on the verso of fos. 2–86; wants lxi–lxxii, lxxxv–cix). $12 \times 8\frac{3}{4}$ in. Paper. Found in a London junk-shop, 20th cent., by T. S. Blakeney.

¶ *Other registers etc.*

282.　**H. L. Bradfer-Lawrence Esq., F.S.A.,** Sharow End, Ripon. Register of terriers, rentals etc., *c.* 1342 etc.

283.　**BM., Campbell Ch. xxi. 8.** Terriers for E. & W. Rudham, 1410–11, 1489.

CRABHOUSE　co. Norf.
Aug. Priory (Canonesses)　　f. *c.* 1181
　No cartulary recorded.

¶ *Other registers etc.*

284.　**BM., Add. 4733,** fos. 1–54. Register comprising: (1) fos. 1–29, a narrative account in French of the priory's foundation, lands etc., written in a series of 13th–14th cent. hands, apparently for instructional purposes, and consisting mainly of notes of grants, sometimes with references to the number and type of the relevant charters etc.; (2) fos. 36 ff., terrier and rental, 1420, in Latin; (3) fos. 50v ff., an annalistic account, late 15th cent., in English, of building work carried out at the priory, 1420–44 and after 1461, incomplete at the end. Mary Bateson, 'The Register of Crabhouse Nunnery', *Norfolk Archaeology* xi (1892), 1–71, edits (1) and (3). Presented by the Rev. Henry Robinson, 1765.

CREAKE, NORTH co. Norf.
Aug. Abbey *f.* (as a priory) 1206
285. **Cambridge, Christ's Coll.,**
Muniments (Creake At. 2). Two bifolia
from a cartulary, begun in a 13th cent. hand
which has inserted the headings etc. and
made usually only two or three entries on
each page, and continued in a succession of
other hands down to *temp.* Edw. III. They
contain copies of about 25 private deeds
rel. Burnham, Docking, Brancaster, Deep-
dale, Stanhoe etc., the verso of one leaf
being blank.
Fos. 4. $9 \times 6\frac{1}{2}$ in.

286. **Ditto.** (Creake 7.) Copies, 13th
cent., of papal, episcopal etc. charters to the
abbey rel. its churches, followed by an
added 14th cent. terrier.
Roll of 4 membrs. *c.* $67 \times 8\frac{1}{4}$ in.

287. **H. L. Bradfer-Lawrence Esq.,**
F.S.A., Sharow End, Ripon. Cartulary,
early 14th cent. (*temp.* Edw. II ?), with red
etc. initials, sometimes decorated, occasional rubrics etc. and additions (mainly
temp. Edw. III). Contains copies of private
deeds and some grants by the abbey,
arranged topographically, for Creake,
South Creake, Quarles, North Barsham,
Holkham, Thorp and Burnham. A historical preface (fos. 1–2) is printed in *Mon.
Angl.* vi, 487–8.
Fos. 76 (post-medieval numeration, 1–
79; wants 14–16). $11\frac{1}{4} \times 7\frac{3}{4}$ in. *FO:* H.
Dereham, 1633 (*D*); R. Bryer (*P*); Taylor
Combe; Sir T. Phillipps, 1827 (MS. 85).

288. **Untraced.** Part of a register rel.
Gateley and Ryburgh *penes* Bp. John
Moore, 1698 (*T*).

CRICH co. Derby
Parish Church
289. **BM., Harley 3669.** Cartulary, late
14th cent., of deeds etc., incl. copies of a
few royal and episcopal documents, rel.
the foundation and endowment by W. de
Wakebridge of two chantries there and
(fos. 88–91) of a third at Annesley, 1350–68,
with misc. additions on the fly-leaves (fos.
1–5, 104–6). Bound up with two kalendars
(fos. 6–11, 98–103). Used extensively by
J. C. Cox, *Notes on the Churches of Derbyshire* iv (1879), 35–50, and 'A Parochial
Chartulary of the 14th cent.', *The Ancestor*
vi (1903), 103–19.
Fos. 106. $12\frac{1}{4} \times 8$ in.

CROXDEN co. Staff.
Cist. Abbey *f.* (at Cotton) 1176
290. **Untraced.** 'Registrum . . . nuper
penes Will. Pierrepoint de Tong Castle,
modo penes honoratiss. Thomam com.
Macclesfield' (*T*), i.e. Thomas, 1st earl of
Macclesfield, d. 1732.

CROXTON co. Leic.
Praem. Abbey *f.* bef. 1160
No proper cartulary recorded. For the
material at Belvoir see J. H. Round, *HMC.
Rutland* iv (1905), 174–82. For extracts
from Nos. 291–2, see BM., Add. 4934, fos.
145 ff. & 4935, fos. 95 ff. (by F. Peck, 1731);
J. Nichols, *Hist. Leicester* ii, pt. 1 (1795),
App. xi, 77–104 and his accounts of the
abbey's manors *passim.*

¶ *Other registers etc.*
291. **The Duke of Rutland,** Belvoir
Castle (Add. MS. 70). The 'Large Cartulary' *al.* 'Croxton Domesday'. An account
of the abbey's lands, incl. the names of
benefactors and tenants, compiled 13th
cent. (*temp.* Hen. III) by Wm. de Lough-
borough. Rubricated initials. Followed
(fo. 41v) by rentals down to *temp.* Hen.
VIII, fos. 46 ff. being additional to the
original compilation.
Fos. 92. $8\frac{1}{2} \times 6\frac{1}{2}$ in.

292. **Ditto** (Add. MS. 71). 'Croxton
Abbey Register'. Memoranda (fos. 1–70),
13th cent. (*temp.* Hen. III), rel. the acquisition etc. of lands in co. Leic., based on
charters which are sometimes summarised
and occasionally transcribed in full, with
place-names in red at the top of each leaf.
Followed by: (*a*) similar added memoranda rel. the abbey's churches, fos. 84–9;
(*b*) a formulary (fos. 73, 95–149), etc. A
transcript, 1755, omitting (*b*), is in BM.,
Stowe 928 (*FO:* T. Astle).
Fos. 150. $6 \times 3\frac{1}{2}$ in.

293. **Ditto** (Muniment room ii, case 29,
shelf 3). Roll, late 13th cent., with pen-
decorated paragraphs, the recto containing
memoranda similar to those in No. 292,
and the verso abstracts of grants to and by
the abbey.
Roll of 3 membrs. 57×9 in.

CROYLAND co. Linc.
Ben. Abbey *f.* aft. 966
294. **Spalding, Gentlemen's Society.**
Gen. cartulary, mid-14th cent. (aft. 1343),

with rubrics etc. and additions *passim*. Arranged topographically in sections, the royal (from Stephen), papal and episcopal charters being grouped at the beginning under Croyland. Also includes copies of a few grants by the abbey. A contemp. Table (fos. 3–23) shows a small section for Standon, co. Hertf., to be uncompleted or wanting at the end. A transcript and some rotographs are in Lincolnshire Archives Office (Foster Libr.).

Fos. 257 (wants single leaves aft. fos. 90, 121). $14\frac{1}{2} \times 9\frac{1}{4}$ in. *FO:* R. Ogle; William Cecil, Ld. Burghley; the Earls & Duke of Kent and their descendants at Wrest Park (Marchioness Grey, Philip Yorke 2nd earl of Hardwicke, Earls de Grey, Earls Cowper etc.); A. K. Maples.

295.   Oxford, All Souls Coll., MS. 32. A composite 15th cent. register comprising: (1) fos. 1–8 (a quire), copies of charters of Anglo-Saxon kings etc., 716–966 (of which other texts occur in Ingulph, 'Historia Croylandensis'), with pen-decorated initials, and place-names in the text written in red; (2) fos. 9–23 (a quire of coarser vellum), copies of pleas, *temp.* Hen. V–VI, followed by two further Anglo-Saxon private charters, 819–20, and six 12th–13th cent. fines. H. O. Coxe, *Cat. MSS. Oxon.* ii (Oxford, 1852), *ad loc.*

Fos. 23. $12\frac{1}{2} \times 8\frac{1}{2}$ in. Presented by Daniel Prince, bookseller, 1755.

¶ *Other registers etc.*
296.   Untraced. Leiger-book, 14th cent., of about 250 fos., to many of which small deeds etc. were sewn. Apparently a misc. register of pleas, terriers, rentals etc., see the extracts, 1772, by W. Cole in BM., Add. 5845, fos. 18–108 & 5887. *Mon. Angl.* ii, 105–6 etc. *FO:* J. Oldfeild; Maurice Johnson; lent, bef. 1772, by Mrs. Elizabeth Wingfield to W. Greaves *al.* Beaupré-Bell.
297.   BM., Add. 25302, fos. 1–8. Fragm. of a 15th–16th cent. register on paper, containing copies of inquisitions etc. and one or two deeds. *FO:* Ld. Robert Montagu.

DALE   co. Derby
Praem. Abbey   *f.* (as a priory) aft. 1180
298.   BM., Cotton Vesp. E. xxvi. Gen. cartulary, early 14th cent., with uncompleted rubrication and red initials. Imperf. at the beginning. Contains copies of private deeds etc. arranged topographic-

ally, preceded (fo. 5) and followed (fos. 178 ff.) by misc. additions, incl. a list of abbots and T. de Musca's history of the abbey, with occasional other additions *passim*. Calendared by J. C. Cox, 'The Chartulary of . . . Dale', *Derbyshire Arch. & Nat. Hist. Soc. J.* xxiv (1902), 82–150. *Mon. Angl.* vi, 892 (*g*) lists the places.

Fos. 196 (lacks the first quire (16 leaves ?) and part (6 leaves ?) of the second). $8\frac{3}{4} \times 6\frac{1}{2}$ in. *FO:* Anchitell Grey, 17th cent.

DARLEY   co. Derby
Aug. Abbey   *f. c.* 1137
R. R. Darlington, *The Cartulary of Darley Abbey*, 2 vols. (Kendal, for the Derbyshire Arch. Soc., 1945), edits No. 299, with supplementary extracts from No. 300, and describes the MSS., vol. i, pp. lxxv–lxxix.

299.   BM., Cotton Titus C. ix, fos. 39–166. Cartulary, late 13th cent. (*c.* 1275 ?), with rubrics etc., pen-decorated initials (occasionally in red) and additions, incl. copies of a few 13th–14th cent. royal documents, on blank and added leaves *passim*. Consists mainly of copies of private etc. charters, arranged topographically in sections lettered *A–P* (*O* episcopal, *P* capitular, *J* & *M* apparently never written; much of *L*, for Crich, Sandiacre and Wingfield, wanting). Contemp. Table, fos. 43–7. Ed. Darlington, *op. cit.* Calendared by J. C. Cox, 'History and Chartulary of . . . Darley' etc., *Derbyshire Arch. & Nat. Hist. Soc. J.* xxvi (1904), 100–38.

Fos. 128 (wants 12 leaves aft. fo. 149 and 4 others *passim*). 11×8 in.

300.   Oxford, Bodl., Gough Derby 1 (*SC.* 17857). Fragm. (quires *xvi* (?), *xvii*) of a late 14th cent. cartulary with red page-headings, mainly cropped off, and touching of capitals. Contains copies of about 100 charters rel. Oakerthorpe, Wessington, Crich etc., arranged topographically. An 18th cent. transcript by W. Cole is in BM., Add. 5822, fos. 150–70.

Fos. 21. $10 \times 7\frac{3}{4}$ in. (cropped). *FO:* Dr. R. Farmer.

¶ *Other registers etc.*
301.   Untraced. Register, 13th cent. (*temp.* Hen. III), of upwards of 344 fos., in the possession, 1647, of Samuel Roper of Monks Kirby. Described as containing 'plurima ad abbatiam de Darley . . .

necnon historica quaedam', see the extracts in Bodl., Dugdale 20 (*SC.* 6510), fos. 136v–142. N. Denholm Young, 'Documents of the Barons' Wars', *Engl. Hist. Review* xlviii (1933), 569–75.

DAVENTRY co. Northt.
Clun. Priory *f.* (at Preston Capes) *c.* 1090
302. **BM., Cotton Claud. D. xii.** Gen. cartulary, late 14th cent. (aft. 1366), with rubrics and red initials. Arranged in sections mainly topographically (fos. 159 ff., rel. churches) with a few additions, incl. a list of priors (fo. 172), on fly-leaves and at the end (fos. 172 ff.), and incl. copies of some royal (English and Scottish), papal and episcopal charters *passim*. *Mon. Angl.* v, 177 ff., lists the places and some of the contents, with extracts.
Fos. 179 (139–50 misbound after 126). 12½ × 9½ in. *FO:* Sir H. Spelman (*D*); J. Rushworth, 1651 (*D*); Sir J. Legard, bart.

DAVINGTON co. Kent
Ben. Priory (Nuns) *f.* 1153
303. **Untraced.** Ledger-book cited by E. Hasted, *Hist. Kent* ii (1782), 725 (*u*), and perhaps then in the possession of Wm. Sherwin, owner of Davington manor and the priory's site.

DEEPING, EAST co. Linc.
Ben. Priory of St. James *f.* 1139
304. **BM., Harley 3658.** Gen. cartulary, 1332, with rubrics, some decorated initials etc. Contains copies of deeds and other evidences, incl. one or two royal charters, arranged mainly topographically (fos. 12–4, Lords of Wake) with a summary Table at fo. 1. Misc. additions at the beginning, end (fos. 54v ff.) and *passim*, include a kalendar (fos. 2–7), rental of 1473 (fos. 66v–72) and library list (fo. 74v). *Mon. Angl.* iv, 168 (*e*) (partial list of contents).
Fos. 76 (excl. blank leaves). 10½ × 7 in. *FO:* Symon Lowe, 16th cent.; Z. Grey, LL.D.

DENNY co. Cambr.
Franciscan Abbey (Nuns) *f.* (at Water-beach) 1294
No cartulary recorded.
¶ *Other registers etc.*
305. **Untraced.** Transcript (pp. 764, paper, folio) of court rolls of the manor of Denny, 1327–1630, from which extracts, late 18th cent., by W. Cole are in BM., Add. 5830, fos. 130v ff. *FO:* Peter Stanley, 1773 (but in the custody of Mr. Day, town clerk of Cambridge and steward of the manor).

306. **Ely, Diocesan Registry,** 'Denney Abbey MS.'. Proceedings on the appropriation of Eltisley and Biddenham churches, 1512. A Gibbons, *Ely Episcopal Records* (Lincoln, 1891), 153. *FO:* Sir R. Naunton; the Rev. J. Leman, who presented it to the Bp. of Ely in 1776.

DEREHAM, WEST co. Norf.
Praem Abbey *f.* 1188
307. **BM., Add. 46353.** Gen. cartulary, 1315, with rubrics etc., spaces for initials and a few additions on fly-leaves and *passim*. Arranged in sections topographically, and incl. copies of royal charters in the first, for Dereham. Uncompleted Table, fos. 5–7. Contains no papal privileges, although these are referred to in the title (fo. 8), but at least one quire (12 leaves ?) is lacking at the end. An early 17th cent. transcript of 277 deeds rel. Wiggenhall St. Mary etc. is in BM., Stowe 929 (*FO:* R. Underwood; T. Martin; J. Ives; T. Astle, 1777).
Fos. ii + 346 (earlier post-medieval foliation, 1–336, from fo. 8). 14 × 10¼ in. *FO:* Sir S. Stuart, bart., 18th–19th cent., presumably by descent from the Dereham fam., barts.; J. Towneley; R. Heber; Sir T. Phillipps (MS. 8134).

DIEULACRES co. Staff.
Cist. Abbey *f.* (at Poulton) 1153
308. **Untraced.** 'Liber cartarum Abbottes (*sic*) et conventus de Dulacres iuxta Leek.' Perhaps the cartulary reported, 17th cent., in the hands of the Rudyard fam. of Leek, see R. Holme's extracts from this and other sources in BM., Harley 2060, fos. 24–30v, copied in Bodl., Dodsworth 31 (*SC.* 4173), fos. 20v–32v, and partly printed in G. Ormerod, *Hist. Chester*, ed. T. Helsby, ii (1882), 864–5. A partial (?) 17th cent. transcript of the original, by B. Rudyard, in Leek Public Libr. (*FO:* the Parker fam., earls of Macclesfield; presented by A. C. Parker Esq., 1947) contains copies of 184 deeds, 1150–1257, rel.

Poulton and Dieulacres. Typewritten copies of this transcript by H. E. Salter, 1903, are in BM., Add. 36869 and Bodl., Top. Gen. c. 26 (*SC.* 33216); and it is edited by G. Wrottesley, 'Chartulary of Dieulacres Abbey', Wm. Salt. Arch. Soc., *Coll. Hist. Staffordshire*, New ser. ix (1906), 310–62.

309.　**Stafford, Wm. Salt Libr.**, 'Dieulacres Chartulary'. Cartulary roll, 14th-15th cent., with rubrics etc., red numeration of the entries, and one or two additions. Contains copies of 63 charters etc. arranged mainly by properties, the royal etc. (John–Hen. III) being placed at the beginning, and the episcopal and one papal entered *passim*. Contemp. Tables, at the head of both the recto and the verso. A 19th cent. transcript by A. Huntbach is *ib.*, MS. 302/29. Wrottesley, *l.c.*, 363–6 (descriptive note).

Roll of 6 membrs. (incl. the wrapper). 126 × 9 in. *FO:* R. Fenton; the Rev. C. Swynnerton.

310.　**Untraced.** 'Registrum . . . penes . . . Jolly de Leak arm.' (*T*). Perhaps identical with No. 308.

DONCASTER　　　　co. York
Hosp. of St. James　　　*f.* bef. 1122–3
v. No. 622 below.

DORE　　　　　　co. Heref.
Cist. Abbey　　　　　　*f.* 1147
311.　**Untraced.** 'Registrum . . . penes . . . dom. Scudamore' (*T*), i.e. the viscounts Scudamore of Holme Lacy. The material in BM., Add. 5937, f. 173; Harley 2044, fos. 127, 182v–3; Harley 5804, fos. 258–63; and Cotton Julius C. vii, fos. 252 ff., appears all to be derived from original charters and to some extent interrelated.

DOVER　　　　　　co. Kent
Praem. Abbey of St. Radegund, Bradsole
v. ST. RADEGUND'S.

DOVER　　　　　　co. Kent
Ben. Priory　　　　　　*f.* 1136
312.　**London, Lambeth Palace, MS. 241.** Gen. cartulary, 1372, compiled by R. de Welle and J. Hwytefeld. Red pageheadings, underlining of titles, ruling of margins, initials (which are decorated with blue) etc. Arranged topographically, with pressmarks. The opening section for Dover

(fos. 2–105), which includes copies of royal and papal charters, is subdivided according to subject matter etc. and preceded by a preface describing the organisation of the muniments (printed by C. R. Haines, *Dover Priory* (Cambridge, 1930), 490–1) and a list of *Tituli*. M. R. James, *Cat. Lambeth MSS.* (Cambridge 1932), 393–7 (description).

Fos. 6 + 262. 13¾ × 9 in. *FO:* H. Dyneley *al.* Dingley, 1570; restored to Archbp. J. Bancroft by the Court of Wards, 1602/3.
¶ *Other registers etc.*
313.　**BM., Add. 26766.** Four leaves (6 × 4½ in.) from a misc. 14th cent. register of memoranda rel. lands. *FO:* Sir E. Dering.

DOVER　　　　　　co. Kent
Hosp. of St. Bartholomew (dep. on the Ben. Priory)　　　　　*f.* 1141
314.　**Oxford, Bodl., Rawlinson B. 335.** Gen. cartulary, 1373, compiled by R. de Welle and J. Hwytefeld, monks, with decoration similar to that of No. 312. Arranged topographically, with copies of the *Privilegia* at the beginning (fos. 5–8), and preceded by an index of places on an unnumbered leaf and (fos. 1–4) *Ordo suscipiendorum fratrum*. Originally followed (fos. 99 ff., now wanting) by rentals, inventories etc. W. D. Macray, *Cat. MSS. Bibl. Bodl.* v (i) (Oxford, 1862), 603–4, prints the contemp. heads of contents.

Fos. 100 (lacks at least 14 fos. at the end). 8 × 5¼ in. *FO:* W. Clavell, 1719.

DRAX　　　　　　co. York
Aug. Priory　　　　　*f.* 1130–9
315.　**Oxford, Bodl., Top. Yorks c. 72.** Gen. cartulary, mid-14th cent., with rubrics and spaces for initials. Arranged mainly topographically with sections of pleas and fines at the end (fos. 80 ff.), and incl. copies of royal, papal and episcopal charters *passim*. Additions, mainly 14th cent. and at the end, include (fos. 98–109) an 18th cent. Table. Extracts are in Bodl., Dodsworth 26 (*SC.* 4168), fos. 24–95. Cited by J. Burton, *Mon. Ebor.* (York, 1758), 100–12.

Fos. ii + 123. 13 × 8⅛ in. *FO:* the Constable, afterw. Constable-Maxwell fam., barons Herries; Gwendolen, duchess of Norfolk.

316.   **Oxford, Bodl., Dodsworth 76**
(*SC.* 5018), fos. 124–6. Three leaves from a
register written, without decoration, in the
same mid-14th cent. hand as some of the
additions (fos. 90–3) in No. 315. Copies of
13 documents rel. the appropriation of
Roxby church.
    Fos. 3. $11\frac{1}{2} \times 8$ in.

DUNKESWELL   co. Devon
Cist. Abbey   *f.* 1201
317.   **Untraced.** Register cited as the
authority for a note rel. the abbey's
founder, W. de Brewer, in P. Holland's
translation of Wm. Camden's *Britannia*,
sub Odcombe, co. Som. (ed. 1637, p. 222E).

DUNMOW, LITTLE   co. Essex
Aug. Priory   *f.* 1106
318.   **BM., Harley 662.** Gen. cartulary,
1274, written in double columns with
rubrics etc. Arranged topographically and
incl. copies of royal, episcopal etc. charters,
mainly in the first section, for Little Dunmow, with misc. additions at the beginning (fos. 2–5), end (fos. 114 ff.) and
passim.
    Fos. 130. $12\frac{1}{4} \times 9$ in. *FO:* C. Blencow,
16th cent.; J. Martin, 16th cent. (?); Bp.
Wm. Nicholson.
319.   **The Vicar & Churchwardens of
Gainsborough,** deposited at Lincoln,
Lincolnshire Archives Office (Misc. Deposit 31). Inventory or abstract, 13th–14th
cent., of about 75 private deeds rel.
Poslingford. Arranged by grantors. The
material is partly additional to that copied
in No. 318. fos. 82–93. Typewritten transcripts are *ib.*, at Chelmsford, Essex R.O.,
and at Bury St. Edmunds, Bury and W.
Suffolk R.O. *Lincolnshire Archives Office
Report for* 1952–3 (notice).
    Roll of 4 membrs. 113 × 8 in.

DUNSTABLE   co. Bedf.
Aug. Priory   *f.* 1131–2
320.   **BM., Harley 1885.** Composite
cartulary (fos. 4–79), begun apparently
soon after the election of R. de Morins,
prior 1202–42, and written mainly in
double or (fos. 4–12) three columns in a
series of mainly early 13th cent. hands, with
some rubrication, red or green initials, and
a few subsequent additions. Besides copies
of royal, episcopal etc. and private chart-

ers, sometimes duplicated, the contents include: (*a*) a classified inventory of the
muniments, opening with a list of papal
charters and followed by lists of lands, fos.
4–13r; (*b*) copies of grants by the priory,
temp. R. de Morins, fos. 35 ff.; (*c*) notes of
grants to the almoner, fos. 59 ff.; (*d*) a
draft of the beginning of the Dunstable
Annals (cf. No. 322), fo. 41v; and (*e*) other
misc. memoranda. Bound up (fos. 80–136)
with (part of ?) a 14th cent. register of
documents rel. legal proceedings etc.,
temp. Edw. III–Ric. II etc., with misc.
additions incl. (fos. 101v–3) a copy of a
royal charter of *Inspeximus*, 1377, etc. G. H.
Fowler, *Digest of the . . . Cartulary . . . of
Dunstable* (Bedfordshire Hist. Record Soc.
x, 1926). T. Hearne, *Chronicon . . . de Dun-
staple* i (Oxford, 1733), lxviii–xcvii (notice
etc. by H. Wanley) and ii, 676–713
(extracts).
    Fos. 137. $12\frac{1}{4} \times 8\frac{3}{8}$ in. *FO:* W. Dun-
comb, 1614 (*T*); bound at the expense of
John Ward, citizen and vintner of London,
1655; the Rev. J. Clithero (*T*); H. Wanley,
1714.
321.   **Untraced.** 'Registrum . . . penes
. . . Parson(s), unum ex auditoribus scac-
carii regii, postea penes Jacobum Mickleton
de Furnivals Inn, Gen.' (*T*), early 18th
cent. (cf. No. 750).
❡ *Other registers etc.*
322.   **BM., Cotton Tib. A. x,** fos. 5–
115. Annals down to 1297, ed. H. R.
Luard, *Annales Monastici* iii (Rolls ser.,
1866), 1 ff.; followed (fos. 89v ff.) by misc.
additions incl. copies of 14th cent. documents rel. legal proceedings, lists of fees
etc.

DURFORD   co. Suss.
Praem. Abbey   *f.* bef. 1161
323.   **BM., Cotton Vesp. E. xxiii.**
Gen. cartulary, late 13th cent., with rubrics. Contains copies of deeds arranged
(mainly topographically) and numbered in
two sections, with the royal charters placed
at the beginning of the first, and misc.
additions on fly- and added leaves at
the beginning and end of each. Fos. 46–51
should follow fo. 76 to form the first quire
of the second section, opening with material rel. the abbey's properties in co.
Southt.
    Fos. 117. $9\frac{1}{4} \times 7\frac{1}{2}$ in.

DURHAM co. Durh.
Ben. Cath. Priory *f.* 1083

W. A. Pantin, *Report on the Muniments of the Dean & Chapter of Durham* (privately printed, 1939) gives an account of the organisation and history of the muniments at Durham, with a list of the registers there.

324. **Durham, D. & C.,** Muniments. Fragms. of a cartulary written, *c.* 1230 (?), in double columns with alternate plain red or blue initials: (*a*) three leaves, numbered xviii, xix, xx, in a later medieval foliation, containing the end of a section of episcopal charters, the latest entry being of *temp.* R. Poore, bp. 1228–37; (*b*) two leaves (xxv, xxxii) containing copies of papal bulls. Photostat copies are bound with No. 325.

Fos. 5. $16\frac{1}{8} \times 11\frac{5}{8}$ in. *FO:* Granville Sharp.

325. **Oxford, Bodl. Carte 177** (*SC.* 10622), fos. 41–2. Further fragms. of the same (cf. No. 324), viz. two leaves (lvi, lxiiii) containing copies of deeds rel. 'Haliwarfolk'. Bound at the end of a 14th cent. inventory of the muniments (No. 340 below). Photostat copies are kept with No. 324.

Fos. 2. $16\frac{1}{4} \times 11\frac{1}{4}$ in.

326. **Durham, D. & C.,** Muniments, 'The Small Cartulary'. Cartulary, mid-13th cent., of episcopal, papal, royal, baronial and other charters (English and Scottish), mainly rel. the priory's rights, privileges etc. Rubrics etc. and red and blue decorated initials. Arranged partly by grantors and partly topographically by counties, the first 34 leaves being misbound as fos. 126–158. Includes a contemp. Table (fos. 1–7) and a few additions *passim.*

Fos. 173. $9\frac{1}{4} \times 6\frac{1}{2}$ in.

327. **Ditto,** 'Cartuarium I'. Vol. i of a Gen. cartulary, *c.* 1400, with partial rubrication and spaces for initials throughout. Contains sections of papal, royal, episcopal (Durham), archidiaconal (Durham), archiepiscopal etc. charters, each with its own Table, followed (fos. 201–47) by copies of other misc. charters. A few later additions have been made at the ends of sections *passim.*

Fos. iii + 237 (medieval foliation, 1–249; wants 164–75). $13\frac{3}{8} \times 9\frac{5}{8}$ in.

328. **Ditto,** 'Cartuarium II'. Vol. ii (cf. No. 327), 'De munimentis specialibus infra dioc. Dunelm.' Copies of local deeds rel. the diocese of Durham, arranged by places, with a contemp. Table on 20 preliminary leaves and some misc. additions at the end (from fo. 293).

Fos. xxii + 307 (medieval foliation, 1–318; wants 289–99). $14\frac{1}{8} \times 9\frac{3}{4}$ in.

329. **Ditto,** 'Cartuarium III', pt. ii, fos. 1–152. Vol. iii (cf. Nos. 327–8), 'De munimentis specialibus et generalibus in diocesibus Ebor. et Lincoln'. Copies of local deeds rel. the dioceses of York and Lincoln. Subsequently incorporated with No. 332.

Fos. 152. $13\frac{5}{8} \times 9\frac{3}{4}$ in.

330. **Ditto,** 'Cartuarium III', pt. ii, fos. 153–353. Vol. i of a gen. cartulary written in several 15th–16th cent. hands, apparently as a revision of Nos. 327–9, to take account of a reorganisation of the muniments. Contains copies of royal, papal, episcopal etc. charters.

Fos. 201. $13\frac{5}{8} \times 9\frac{3}{4}$ in.

331. **Ditto,** 'Cartuarium IV'. Vol. ii (cf. No. 330), *Specialia.* Copies of local deeds rel. the Palatinate of Durham, arranged in order of pressmarks by places.

Fos. 309. $13\frac{3}{4} \times 10\frac{1}{4}$ in.

332. **Ditto,** 'Cartuarium III', pt. i, fos. 1–48. Vol. iii (cf. Nos. 330–1), *Eboracensia* (incomplete). Preceded by indexes to the whole of 'Cartuarium III', incl. the section of the earlier compilation incorporated with it (No. 329).

Fos. 48. $13\frac{5}{8} \times 9\frac{3}{4}$ in.

¶ *Inventories*

333. **Ditto** (Misc. Ch. 2585). Inventory, early 13th cent., of 34 episcopal charters to the priory, *temp.* H. of le Puiset—P. of Poitou, 1153–1208, with one added of R. Marsh, bp. 1217–26.

Roll of 2 membrs. $18 \times 5\frac{7}{8}$ in.

334. **Ditto** (Ia. Ie. Papales 30). Inventory, early 13th cent., of 51 papal and 5 archiepiscopal privileges to the priory, 11th–13th cent.

Roll of 1 membr. $23\frac{1}{2} \times 4$ in.

335. **Ditto** (Misc. Ch. 7174). A later 13th cent. inventory of 52 papal privileges to the priory, 12th–13th cent.

Roll of 2 membrs. *c.* $30 \times 3\frac{1}{2}$ in. (mutilated at the top).

336. **Ditto** (Misc. Ch. 5678). 'Rotulus cartarum de halywarfolc., scilicet inter Tynam et Theysam.' Inventory, late 13th

cent., of 123 deeds etc., arranged topographically in four parts.

Roll of 2 membrs. 21 × 7 in.

337. **Ditto** (Ia. Ie. Papales 31). Inventory, 13th–14th cent., of papal privileges to
the priory, lettered *A–U* with additions
V–Z.

Roll of 2 membrs. $23\frac{3}{4} \times 7\frac{1}{2}$ in.

338. **Ditto** (Misc. Ch. 7172). Pt. *vii*,
with portions of pts. *vi* & *viii*, of a 13th–
14th cent. inventory of charters written in
the same hand as No. 337. About 100
entries.

Roll of 2 membrs., with a schedule
attached. $22\frac{1}{2} \times 6\frac{7}{8}$ in.

339. **Ditto** (Misc. Ch. 426). Inventory
of the muniments, mid-14th cent., written
in double columns with rubrics, red and
blue initials, pressmarks etc. and the added
title, *c.* 1400, 'Antiquum cartuarium
pertinens ad officium cancellarii Dunelm.'
Lists papal, royal, episcopal etc. charters
and local deeds arranged topographically
under the heading *Generales*.

Fos. 25. $13\frac{1}{4} \times 8\frac{1}{2}$ in.

340. **Oxford, Bodl., Carte 177** (*SC.*
10622), fos. 1–39. 'Tabula bullarum
papalium, cartarum regalium et episcopal-
ium, ac eciam omnium cartarum general-
ium que continentur in armariolo interiori
in le spendement.' Inventory of the muniments, mid-14th cent., similar in arrangement to No. 339. Written in double
columns with rubrics, and bound (fos.
40–1) with two leaves of an early cartulary
(No. 325).

Fos. 39 (v + 56 in the MS., incl. blank
leaves). $17\frac{1}{8} \times 11\frac{3}{8}$ in.

341. **Durham, D. & C.,** Muniments,
'Repertorium Parvum'. Inventory of the
muniments, *c.* 1400, in two parts, written
perhaps in the hand of the cartulary of that
date (Nos. 327–9). Rubrics, red pressmarks,
touching of capitals etc. and later additions
and corrections *passim*. Pt. 1, from which
the first three leaves (*papalia*) have been
excised, lists royal and episcopal charters;
and pt. 2 local deeds arranged topographically under the headings *Speciales* (rel. the
Palatinate) and *Generales* (elsewhere).
Index of places, fo. 1.

Fos. 26 (unnumbered) + 79 (medieval
foliation). $11\frac{1}{4} \times 6\frac{3}{4}$ in.

342. **Ditto,** 'Repertorium Magnum'.
Inventory of the muniments, *c.* 1456–62,

with red titles, pressmarks, touching of
capitals etc. and later additions and corrections *passim*. The arrangement is similar to,
but more complex than, that of No. 341.
Contemp. index of places on 56 preliminary
ary leaves.

Fos. 56 + 159. $15\frac{1}{8} \times 11\frac{1}{4}$ in.

¶ *Camerarius*

343. **Ditto,** 'Chamberlain's Cartulary'.
Two quires from a cartulary of the
chamberlain, bound in a limp medieval
vellum cover. The first (4 leaves) contains
copies, late 13th cent. (*temp.* Edw. I), of
about 10 charters, incl. one or two papal
and episcopal ones; and the second (8
leaves) contains additions in two consecutive mid-14th cent. hands.

Fos. ii + 12. $10\frac{1}{4} \times 6\frac{3}{4}$ in.

¶ *Communarius*

344. **Ditto,** 'Cartuarium Evidenciarum
Communarii'. Cartulary of the com-
munar, 15th–16th cent., arranged topographically in sections, with pressmarks.

Fos. 55. $11 \times 7\frac{3}{4}$ in.

¶ *Elemosinarius*

345. **Ditto,** 'Cartuarium Elemosinarie'.
Cartulary of the almoner (pp. 81–154),
early 13th cent., with rubrics and a few
additions at the end. Includes copies of
some episcopal charters *passim*. Preceded
and followed by added quires etc. containing misc. 13th–14th cent. additions,
incl. (pp. 69–73) a later 13th cent. Table
and (pp. 39–66) a rubricated inventory,
1399, of the almoner's muniments.

Fos. 117 (paginated, 1–234). $8\frac{1}{4} \times 6$ in.

346. **Ditto,** 'Rentale et Cartuarium
Elemosinarie', fos. 71–196. Cartulary of
the almoner, written in the same 15th–
16th cent. hand as No. 330, with marginal
titles and spaces for initials. Wants material
at the beginning and end, part of the latter
being transcribed in *ib.*, D. & C. Libr.,
Hunter 37, pp. 28 ff. Bound (fos. 1–70)
with rentals of the almoner, 1424–40.

Fos. 126 (v + 196 in the MS.). $14\frac{3}{4} \times 10\frac{1}{4}$
in.

¶ *Sacristarius*

347. **Ushaw College Libr.** (xviii. F. 5.
11). 'Liber Sacriste', 15th–16th cent. (aft.
1493), containing copies of charters,
records of legal proceedings etc. arranged,
apart from a few misplaced items, in the
order of the muniments with pressmarks,

partly added. Contemp. blind-stamped binding.

Fos. i+131. $14\frac{1}{2}\times9\frac{1}{2}$ in.

348. **Durham, D. & C.,** Muniments, 'Sacrist's Cartulary'. Register comprising: (1) an inventory, *c.* 1500, by pressmarks of the sacrist's muniments with some later additions and corrections, fos. 1–10; (2) a section of misc. charters etc. rel. his lands etc., fos. 12–17; (3) a rental dated 1500, fos. 21–30.

Fos. 32. $12\frac{1}{2}\times8$ in.

❡ *Other registers etc.*

For other registers at Durham, see also W. A. Pantin, 'English Monastic Letter-Books', *Historical Essays presented to James Tait,* ed. J. G. Edwards, V. H. Galbraith, E. F. Jacob (Manchester, 1933), 215–7.

349. **BM., Cotton Domit. A. vii.** Obit-book, 9th–16th cent., incl. a few memoranda and copies of documents rel. early grants to the priory. Ed., in facsimile, A. Hamilton Thompson, *Liber Vitae Ecclesiae Dunelmensis* (Surtees Soc. cxxxvi, 1923).

350. **BM., Stowe 930.** Composite misc. register, 13th–14th cent. A leaf wanting bef. fo. 35 is in **Durham U.L., Mickleton & Spearman 13,** cf. BM., MS. Facsimiles Suppl. ix (18). BM., *Cat. Stowe MSS.* i, 613–17, lists the contents. *FO:* M. Lort, D.D.; T. Astle,

351. **BM., Cotton Faust. A. vi,** fos. 1–112. Priors' register 1302–1406, continued down to 1519 etc. in **Durham, D. & C.,** Muniments, 'Reg. Parva I–III.'

352. **London, Lincoln's Inn, MS. 114,** fos. 1–133. 'Libellus de exordio et statu ecclesiae cathedralis quondam Lindisfarnensis' etc. A history of the priory and See down to 1195, incorporating copies of some early royal, papal, episcopal and other charters *passim.* A 15th cent. MS. *FO:* J. Barnes; Sir M. Hale, 1657.

353. **BM., Cotton Claud. D. iv,** fos. 3–89. Another 15th cent. MS. of the same work (cf. No. 352).

EARLS COLNE   co. Essex
v. COLNE, EARLS.

EASBY   co. York
Praem. Abbey of St. Agatha   *f.* bef. 1155

354. **BM., Egerton 2827.** Gen. cartulary, late 13th cent. (aft. 1281), with marginal titles underlined in red etc. Arranged in sections mainly topographically (fines, fos. 282–8 etc.; papal charters, fos. 307–20; *Comites* (incl. royal charters), fos. 321–4) with misc. additions at the ends of the sections *passim* and fos. 325 ff. Fos. 342–55 are part of a contemp. register of deeds rel. acquisitions 'in tempore fratris W. de Wauz, ab anno domini MCC'. A photostat copy is at Leeds, Yorks. Arch. Soc. Libr. *BM. Cat. Add. MSS.* 1900–1905, 383–4.

Fos. 364. $9\frac{1}{4}\times6$ in. *FO:* the Constable fam., barts., Burton Constable.

EDINGTON   co. Wilts
Coll. Church (Bonshommes)   *f.* 1352–8

355. **BM., Lansdowne 442.** Gen. cartulary, late 14th cent. (*temp.* Ric. II), with rubrics, blue initials decorated with red etc. and additions. Arranged topographically in sections and incl. copies of royal, episcopal and occasional papal charters *passim.* Also includes some antecedent material rel. Romsey Abbey upon which the church was previously dependent. *Mon. Angl.* vi, 535 (*i*) (list of places).

Fos. 218. $13\frac{1}{2}\times10$ in.

ELMHAM, SOUTH   co. Suff.
Parish of St. Michael in

356. **Oxford, Bodl., Top. Suff. d. 15** (*SC.* 29006). Register, 1500, rel. lands etc. of various ownership situated within the parish, made by John Ledell, monk and afterw. prior of Rumburgh, apparently for the use of St. Michael's Church. Occasional underlinings in red. Comprises misc. terriers, rentals etc. and (fos. 35–69) a section of charters, incl. some rel. the priory.

Fos. 135. $9\frac{1}{2}\times6\frac{1}{2}$ in. *FO:* the North fam., barons North and earls of Guilford.

ELY, See of   *f.* 1109
E. Miller, *The Abbey & Bishopric of Ely* (Cambridge, 1951), lists the MS. sources, pp. 292–3, with discussion *passim.* A. Jessopp, *HMC. Twelfth Report,* App. ix (1891), 375–96, describes the episcopal and cathedral muniments at Ely. S. J. A. Evans, 'Ely Chapter Ordinances etc.', *Camden Miscellany* xvii (Camden Third ser. lxiv, 1940), xvii–xix, notices the history of some registers. No cartulary recorded.

¶ *Inventory*

357.   **BM., Cotton Nero C. iii**, fos. 202–7. Inventory of deeds etc., late 13th cent., with a few 14th cent. additions at the end. Arranged by *Puncta* (*A–D*), mainly topographically, with the entries for royal and other general charters grouped at the beginning, which may be imperfect.

Roll, now in 7 pieces mounted as 6 fos. *c.* 67 × 7½ in.

¶ *Other registers etc.*

For material at Ely see A. Gibbons, *Ely Episcopal Records* (Lincoln, 1891).

358.   **BM., Cotton Tib. B. ii**, fos. 86–259. Survey (1222) of the bishop's demesne manors. A 13th cent. MS. followed (fos. 234 ff.) by added leaves containing misc. 13th cent. memoranda, incl. copies of a few deeds etc. and (fos. 255–9) a section of fines. *FO:* R. Massy.

359.   **BM., Cotton Claud. C. xi.** Survey (1251) of the bishop's demesne manors, preceded (fos. 1–7) by a kalendar and (fos. 8–20) by copies of 13th cent. royal and other charters headed 'Iste libertates allocate sunt episcopo Elyensi in scaccario'. A 13th cent. MS. with misc. additions, incl. copies of further charters, at the end (fos. 312v ff.).

360.   **Cambridge, Gonville & Caius Coll., MS. 485.** Similar to No. 359, 14th cent. with additions. A partial 17th cent. transcript is in Cambr. U.L., Dd. 8. 24. M. R. James, *Cat. MSS. Gonv. & Caius Coll.* ii (Cambridge, 1908), no. 489. *FO:* Augustine Steward.

361.   **Cambridge U.L., Add. 3468.** 'The Black Book', 13th–14th cent. 'Registrum taxe bonorum' (fos. 53–84) and other misc. material, incl. occasional added copies of charters. *FO:* J. Meyrick; R. Heber (MS. 407); Sir T. Phillipps (MS. 8121).

362.   **Ely, Diocesan Registry,** 'Liber R' *al.* 'The Old Coucher Book'. Survey (1251) of the bishop's demesne manors. A 14th cent. MS. followed (fos. 209–42) by 15th cent. copies of misc. documents, incl. royal and other charters, rel. his manors, rents etc., 12th–15th cent.

363.   **BM., Cotton Domit. A. xv**, fos. 96–151. Register, 15th cent., of terriers and other misc. documents (incl. some royal and papal charters etc.) rel. the bishop's possessions, *temp.* Hen. VI.

ELY   co. Cambr.

Ben. Cath. Priory   *f.* (as an abbey) 970.
General bibliography as for the See.

364.   **Cambridge, Trinity Coll., MS. O. 2. 41,** pp. 81–159. 'Collectio privilegiorum Eliensis Ecclesie.' Copies, 12th cent., of royal, papal, episcopal etc. privileges to the church, 10th–12th cent., with rubrics, red and green initials etc. Arranged chronologically, the last three entries (bulls of Eugenius III, d. 1153) being added in another hand. Preceded by a kalendar, life of St. Aethelwold etc. and followed by a copy of the 'Inquisitio Eliensis', 1086–7, for which see N. E. S. A. Hamilton, *Inquisitio Comitatus Cantabrigiensis* (Royal Soc. of Literature, 1876). M. R. James, *Cat. MSS. Trinity Coll.* iii (Cambridge, 1902), no. 1145.

Fos. 39 (11 + 148 in the MS.; postmedieval pagination, 1–294). 8¼ × 6 in. *FO:* T. and R. Gale.

365.   **BM., Cotton Tib. A. vi**, fos. 36–120. A similar, later 12th cent., collection of privileges (fos. 99 ff.), written in double columns with rubrics and red, blue or green initials. Imperf. at the beginning. Preceded (fos. 36 ff.) by another copy of the 'Inquisitio Eliensis', 1086–7, and the 'Inquisitio Comitatus Cantabrigiensis' (ed. Hamilton, *op. cit.*).

Fos. 85 (17th cent. foliation, 38–139; wants four leaves bef. fo. 99 and two others aft. fos. 70, 74). 9¼ × 6½ in.

366–368.   THE HISTORIA ELIENSIS in three books, of which *ii* and *iii* incorporate copies of numerous royal, papal, episcopal and other privileges etc. down to the mid-12th cent., arranged chronologically. D. J. Stewart, *Historia Elyensis* (Anglia Christiana Soc., 1848) edits bks. *i* & *ii*. An edition of the whole is in preparation by E. O. Blake. For discussion, and citation of later MSS. not listed here (Bodl., Laud misc. 647; BM., Cotton Vesp. A. xix, fos. 29v–51 etc.), see W. Holtzmann, *Papsturkunden in England* ii (Göttingen, 1936), 78 ff. Three early MSS., as follows:—

366.   **Cambridge,   Trinity   Coll., MS. O. 2. 1.** Late 12th cent., with rubrics and red or green initials. Followed (fos. 177v ff.) by a copy of the 'Inquisitio Eliensis', 1086–7, and lives of saints, in similar format. A contemp. kalendar is bound in at the beginning.

Holtzmann, *l.c.*, 80–93, lists the *Capitula* of bk. *iii*. M. R. James, *op. cit.*, no. 1105. Fos. 256+2. 9 × 6½ in. *FO:* R. Gale.

367. **Ely, D. & C.,** Muniments. Written, 12th–13th cent., in double columns with rubrics and red, green or occasionally blue initials, and continued from fo. 112 in slightly later hands. C. W. Stubbs, *Hist. Memorials of Ely Cathedral* (1897), 58–66, lists the *Capitula* of bk. *iii*. Fos. 189. 10¾ × 7½ in.

368. **BM., Cotton Titus A. i,** fos. 3–56. A version of the narrative part of bk. *ii*, followed (fos. 24 ff.) by the charter material of bks. *ii* & *iii*. Written, 12th–13th cent., with rubrics and red or green initials. Fos. 54. 7¼ × 5¾ in.

369. **Ely, Diocesan Registry,** 'Liber M'. Gen. cartulary, *c.* 1290–1300, written in double columns with rubrics etc. and red and blue decorated initials. Arranged in sections partly by grantors etc. (papal, royal, episcopal, fines) and partly by *Officia* (unassigned, precentor, refector, hostiller, infirmarer, altar of the BVM., pittancer, chamberlain, gardener, almoner). The internal arrangement of the sections is mainly topographical with additions, mainly 14th cent., at the end. Further additions have been made on the last 15 leaves of the volume.

Fos. 301 (medieval pagination, 1–628, duplicating 160–9; lacks leaves *passim*). 13¾ × 9½ in.

370. **Oxford, Bodl., Cambr. Rolls 9.** Copies, late 13th cent., of 52 charters rel. Teversham, Haddenham, Ditton, Fulbourn, Littlebury and Willingham, each headed with the name of the grantor. W. H. Turner & H. O. Coxe, *Cal. Charters & Rolls . . . in the Bodl. Libr.* (Oxford, 1878), 40–5 (calendar). Roll of 9 membrs., now in three unequal pieces, 43¼ etc. × 6½ in.

371. **BM., Egerton 3047.** The first part (cf. No. 372) of a 15th cent. gen. cartulary (*temp.* Edw. IV?), with occasional additions. Arranged mainly topographically with the copies of royal and episcopal charters at the beginning, and pressmarks. Bears on the front cover (18th cent.) the letter 'L'. *BM. Cat. Add. MSS.* 1926–1930, *ad loc.*

Fos. iii+256 (contemp. foliation, 1–276; lacks 81–96 etc.). 11½ × 8¾ in. Paper. *FO:*

the Bps. of Ely, Holborn (?); produced in the Exchequer Court, early 18th cent. and 1804; Messrs. J. Wilson, booksellers, 1930, who stated that they acquired it, *c.* 1902, with the library of Mr. Beale of Bengeworth.

372. **Oxford, Bodl., Ashmole 801,** fos. 74–143. Continuation (six quires) of No. 371. W. H. Black, *Cat. MSS. Bibl. Bodl.* x (Oxford, 1845), 442.

Fos. 69 (contemp. foliation, 278–349). 11¾ × 8¼ in. Paper.

¶ *Elemosinarius*

373. **BM., Cotton Vesp. A. vi,** fos. 90–133. Cartulary of the almoner, 14th cent. (*temp.* Edw. II), with rubrics and spaces for initials. Arranged in sections topographically with a few later editions *passim* and a Table, partly added, on the last two leaves. The contents relate to Ely etc., Stretham, Cambridge, Foxton, Upwell and other places.

Fos. 45 (contemp. foliation). 8¾ × 6½ in. (cropped).

374. **Ely, D. & C.,** Muniments. Cartulary of the almoner, of similar or slightly later date to No. 373, without coloured decoration. Arranged topographically in sections and contains material for Ely, Downham, Witcham, Stuntney and Stretham, with some additions for Cambridge. A number of leaves at the beginning and end, which is incomplete, are damaged by damp.

Fos. 107 (medieval foliation, 1–135; wants 1–18 and other leaves *passim*). 9⅝ × 6¾ in.

¶ *Other registers etc.*

375. **BM., Add. 41612.** Chapter Register, *c.* 1273–1366 etc. Extracts, 18th cent., are in Cambridge U.L., Mm. i. 49, pp. 107–82 and the former Phillipps MS. 4806 (untraced). Calendared by A. J. Horwood, *HMC. Sixth Report* (1877), App., 289–300. *BM. Cat. Add. MSS.* 1926–1930, *ad loc. FO:* Sir Wm. Wyndham, bart., 1735; the Wyndham fam., earls of Egremont and barons Leconfield, Petworth.

376. **Ely, D. & C.,** Muniments. 'Registrum Domini Edwardi Walsingham prioris.' Fragm. of a register, containing copies of 69 misc. letters etc., 14th–15th cent. Jessopp, *l.c.*, 394–5.

377. **Ely, Diocesan Registry,** 'Liber B'. Priory Register, *c.* 1407–1515. W. A.

Pantin, 'English Monastic Letter-Books', *Historical Essays presented to James Tait*, ed. J. G. Edwards, V. H. Galbraith, E. F. Jacob (Manchester, 1933), 217. *FO:* the Bp. of Ely, Holborn, 1771; R. Almack, 1849, by gift of 'T.M.G.' in whose late father's library it had been for many years; Ld. A. Compton, bp. of Ely, 1889.

378. **BM., Add. 9822.** 'Liber A'. A misc. 14th–15th cent. register, mainly of contemp. royal, papal and episcopal documents. Wants about 40 leaves at the beginning and end. Cited by J. Bentham, *Hist. Ely* (Norwich, 1771), when it was with the Bp. of Ely, Holborn. Acquired of J. Graham, a dealer, 1835.

379. **BM., Cotton Vesp. A. xix,** fos. 61–102. Copy of an *arbitrium*, 1417, between the bishop and prior, rel. their respective rights in fees, jurisdiction etc.

EPWORTH (*al.* **AXHOLME**) co. Linc.
Carthusian Priory *f.* 1397–8
380. **PRO., Exch., K.R.** (Eccl. Docs., E/135/2/24). Quire from a 16th cent. cartulary or register, with spaces for titles and initials. Contains copies of papal (Boniface IX), royal (Richard II) and other charters rel. the priory's foundation (seven documents in all, the last incomplete).
Fos. 8. 14¾ × 10½ in.

EVESHAM co. Worc.
Ben. Abbey *f.* aft. 701
The principal contents of the cartularies are listed with extracts in *Mon. Angl.* ii, 10 ff. See also W. Tindal, *Hist. Evesham* (Evesham, 1794).
381. **BM., Cotton Vesp. B. xxiv.** Misc. 12th–13th cent. register of terriers, fees, rentals etc. and copies of royal, episcopal, papal and some other misc. charters and documents, 8th–13th cent., mainly rel. the abbey's rents, churches, tithes etc. Written in a number of hands with red initials, marginal rubrication etc. and some later additions. Apparently incomplete at the end. Extracts, 17th cent., by R. James are in Bodl., James 29 (*SC.* 3866), p. 40. A 17th cent. Table and an 18th cent. transcript are in BM., Lansdowne 1233 (fos. 23–38) and 411 respectively.
Fos. 80. 10 × 7¼ in. *FO:* Dr. (Samuel?) Fell (James, *l.c.*).
382. **BM., Harley 3763.** A similar

compilation to No. 381 (fos. 58–94), written in similar hands and format with some duplication of material and thus presumably distinct from it. Bound up in the medieval period with: (*a*) fos. 3–57, proceedings rel. the church of Ombersley, 1284, followed (fo. 45) by copies of misc. 14th cent. letters etc. rel. churches, pensions etc. (mainly *temp.* Abbot W. de Cheriton); (*b*) fos. 95–198, a late 14th cent. compilation, with some rubrication and many letters touched with red, comprising sections of 13th–14th cent. papal and royal charters (fos. 95–149) followed by copies of further misc. documents, memoranda etc. rel. churches, pensions etc. W. A. Hulton, *Documents rel. to the Priory of Penwortham* (Chetham Soc. xxx, 1853), prints extracts.
Fos. 201 (excl. blank leaves; a medieval foliation, i–ccxiiii, from fo. 3 is followed by *Mon. Angl., l.c.*). 10¼ × 7½ in. *FO:* H. Fleetwood, Penwortham.
¶ *Other registers etc.*
383. **BM., Cotton Vit. E. xvii,** fos. 224–50. Fragms. of a 14th cent. register containing misc. material rel. the assignment of rents to obedientiaries etc., and a kalendar. Damaged by fire, 1731.
384. **BM., Cotton Nero D. iii,** fos. 219–23, 226. Fragm. of a misc. 14th–15th cent. register, apparently of the sacrist, incl. some notes and copies of deeds.
385. **BM., Cotton Titus C. ix,** fos. 1–38. Register of R. Bromsgrove, abbot 1418–35.
386. **PRO., Duchy of Lanc.** (Miscellanea, DL/41/3/29). Copies (a roll), 15th cent., of 11 charters of magnates rel. the abbey's possessions in co. Lanc., 12th–14th cent.

EWYAS HAROLD co. Heref.
Ben. Priory *f.* 1100
The source of the 18th–19th cent. transcript in the Rev. J. Webb's collections (Hereford City Libr., LC. 274. 244) and of the abstract printed by A. T. Bannister, *Hist. Ewias Harold* (Hereford, 1902), 48–60, is apparently Gloucester, D. & C., 'Reg. A', fos. 78 ff. (No. 455 below).

EXETER co. Devon
Cath. Church *f.* 1050
The muniments of the Dean & Chapter

at Exeter are described by R. L. Poole, *HMC. Various Collections* iv (1907), 23–95.

387. **Exeter, D. & C.,** Muniments (3672). Gen. cartulary, early 15th cent., arranged topographically, with a few later additions.

Pp. 418. 10⅝ × 7¾ in.

388. **Ditto** (3681, 3681 (a)). Fragm. of a 15th cent. cartulary with some marginal rubrics and red initials. Much decayed by damp. Contains copies of royal, episcopal and private charters, mainly 14th cent., rel. various places.

Fos. 17 (non-consecutive) with some blank leaves. 14¾ × 10⅝ in.

❡ *Inventories*

389. **Ditto** (4614). Fragm. (one small sheet) of a 14th cent. inventory of muniments. Much decayed and almost illegible.

390. **Ditto** (571). Schedule, 15th cent., of some 20 charters contained 'in pixid(ibus) qui intitulantur extra in capite sic "Carte diversorum in civitate Exonie facte Decano et Capitulo Exonie" cum diversis asisis captis ibidem que fuerunt in magno rotundo lign(e)o pixide antico'.

Fos. 1. 12 × 9 in. Paper.

391 **Ditto** (2862). Inventory of the muniments, *c.* 1500, entitled 'Tabula diversorum Munimentorum de Scaccario Ecclesie Cathedralis Exon. videlicet de diversis pixidibus, hampers, skebettis et aliis locis ut hic patet sequenter'.

Roll of great length, 6 in. wide.

EXETER co. Devon
Ben. Priory of St. Nicholas *f.* 1087

392. **BM., Cotton Vit. D. ix.** Gen. cartulary (fos. 24–182), begun in a 13th cent. hand (aft. 1227) with rubrics etc. and continued, from fo. 82, without decoration in a 14th cent. hand (aft. 1333), with some intermediate and later additions *passim*. Contains copies of royal, papal, episcopal etc. and private charters without obvious arrangement, preceded (fos. 5–22) by Annals to 1333 and (fo. 23) a list of priors. (Sir T.) P(hillipps), 'List of Charters in the Cartulary of St. Nicholas Priory at Exeter', *Coll. Top. et Genealogica* i (1834), 60–388 *passim*.

Fos. 182. 7¾ × 5¾ in. *FO*: Sir R. Cotton; Scipio Le Squyer, 1632; Sir W. Le Neve (T); A. Cooper; Sir T. Phillipps (MS. 6477); reacquired by the BM., 1854.

EXETER co. Devon
Hosp. of St. John Bapt. *f.* bef. 1220

393. **Exeter, City Archives** (Muniment Bk. 53A). Gen. cartulary, 15th cent., with some later additions. Contains copies of royal, episcopal and private grants to the hospital, 13th–15th cent., arranged roughly topographically.

Fos. 95. 13½ × 9½ in. A modern acquisition; previous history unknown.

EXETER co. Devon
Hosp. of St. Mary M. *f.* bef. 1163

394. **Exeter, City Archives** (D. 2). Two quires from a 15th cent. cartulary containing copies of: (1) private grants, opening in the middle of an entry; (2) episcopal and papal charters, statutes etc. of the hospital, and a rental (1428). The last leaf of each is blank.

Fos. 16. 10¼ × 7 in.

395. **Ditto** (D. 23). Copies, 15th cent., of 21 private grants to the hospital, 13th–14th cent., arranged topographically.

Roll of 4 membrs. (apparently written singly on the recto and verso before the roll was made up). 94 × 9½ in. etc.

❡ *Other registers etc.*

396. **Ditto** (D. 20). Two small rolls of charters rel. grants by the Sokespiche family, 13th–14th cent.

EYE co. Suff.
Ben. Priory *f. c.* 1080

Extracts, 1636, from Nos. 397–8 by Sir S. D'Ewes, who entitled them respectively 'Malet' and 'Danoun', are in BM., Harley 294, fos. 171–2; 298, fo. 69; 312, fos. 79v–80; 639, fos. 58–71. Cf. *Mon. Angl.* iii, 403 (*e*).

397. **Audley End Estate Archives,** deposited at Chelmsford, Essex R.O. (D/DBy Q 19). 'Liber Albus' *al.* 'Registrum Malet'. Gen. cartulary, late 13th cent., with rubrics etc. Arranged topographically in sections, with additions at the beginning, between the sections and at the end. Copies of the foundation, royal, episcopal etc. charters are included in the first section, for Eye, which is preceded (fos. 10v–16v) by a contemp. Table. Transcripts, 1814, are in BM., Add. 8177, fos. 109–204; 19089, fos. 189–244v.

Fos. 138 (17th cent. foliation, 4–142). 7¾ × 5⅞ in. *FO*: Sir T. Deye, 1636; T.

Martin, 1731 (Blomefield); Charles, 2nd marquis Cornwallis, 1814; found among the papers of the latter's executor, J. T. Townshend, 2nd viscount Sydney, and presented by his grandson, the Hon. R. Marsham-Townshend to the 5th baron Braybrooke, 1893.

¶ *Other registers etc.*
398. **BM., Egerton 3140.** 'Registrum Danoun.' A late 13th cent. rental and custumary (fos. 20–49, originally quires *xvi–xix* of No. 397) with similar material, some misc. copies of deeds etc. and a kalendar added. B. Schofield, 'A Register of Eye Priory', *Brit. Mus. Quart.* xii (1937–8), 9–10. *FO:* Sir T. Deye, 1636; T. Martin; F. A. O'B. Bedingfield.

EYNSHAM co. Oxon
Ben. Abbey *f.* 1005
399. **Oxford, Christ Church,** Chapter Libr. (Kitchin's cat., no. 341). Gen. cartulary. The original compilation (fos. vii–xlv), to which there is a Table at fos. v–vi, and of which fos. cxlvii–viii appear to be the original parchment cover, is late 12th cent. (*c.* 1196–7 ?) with rubrics and red and green initials, and has the foundation and other Anglo-Saxon, early royal, papal, episcopal etc. charters copied at the beginning. Continuations on added quires, in a succession of hands down to the mid-14th cent., include copies of grants by the abbots and other misc. material. Medieval binding. Ed. H. E. Salter, *Cartulary of Eynsham Abbey* i (Oxford Hist. Soc. xlix, 1906–7).
Fos. 152 (post-medieval roman foliation). 10½ × 7 in.
¶ *Other registers etc.*
400. **Ditto** (Kitchin's cat., no. 342). Misc. late 14th cent. etc. register of inquisitions, pleas, extents etc., incl. copies of a few charters *passim*. Ed. Salter, *op. cit.* ii (Oxford Hist. Soc. li, 1908), 1–154.

FARLEIGH, MONKTON co. Wilts
v. MONKTON FARLEIGH.

FAVERSHAM co. Kent
Ben. Abbey *f.* 1148
No cartulary identified.
¶ *Other registers etc.*
401. **Comdr. Sir Michael Culme-Seymour, bart.,** Rockingham Castle

(Muniments C. 10). Misc. register or memorandum book, 15th–16th cent., containing copies of rentals, inquisitions, proceedings of the hundred court of Faversham, 1377–1461, and other evidences incl. some charters. Paper. *FO:* J. Diggs (?); Sir G. Sondes, 1st earl of Feversham; Lewis Watson, 1st earl of Rockingham, and his descendants at Rockingham Castle.

FELLEY co. Nott.
Aug. Priory *f.* 1152
402. **BM., Add. 36872.** 'The Booke of Felley called the Domesday.' Gen. cartulary, 16th cent. (aft. 1505), with red initials. Arranged topographically with the papal, royal, episcopal etc. material at the beginning. Added leaves at the front and back contain later copies of deeds rel. Newthorpe, co. Nott. *BM. Cat. Add. MSS.* 1900–1905, 241.
Fos. 141 (lacks leaves aft. fos. 24, 70). 10¼ × 8 in. *FO:* G. Millington, 1690; the Savile fam., earls of Mexborough.

FERRIBY, NORTH co. York
Aug. Priory (Order of the Temple of Our Lord at Jerusalem) *f. c.* 1140 (?)
403. **Oxford, Bodl., Add. C. 51** (*SC.* 30241). One quire ('*f*') from a late 14th cent. cartulary, with rubrics etc. and large red initials decorated with mauve. Contains copies of deeds rel. Tranby, Hessle etc., numbered marginally by places.
Fos. iii + 8. 11⅞ × 7⅜ in. Acquired bef. 1863.

FINESHADE co. Northt.
Aug. Priory *f.* bef. 1208
404. **London, Lambeth Palace,** Records of the Court of Arches (Exhibits). Abstract of the priory's charters (fos. 8–27), 14th cent. (*temp.* Edw. II), with red and green paragraphs and red underlining etc. of headings. Arranged topographically and followed (fos. 29–59) by surveys, 1317 etc., in similar format, with misc. contemp. and later additions *passim* and at the end. Preceded (fos. 1–7) by an added section of deeds (26) rel. Bulwick, written apparently at a slightly later date with spaces for initials and titles.
Fos. 64 (17th cent. foliation) + 4. 10½ × 6¾ in. *FO:* R. Kirkham, 1640; deposited in a suit, Kirkham *v* Lovell, 1670 (see *ib.*, Deposition Book Eee. 4, fos. 159v–60).

FLAMSTEAD co. Hertf.
Ben. Priory (Nuns) *f. c.* 1150
405. **Hertford, Hertfordshire R.O.**
(No. 17465). Cartulary (fos. 5–27), 13th
cent. (*temp.* Hen. III?), with rubrics and
red or, in the case of the rubrics, blue
initials etc. Contains copies of private
deeds arranged by grantors. Fos. 1–4, 27–
33 (folded round from the front of the
volume when it was sewn into its cover),
contain 13th–14th cent. additions, incl.
copies of some royal charters.
Fos. 33. 6¾ × 8¾ in. *FO:* T. Saunders (*T*);
Sir E. Sebright, 3rd bart., and his descendants at Beechwood.

FLAWFORTH co. Nott.
Church of St. Peter
No cartulary recorded.
❡ *Other registers etc.*
406. **BM., Harley 174.** Recital, 15th
cent., of royal and other documents, 1459–
78, rel. the foundation of Babington's
chantry. *FO:* R. St. George, 1605.

FLAXLEY co. Glouc.
Cist. Abbey *f.* 1151
407. **Untraced.** Roll, 13th cent., containing copies of charters, incl. papal bulls,
rentals etc. and a list of books (97 items in
all). Ed., from a 19th cent. transcript
(Phillipps MS. 1310), A. W. Crawley-
Boevey, *Cartulary . . . of Flaxley* (Exeter,
1887), 124 ff. *FO:* T. Wynniatt; Sir T.
Phillipps (MS. 24180); reported, 1933, at
Thirlestaine House by W. Holtzmann
(*Papsturkunden in England* iii (Göttingen,
1952), 78), but previously stated to have
been mislaid.

FOLKESTONE co. Kent
Ben. Priory *f.* 1095
No cartulary recorded.
❡ *Other registers etc.*
408. **The Earl of Radnor,** deposited at
Maidstone, Kent R.O. (U. 270/Q. 4). Roll
(81 × 18 in.) containing copies, early 15th
cent., of four confirmations of charters by
the earls of Folkestone, *temp.* Hen. I–1340.

FORDE co. Dors. (formerly Devon)
Cist. Abbey *f.* 1136
409. **G. D. Roper Esq.,** Forde Abbey.
Gen. cartulary, early 15th cent., with a few
decorated headings in red. Arranged topographically by counties (Dors., Devon,

Som.) and incl. copies of royal and episcopal charters etc.
Fos. 287 (contemp. foliation by counties,
1–130, 1–52, 1–105; later pagination, 1–
574). 11 × 8 in. *FO:* Sir W. Drake, bart.
(*T*); the Gwynne fam., Forde; Sir T.
Phillipps, 1848 (MS. 13823); the Roper
fam., Forde, 1911.
410. **Untraced.** 'Registrum . . . penes
. . . Ruswell de . . . in com. Somerset'
(*T*).

FOUNTAINS co. York
Cist. Abbey *f.* 1132
Extracts from the cartularies are printed
by J. R. Walbran, *Memorials of . . .
Fountains*, 3 vols. (Surtees Soc. xlii, lxvii
and (ed. J. T. Fowler) cxxx, 1862–1918).
They are described *ib.* ii, 86–106.
411. **Oxford, Bodl., Rawlinson B.
449.** (The first?) part of a late 13th cent.
cartulary written in double columns with
rubrics, red or sometimes green initials and
some later additions, the whole being
arranged in sections by granges, and each
section arranged by pressmarks and preceded by its own Table. W. D. Macray,
Cat. MSS. Bibl. Bodl. v (i) (Oxford, 1862),
682–3.
Fos. 152 (for fos. 13–18, 111–22, see No.
423 below). 9¼ × 8¼ in. *FO:* Dame Honor
Proctor, 1619; St. Mary's Tower, York,
bef. 1630.
412. **Oxford, Univ. Coll. MS. 170,**
deposited in the Bodleian Libr. Continuation of No. 411. H. O. Coxe, *Cat. MSS.
Oxon.* i (Oxford, 1852), *ad loc.*
Fos. 117 (for fos. 87–111, see No. 423
below). 9⅜ × 8¼ in. *FO:* H. Todd, D.D.
413. **BM., Egerton 3053.** Similar to
No. 411, repeating, with variations, its
first section (Aldborough) on quires numbered '12', '13' etc. H. I. Bell, *Brit. Mus.
Quart.* vii (1932–3), 16–18.
Fos. i+21. 9¼ × 8¼ in. *FO:* Lady M. E.
Lawson-Tancred, 1922.
414. **BM., Cotton Tib. C. xii.** Vol. i
(A–C) of a 15th cent. cartulary, with uncompleted page-headings etc. and number-
ing of the deeds in red, arranged by pressmarks in alphabetical order of places and
incl. copies of some royal, papal, episcopal
etc. charters *passim*. W. T. Lancaster,
Chartulary . . . of Fountains, 2 vols. (Leeds,
1915), prints an abstract of the whole.

Fos. 332. *c.* 11½ × 8 in. (shrunk and damaged by fire, 1731, and the leaves now mounted).

415. **BM., Add. 40009.** Vol. ii (D–I), cf. Nos. 414, 416. *BM. Cat. Add. MSS.* 1916–1920, 286–7.

Fos. iv + 291 (wants at least 34 further leaves). 12¼ × 8¼ in. *FO:* Ld. Wm. Howard; the Ingilby fam., Ripley Castle.

416. **Comdr. G. C. Vyner,** Studley Royal, Ripon. Detached leaves from No. 415, of which six (Fountains) should follow fo. 171 and nineteen (Hopperton-Ilkley), fo. 281.

Fos. 25. 12¼ × 8¼ in.

417. **BM., Add. 37770.** Vol. iii (K–M), cf. No. 414.

Fos. iii + 368. 11⅝ × 8 in. *FO:* the Ingilby fam.; H. Wythens; Col. Charles Fairfax, 1644; Sir T Pulleyn, 1751; Sir T. Phillipps (MS. 11122); Sir T. Brooke, bart., 1898.

418. **Untraced.** Vol. iv (N–P), cf. No. 414.

419. **Manchester, Rylands Libr., Lat. MS. 224.** Vol v (Q–Z), cf. No. 414.

Fos. ii + 420. 12¼ × 8¼ in. *FO:* Scipio Le Squyer.

420. **Oxford, Univ. Coll. MS. 167,** deposited in the Bodleian Libr. Cartulary, late 15th cent., of royal and papal privileges, in two parts: (1) fos. 1–46, with rubrics and red initials, copies of royal and papal privileges to the abbey, 12th–15th cent., with a Table and index at the end; (2) fos. 61–149, with headings etc. and pen-decorated initials in black ink, privileges of the Cistercian order down to 1490.

Fos. 149. 13 × 9 in. *FO:* T. Ingilby; H. Todd, D.D.

❡ *Inventories*

421. **Comdr. G. C. Vyner,** Studley Royal, 'The Coucher Book'. Inventory or abstract of charters, late 14th cent., with some misc. additions *passim.* Arranged in alphabetical order of places, with press-marks.

Fos. 253. 11¾ × 8¾ in. Paper.

422. **BM., Add. 18276.** 'Antiquum registrum terrarum feodorum ac possessionum etc.': an inventory or abstract of deeds, 1509, written by Stephen Green. Similar to No. 421, of which, or of some other such compilation, it was apparently intended as a revision, see the colophon

(fo. 255v). Followed (fo. 256) by genealogies of De Fortibus, Mowbray and Percy.

Fos. 260. 15½ × 11 in. *FO:* the Feilding fam., earls of Denbigh.

❡ *Pitanciarius*

423. **Oxford, Bodl., Rawlinson B. 449,** fos. 13–18, 111–22; **Univ. Coll. MS. 170** (deposited in the Bodleian Libr.), fos. 87–111. Cartulary of the pittancer, late 13th cent., with rubrics etc. and red initials. Contains copies of deeds numbered consecutively *i–lxxxxvi,* with one unnumbered addition, and a Table at the beginning.

Fos. 43. 9¼ × 6½ in. *FO:* cf. Nos. 411–12.

❡ *Other registers etc.*

For other material at Studley Royal, not all of which can now be traced, see also Walbran, *op. cit.* ii, 86–93.

424. **BM., Add. 40010.** Rentals, 15th cent. *FO:* the Ingilby fam.

425. **BM., Add. 40011(A).** 'Liber penes servos seu famulos' *al.* 'The Memorandum Book of Thos. Swynton,' 1446–60. Fowler, *op. cit.* iii, 93–255. *FO:* the Ingilby fam.

426. **Comdr. G. C. Vyner,** Studley Royal, 'The President's Book'. A misc. 15th cent. register of homages etc., incl. (pp. 45–127) a digest of records rel. certain estates in Craven and (pp. 141–55) copies of 36 charters rel. Ripon. Paper. Walbran, *op. cit.* ii, 86–7.

427. **Leeds, Yorks. Arch. Soc., MS. 284.** Register of leases, *temp.* Hen. VII–VIII etc., made by Abbot W. Thirsk. *FO:* Sir H. Savile; Sir T. Phillipps (MS. 25263); Sir T. Brooke, bart.

FURNESS co. Lanc.
Cist. Abbey *f.* (at Tulketh) 1124

428. **PRO., Duchy of Lanc.** (Misc. Bks. 3). Vol. i of a gen. cartulary made, 1412, by John Stell for Abbot W. de Dalton. The whole is elaborately written in double columns with illuminated initials (miniatures, coats of arms etc.), rubrics etc. and arranged topographically, with sections of papal and other general charters at the end of vol. i (fos. 215 ff.) and copies of royal and one or two archiepiscopal etc. charters included *passim.* Each vol. is prefaced by a contemp. Table, uncompleted in vol. i. Ed. (vol. i) J. C. Atkinson, *The Coucher Book of Furness Abbey,* 3 vols. (Chetham Soc., New ser.

ix, xi, xiv, 1886–8); cf. C. T. Flower, 'The Cowcher Book of Furness Abbey', in *Chetham Miscellanies* vi (*ib.* xciv, 1935).

Fos. 293 (wants about 25 leaves *passim*; **Cambridge U.L., Add. 4407** (12), taken from a binding, is the upper half of fo. 178 ('Roos')). 16 × 10½ in.

429. **BM., Add. 33244.** Vol. ii, cf. No. 428. Ed. J. Brownbill, *The Coucher Book of Furness, Volume ii*, 3 vols. (*ib.* lxxiv, lxxvi, lxxviii, 1915–19).

Fos. 227. 15¼ × 9¾ in. *FO:* the Duchy of Lanc. Office, 16th–17th cent.; R. Palmer, 1747; Ralph, 2nd earl Verney; Sir W. Burrell, bart.; the Hamilton fam., dukes of Hamilton etc.

430. **Untraced.** 'Cartularium . . . penes doct. Rawlinson, 1742' (*T*). Possibly identical with No. 429. The cartulary referred to by Sir H. Spelman, *Glossarium*, 431, *s.v.* 'Novale', is there said to have been in the Duchy of Lanc. Office and not in his own possession as stated by (*T*).

GARENDON co. Leic.
Cist. Abbey *f.* 1133

J. Nichols, *Hist. Leicester* iii, pt. 2 (1804), prints most of No. 431, pp. 805–30 etc., and an abstract of No. 432, pp. 834–8.

431. **BM., Lansdowne 415.** Elements of at least two cartularies, written in 12th–13th cent. charter- and book-hands with rubrics etc. and misc. additions on the front fly- and blank and added leaves towards the end. Arranged mainly topographically, with some duplication of material, and incl. copies of royal, papal, episcopal etc. charters *passim*.

Fos. iii + 39 (modern foliation, 1–42). 11½ × 7¾ in. *FO:* George Villiers, 2nd duke of Buckingham, 1680; Sir Ambrose Phillipps, 1683; James West, 1763.

432. **W. A. Foyle, Esq.,** Beeleigh Abbey. (The first part of a ?) 15th cent. cartulary, written in book-hand with spaces for titles and initials. Arranged topographically with copies of the foundation, royal and papal charters at the beginning, the latter part (fos. 13 ff.) consisting of bare notes of grants. Apparently lacks material at the end.

Fos. i + 27 (contemp. foliation, i–xxix; wants vi, vii). 13¼ × 10¼ in. *FO:* C. Ord; the Phillipps, afterw. De Lisle, fam., 1829–1943.

GLASNEY co. Cornw.
v. PENRYN.

GLASTONBURY co. Som.
Ben. Abbey *f. c.* 6th cent. (refounded 943)

433. **The Marquess of Bath,** Longleat (Muniments 10592). Fragm. of a late 13th cent. cartulary, written in book-hand with spaces for rubrics and uncompleted red and blue initials, containing copies of deeds rel. Longbridge Deverill (pp. 1–15), Glastonbury (pp. 17–28) and Monkton (pp. 29–58). Followed by two quires written in earlier (*c.* 1260–70) charter-hands ((*a*) pp. 59–72, with pen-decorated initials; (*b*) pp. 73–84, with red initials and rubrics), from which pp. 29–39 and 1–12 respectively appear to be copied. Post-medieval title on the cover, 'Liber R.'

Fos. 42 (19th cent. pagination, 1–83). 9¾ × 7¼ in. etc.

434. **Ditto** (MS. 39). Gen. cartulary, *c.* 1338–40, with rubrics etc. and incompletely decorated red and blue initials. Arranged in two parts, containing copies of: (1) charters etc. rel. the abbey's rights, privileges etc., arranged according to type and incl. sections of royal, papal and ecclesiastical documents; (2) deeds arranged topographically, with contemp. and later additions (aft. fo. ccxiv). Fos. ii–xv contain a contemp. Table and misc. additions, and fos. ccxxx–ccxxxi an inventory, *c.* 1300, of royal and papal charters in the treasury at Wells. Other contemp. additions have been made on inserted slips *passim*. Ed. Dom Aelred Watkin, *The Great Chartulary of Glastonbury*, 3 vols. (Somerset Record Soc. lix, lxiii, lxiv, 1944–56).

Fos. 244 (contemp. roman foliation). 14½ × 10 in.

435. **Oxford, Bodl., Wood empt. 1** (*SC.* 8589). 'Secretum Abbatis.' A fair copy (fos. 20–263) of No. 434 made, *c.* 1340–2, for Abbot W. de Monington. Rubrics, red and blue initials (illuminated at the beginning of each part, fos. 20, 116) and some later additions at the end (fos. 264–90). Preceded (fo. 1) by a short chronicle to 1291 and (fo. 5v) by a Table. Followed (fos. 293–336) by a feodary, 1341–2, ed. F. W. Weaver, *A Feodary of Glastonbury Abbey* (Somerset Record Soc. xxvi, 1910). Watkin, *op. cit.*

Fos. xiv + 344. 15 × 9½ in. *FO:* Thomas

Howard, viscount Bindon, and Thomas Howard, earl of Arundel (so a note by G. Oliver, 1852, inserted in No. 449 below); R. Sheldon, 1677.

436. **Oxford, Bodl., Ashmole 790,** fos. 190–201. Copies, 15th cent., by Prior T. Wason, of deeds rel. the church, tithes etc. of Winford. A rubricated section, placed at the end of a contemp. MS. of J. de Glastonbury, 'Historia Monasterii sui', to which an index by Wason is at fos. 202–9. W. H. Black, *Cat. MSS. Bibl. Bodl.* x (Oxford, 1845), 417–18, lists the entries.

Fos. 12 (209 in the MS.). $7\frac{1}{2} \times 11\frac{1}{4}$ in. Given by Sir R. Tichborne, bart., to Brother Paul Robinson, who inscribed the MS., 1651, in the library of the English monastery of St. Gregory, Douai.

437. **The Marquess of Bath,** *ib.* (Muniments 10586). Part of an early 16th cent. cartulary (*c.* 1503), containing copies of 13th–14th cent. deeds etc., mainly rel. Monkton, West Monkton and Bathpool, co. Som., and (pp. 105–14) Longbridge Deverill, co. Wilts.

Fos. 62 (19th cent. pagination, 17–140; wants leaves at the beginning, end and aft. fo. 52). $12\frac{3}{8} \times 8\frac{5}{8}$ in. Paper.

¶ *Inventories*

438. **Cambridge, Trinity Coll., MS. R. 5. 33,** fos. 77–87. Inventory of charters, 13th cent. (*temp.* Hen. III), written partly in double columns with rubrics, red paragraphs etc. and numerous additions *passim.* Arranged partly by type of charter and partly by obedientiaries, the first section (early royal charters) being headed 'Carte contente in libro terrarum Glaston.'. A single quire bound up, with other misc. quires containing copies of 12th–13th cent. royal, papal and other charters etc., at the end of a contemp. MS. of A. de Domerham's continuation of Wm. de Malmesbury, 'De Antiquitate Glastoniensis Ecclesie' (ed. T. Hearne, Oxford, 1727), which incorporates similar material. Cf. also No. 440. Printed by T. Hearne, *Johannis Glastonie Chronica* ii (Oxford, 1726), 370–418. M. R. James, *Cat. MSS. Trinity Coll.* iii (Cambridge, 1901), no. 724.

Fos. 10+ii (142 in the MS.). $10\frac{1}{2} \times 7$ in. *FO:* W. Bowyer, 1565; T. Nevile (?).

439. **The Marquess of Bath,** *ib.* (MS. 38b (2)). Inventory of deeds, early 15th cent., with red titles, blue initials decorated with red etc. Arranged partly by places (fos. 1–55) and partly by obedientiaries (fos. 56–86), with some later additions. The topographical sections include notes of Anglo-Saxon royal charters, for which see A. J. Horwood, *HMC. Fourth Report* (1874), App., 228.

Fos. 86 (paginated, 1–170). $10\frac{3}{4} \times 7$ in.

¶ *Elemosinarius*

440. **BM., Add. 22934,** fos. 114–25. Quire from an early 14th cent. cartulary (aft. 1313), written in double columns with rubrics and containing copies of deeds, *c.* 1230–1312, rel. the almoner's lands in various places. Breaks off at the end in the middle of an entry (catchword, 'acra iacet'). Bound up at the end of another MS. of A. de Domerham's continuation of Wm. de Malmesbury (cf. No. 438 above), here carried down to 1313.

Fos. 12 (128 in the MS.). $13\frac{1}{8} \times 8\frac{1}{4}$ in. *FO:* W. Fox, 16th cent.; R. Higgs, 18th cent.; T. Clarges (from an Oxford grocer); J. Novell; Bp. T. Tanner; Cox Macro, 1722 (sale-cat., 1820, lot 64: in the hands, 1771, of Osmund Beauvoir); (Sir) F. Palgrave, 1829; Dawson Turner.

¶ *Pitanciarius*

441. **The Marquess of Bath,** *ib.* (Mun. 10587). Quire from an early 16th cent. cartulary, containing copies of sixty-one 13th–14th cent. charters, incl. three papal bulls, rel. the pittancer's lands.

Fos. 20 (wants leaves at the beginning and end). $12\frac{3}{4} \times 8\frac{3}{4}$ in. Paper.

¶ *Other registers etc.*

442. **Ditto** (Mun. 10590). Fragms. of registers of 13th cent. abbots, put together apparently in the early 14th cent. Fos. 87.

443. **Ditto** (Mun. 10591, 10593). Fragms. of registers *temp.* Galf de Fromond, abbot 1302–22, etc. Fos. 21, 25.

444. **Ditto** (Mun. 10588). 'De homagiis et fidelitatibus factis domino Waltero (de Monington) . . . abbati' etc., 1342–9. Fos. 19.

445. **BM., Arundel 2.** Register of Abbot W. de Monington, 1352–66. *FO:* Ld. Wm. Howard; presented by Henry Howard, 6th duke of Norfolk, to the Royal Society, 1678.

446. **BM., Add. 17451.** Register of fines paid to the abbot for grants and reversions of lands, 1533–8. Paper. Acquired of W. Row, 1848.

447.   **The Marquess of Bath,** *ib.* (Mun. 10589). 'Liber Hen. de Soliaco' *al.* 'Liber A'. Inquisitions of the abbey's manors etc., 1189. Ed. J. E. Jackson (Roxburghe Club, 1882).

448.   **BM., Add. 17450.** Register of custumaries, extents etc., 13th cent. Ed. C. I. Elton, *Rentalia et Custumaria* . . . *Glastoniae* (Somerset Record Soc. v, 1891). *FO:* (Sir ?) Egremont Thynne, 16th–17th cent.; acquired of W. Row, 1848.

448A.   **Oxford, Bodl., lat. misc. C. 18*,** fo. 63. Fragm. (6¼ × 2¾ in., approx.) of a leaf apparently from a register of leases, *temp.* M. de Ambresbury, abbot 1235–52. Taken from the binding of a printed book.

449.   **BM., Egerton 3321.** Register of extents and rentals, 14th cent. *FO:* Ld. Rolle; Ld. Clinton.

450.   **BM., Egerton 3034.** Terriers of lands in co. Som., made *temp.* Abbot R. Beere, *c.* 1515–20. Medieval binding. *FO:* the Earls & Marquesses of Ailesbury, 18th–19th cent.

451.   **BM., Egerton 3134.** Similar to No. 450, also for co. Som. Medieval binding. *FO:* E. Goodenough, dean of Wells; Sir T. Phillipps (MS. 12101).

452.   **London, Soc. of Antiquaries, MS. 653.** Similar to No. 450, for Baltonsborough.

453.   **BM., Harley 3961.** Similar to No. 450, for lands in cos. Wilts and Berks. *FO:* H. Spelman; Thomas Rawlinson.

GLOUCESTER   co. Glouc.
Ben. Abbey   *f.* 1058

An account of the cartularies is given by W. H. Hart, *Historia et Cartularium* . . . *Monasterii Gloucestriae*, 3 vols. (Rolls ser., 1863–7), iii, pp. x–xvi, who edits No. 454. For those at Gloucester see also W. H. Stevenson, *HMC. Twelfth Report*, App. ix (1891), 397.

454.   **PRO., Chancery** (C. 150/1). Gen. cartulary, *temp.* J. de Gamages, abbot 1284–1306, with additions. Sumptuously written with red and blue decorated initials, rubrics and an illuminated miniature at the beginning (cf. Hart, *op. cit.* i, frontispiece). Arranged in alphabetical order of subjects and places hotchpotch, in two parallel parts, without obvious distinction,

on leaves numbered i–clxxx, clxxxi–ccxxviii, in a large contemp. foliation, and incl. copies of royal charters *passim*. Preceded by seventeen unnumbered preliminary leaves containing an alphabetical Table of both parts (fos. 10–14) and misc. additions. Followed by: (*a*) fourteen unnumbered leaves in similar format, containing *Transcripta Privilegiorum* (papal) and further additions; (*b*) seventy-two leaves, numbered i–lxvii with five unnumbered, containing extents of manors etc., 1265–7 and undated. Six fly-leaves at the end also contain additions. Ed. Hart, *op. cit.*

Fos. 337 (numbered as above). $11\frac{7}{8} \times 8$ in. *FO:* the Porter fam., Lanthony by Gloucester (?); the Scudamore and Fitzroy-Scudamore fam., Holme Lacy; Frances, duchess of Norfolk (d. 1820).

455.   **Gloucester, D. & C.,** 'Reg. A'. Two parts of a cartulary made, 1393–7, by Abbot W. de Frocester, with rubrics, red and blue paragraphs and a single blue initial decorated with red at the beginning of each part, as follows: (1) fos. 5–72, 'Registrum de donacionibus et confirmacionibus diversorum Regum Angliae et Comitum', 1397, with a contemp. Table (fos. 5–7) and a few later additions (fos. 3v–4, 72v–5); (2) fos. 76–178, 'Registrum pertinens ad ecclesias monasterii . . . et ad earum capellas annexas cum earundem rectoriis vicariis pensionibus' etc., 1393, arranged by places with a contemp. Table at fos. 76–81. Fo. 1 is the first leaf of a Table of a third part, headed 'Registrum de munimentis maneriorum pertinent. ad commune'. Annotations by John Prynne.

Fos. 178 (fos. 9–72, 82–177 with contemp. foliation, i–lxiiii, i–lxxxvi). $11\frac{1}{2} \times 7\frac{3}{4}$ in.

456.   **Ditto,** 'Reg. B'. Cartulary, 1393, in ten parts, of deeds rel. lands assigned to each of the ten *Officia* of the abbey (sacrist, almoner of Standish, hostiller, subalmoner, master of works, abbey chamberlain, refectorer, infirmarer, master of the chapel, precentor), made by Abbot W. de Frocester. Red and blue paragraphs, red underlining of headings etc. Each part is arranged topographically, and there is a contemp. collective Table on fifteen preliminary leaves, preceded by two leaves of index in the hand of John Prynne. The earliest of the deeds copied (more than

1,000 in number) is 11th cent. and the majority concern the city of Gloucester.

Fos. 18+253 (medieval foliation by parts). $12\frac{1}{2} \times 8\frac{1}{4}$ in.

¶ *Other registers etc.*

457. **Oxford, Queen's Coll., MS. 367,** pp. 65–125. 'Donaciones omnium bonorum tam temporalium quam spiritualium,' 15th cent. A list of grantors and their gifts, arranged alphabetically by places and preceded by the treatise 'De Prima Fundacione Monasterii Sancti Petri Gloucestriae'. Ed. Hart, *op. cit.* i, 58–125. *FO:* the Rev. H. Jackson; W. Fulman; T. Halton; A. Hall.

458. **BM., Cotton Domit. A. viii,** fos. 145v–161v. Another version of No. 457, 15th cent. Thought by Hart, *l.c.*, to be copied from it, although possessing some additional sections. *FO:* Sir John Prise; John Dee (?).

459. **Gloucester, D. & C.,** 'Reg. C'. Register of Abbots Braunche and Newton, 1500–13.

460. **Ditto,** 'Reg. D'. Register of Abbot Parker *al.* Malvern, 1514–28.

461. **Ditto,** 'Reg. E'. Register of Abbot Parker, 1528–38.

GODSTOW co. Oxon

Ben. Abbey (Nuns) *f. c.* 1133

A. Clark, *The English Register of Godstow Nunnery*, 3 vols. (Early Engl. Text Soc., Orig. ser. cxxix, cxxx, cxlii, 1905–11), edits No. 463 and describes No. 462.

462. **PRO., Exch., K.R.** (Misc. Bks. i. 20). Gen. cartulary, 1404, with rubrics etc. and some pen-work decoration of initials, made at the charges and labour of Alice de Henley, prioress. Arranged mainly topographically, in alphabetical order of places, with copies of charters rel. the foundation grouped at the beginning and of other royal and papal charters at fos. clxiii–clxxxi. Eighteen unnumbered leaves at the front and back contain a contemp. Table and misc. 15th cent. additions.

Fos. 18 + 190 (numbered i–cxc). $13\frac{1}{4} \times 8\frac{3}{4}$ in. Delivered into the Exchequer by R. Browne, 1585.

463. **Oxford, Bodl., Rawlinson B. 408.** An English abstract of No. 462, begun aft. 1467 by 'a poore broder and well wyller (*blank*) to . . . dame Alice Henley', abbess (d. 1470). Written as a single compilation in three contemp. hands, which copy material extending down to *c.* 1480, with rubrics, uncompleted blue initials and some later additions. Fos. 1–12 contain misc. devotional pieces and a kalendar. Extracts, 17th cent., are in BM., Cotton Julius C. vii, fos. 274–86. *New Palaeographical Soc.*, First ser., pl. 196.

Fos. 224 (wants 12 leaves *passim*). $12\frac{3}{4} \times 8\frac{1}{2}$ in. *FO:* Sir J. Ware; Henry, 2nd earl of Clarendon; James, 1st duke of Chandos.

GORLESTON co. Suff.

Aug. Friary *f. c.* 1261–3 (?)

No cartulary recorded.

¶ *Other registers etc.*

464. **Oxford, Bodl., Twyne 2,** pp. 98–9. Parts of two leaves or membranes from a register or roll, containing copies of about five documents rel. a tithe dispute, 1341. Subsequently used as binding leaves. Noticed by E. A. Webb, *Records of St. Bartholomew's, Smithfield* i (1921), xxxii.

GUISBOROUGH co. York

Aug. Priory *f.* 1119

465. **BM., Cotton Cleop. D. ii,** fos. 112–332. Gen. cartulary, late 13th cent., supplemented throughout in an early 14th cent. hand (aft. 1314) with some later additions *passim*. Arranged mainly topographically in sections, of which the first, for Guisborough (incl. copies of episcopal, royal and papal charters) is followed by: (*a*) fines and further royal charters copied in the hand of the supplementor, fos. 157v–165; (*b*) *Carte Elemosinar.* and *Carte Fabrice Ecclesie* copied in one of the original hands, fos. 166–77. The quires are misarranged, perhaps with loss of material since, in its present state, the MS. does not cover all the priory's known lands. Ed. Wm. Brown, *Cartularium Prioratus de Gyseburne*, 2 vols. (Surtees Soc. lxxxvi, lxxxxix, 1889, 1894 for 1891).

Fos. 223 (earlier post-medieval foliations, (8)–253, 110–352). $10\frac{1}{4} \times 7\frac{1}{2}$ in.

466. **Untraced.** Cartulary stated by Mr. James Yates at a meeting of the Royal Archaeological Institute, 3 June 1868, to have been formerly in the possession of William Hamper of Birmingham, see *Archaeological J.* xxv (1868), 249.

HAILES co. Glouc.
Cist. Abbey *f.* 1246
No cartulary recorded.
⁋ *Other registers etc.*
v. also No. 1041 below.
467. **BM., Royal 12 E. xiv.** Dictaminal formularies, visitations etc., 14th and 15th cent. *FO:* J. Theyer.

HALESOWEN co. Worc.
Praem. Abbey *f.* 1215
468. **Untraced.** Cartulary roll, three or four feet in length, listed by A. J. Horwood, *HMC. Second Report* (1871), App., 38, among the MSS. of the Lyttelton fam., barons Lyttelton (and afterw. viscounts Cobham), at Hagley Hall. Not among the material deposited in Birmingham Reference Libr. Thought to have been destroyed by fire, 1925.
469. **Untraced.** 'Registrum olim penes Hen. Littleton bar.' (d. 1693) (*T*). Thought, 1736, to be in the hands of Mr. Keeling, steward to William, 10th baron Dudley and Ward; see London, Soc. of Antiquaries, Prattinton Collections xvi, fos. 12 ff., cited by H. M. Colvin, *The White Canons in England* (Oxford, 1951), 380.

HARBLEDOWN co. Kent
Hosp. of St. Nicholas *f. c.* 1084
No cartulary recorded.
⁋ *Other registers etc.*
470. **London, Lambeth Palace, MSS. 1131, 1132.** Transcript of the charters, 1763, by the Rev. H. Hall *et al.* An abstract of this by E. H(asted) is in BM., Stowe 855 (*FO:* T. Astle, 1796), and extracts are also printed by J. Duncombe & N. Battely, *Hist. Three Archiepiscopal Hospitals at and near Canterbury* (Bibl. Top. Britannica xxx, 1785). The original muniments of the hospital, lodged with Messrs. Fielding & Pembrook at Canterbury, were destroyed by aerial bombardment, 1 June 1942.

HARROLD co. Bedf.
Aug. Priory (Nuns) *f.* 1140–50
471. **BM., Lansdowne 391.** 'Extractus sive abreviacio cartarum sive munimentorum' etc. Abstract of charters, 15th cent. (aft. 1414), with red or occasionally blue paragraphs, underlining of titles etc. and incl. a few complete transcripts. Arranged topographically, with notes of

a few papal and episcopal documents included *passim*, and of royal ones at fos. 60–1. Ed. G. H. Fowler, *Records of Harrold Priory* (Bedfordshire Hist. Record Soc. xvii, 1935).

Fos. 62. 9½ × 6 in. *FO:* W. Byles, 16th cent. (?); Bernard Baldwyn, 17th cent. (?); W. Clavell, 1709 (*T*); James West.
⁋ *Other registers etc.*
472. **Bristol, Baptist Coll., MS. Z. c. 23.** Psalter, 12th cent., with early 13th cent. copies of 19 documents etc., 12th–13th cent., rel. Stevington church on the back fly-leaves. Ed. C. R. Cheney, '*Harrold Priory: a Twelfth Century Dispute' and Other Articles* (Bedfordshire Hist. Record Soc. xxxii, 1952 for 1951), 1–26. *FO:* J. Sunnyng, 'vicarius de Luswe (?)', 16th cent.; Sir J. Ware; A. Gifford, D.D.

HATFIELD BROAD OAK co. Essex
Ben. Priory *f. c.* 1135
473. **Barrington fam. archives,** deposited at Chelmsford, Essex R.O. (D/DBa Q1). Quire from a 15th–16th cent. cartulary, with rubrics and pen-decorated initials touched with red, containing copies of about 12 charters, incl. royal licences to alienate in mortmain, rel. Hatfield Broad Oak, 1298–*c.* 1327.

Fos. 8 (contemp. numeration, *b* i–*b* viii). 7⅞ × 11 in. *FO:* J. Mountforde (?); the Barrington fam., Hatfield Broad Oak.
474. **Untraced.** Cartulary from which extracts, 1592, from fos. 100–18, are in BM., Lansdowne 860A, fos. 225v–6. Perhaps the source of No. 473.

HAUGHMOND co. Salop
Aug. Abbey *f.* 1130–8
475. **BM., Harley 446.** Fragm. (parts of quires *x–xiii*) of a mid-14th cent. cartulary with rubrics, red pen-decorated initials and misc. additions on fly- or added leaves at the end (fos. 37–9). The contents, incl. copies of some royal and occasional episcopal charters etc., are listed in *Mon. Angl.* vi, 107 (*q*). **BM., Harley 7505,** fo. 22, is a detached leaf which should follow fo. 36.

Fos. 39 + 1 (contemp. roman foliation by quires; wants leaves *passim*). 12⅞ × 9 in. *FO:* Edward Jones (?) (cf. Dugdale, *Antiq. Warwickshire* (2nd ed., 1730), 557 (*f*)); P. Le Neve, 1696.

476. **Shrewsbury, Borough Libr.**
Gen. cartulary, late 15th cent. (aft. 1478),
with rubrics and red initials. Arranged
topographically in alphabetical order of
places, to which there is an index at the
beginning, and incl. copies of royal, papal
and episcopal charters in the section for
Haughmond (fos. 75v ff.) and elsewhere
passim. 16th cent. binding. Partial 18th
cent. transcripts are in BM., Add. 33354
(*FO:* W. Mytton) and Shrewsbury
Borough Libr. MS. 1 (by the Rev. E.
Williams; *FO:* Sir T. Phillipps (MS.
11224)). Extracts by W. A. Leighton *et al.*
in *Coll. Top. et Genealogica* i (1834), 362–74,
are reprinted and expanded by *Id.*, 'Extracts from the Cartulary of Haghmon
Abbey, co. Salop', *Trans. Shropshire Arch.
Soc.* i (1878), 173–214.
Fos. xi + 239. 13½ × 9½ in. *FO:* the
Barker, Kynaston and Corbet fams.,
Sundorne.

HAVERHOLME   co. Linc.
Gilb. Priory   *f.* 1139
477.   **Untraced.** Cartulary *penes* Robert
Pierrepont, 1st earl of Kingston-upon-Hull,
1634, by loan of Gervase Holles of
Grimsby, from which extracts down to fo.
75 are in Bodl., Dodsworth 144 (*SC.* 5085),
fos. 81–96.
478.   **Untraced.** 'Registrum penes Edw.
Lynald de Heling in com. Linc.' (*T*),
17th cent. Possibly identical with No. 477
(*D*).

HAYLING   co. Southt.
Ben. Priory   *f. c.* 1067
v. No. 891 below.

HEALAUGH   co. York
Aug. Priory   *f.* 1218
479.   **BM., Cotton Vesp. A. iv.** Gen.
cartulary written, aft. 1505, for P. Kendayll,
prior 1499–1520, with red initials, marginal
titles etc. Contains copies of deeds, incl.
royal and episcopal charters etc., grouped
to some extent topographically. Preceded
(fos. 1–4) by a *Stemma Fundatoris* and list of
priors, and followed (fos. 175 ff.) by misc.
additions incl. anglicised versions (fos.
176v–7) of bulls of Honorius and Innocent
IV. Ed. J. S. Purvis, *The Chartulary of*
Healaugh Park (Yorks. Arch. Soc., Record
ser. xcii, 1936 for 1935).
Fos. 194 (wants a few leaves *passim*).
9½ × 7 in. Annotated by R. Gascoigne. *FO:*
Sir T. Wharton, 1st baron Wharton; P.
Padmore, 1633.

HEDINGHAM, CASTLE   co. Essex
v. CASTLE HEDINGHAM.

HEREFORD   co. Heref.
Cath. Church   *f.* 7th cent.
480.   **Oxford, Bodl., Jones 23** (*SC.*
8930). (Part (four quires) of a?) late 13th
cent. cartulary (aft. 1277), containing
copies of 71 deeds, incl. one episcopal confirmation. Printed by R. Rawlinson, *Hist.
Hereford* (1717), App., 32–85.
Fos. 40 (post-medieval pagination, i–
lxxx; two leaves excised bef. p. lxxix).
9¾ × 7¾ in.
481.   **Oxford, Bodl., Rawlinson B.**
329, fos. 121–76. Cartulary, 13th–14th
cent. (apparently of later date than No.
480), containing copies of deeds etc., incl.
some episcopal documents, arranged
roughly topographically. Bound up in the
Middle Ages with No. 480, extracts, 1718,
from both in BM., Harley 6203, being
calendared by A. T. Bannister, 'A Lost
Cartulary of Hereford Cathedral', *Trans.
Woolhope Club* 1914–17 (Hereford, 1918),
268–77.
Fos. 56. 13 × 9¼ in. *FO:* Silas Taylor,
1657; Sir T. Thynne, 1st viscount Weymouth.
482.   **Ditto,** fos. 1–120. Cartulary, 15th
cent., with uncompleted rubrication,
underlining of proper names in red etc. or
(fos. 66–103, 119–20, rel. the church of
Diddlebury etc.) alternate red and blue
initials. Contains copies of deeds etc., incl.
papal and episcopal charters, arranged
apparently according to subject matter by
pressmarks, and (fos. 104–18) royal charters etc., Edw. Conf.–Hen. IV, added aft.
fo. 107 in a succession of later hands; with
occasional other additions *passim*. Bannister,
l.c.
Fos. 120 (wants 12 leaves at the beginning and others at the end). 12 × 8½ in. *FO:*
as No. 481.

¶ *Other registers etc.*
483.   **Cambridge U.L., Dd. 10. 18.**
Rentals etc., 14th cent. *FO:* Bp. J. Moore.

HEREFORD   co. Heref.
Ben. Priory of St. Guthlac   *f.* 1107–22
484.   **Oxford, Balliol Coll., MS. 271.**
Gen. cartulary, early 14th cent. (aft. 1311),
with spaces for initials and headings.
Arranged topographically in alphabetical
order of parishes, with copies of *Libertates*,
incl. royal, papal and episcopal confirmations etc., at the end (fos. 92v–110) followed by misc. additions. A contemp.
Table at fos. 11–15r is preceded by further
misc. additions, incl. (fos. 1–5) another
later 14th cent. Table. Described by R. A.
B. Mynors, *Cat. MSS. Balliol Coll.* (forth-
coming), *ad loc.*
     Fos. ix + 137 (later 14th cent. foliation,
i–lxxxxiii, of fos. 16–111). 13¼ × 8½ in.
FO: Sir John Prise; G. Coningsby, D.D.

HEXHAM   co. Northumb.
Aug. Priory   *f.* 1113 (?)
485.   **Leeds, Yorks. Arch. Soc., MS.
542.** Fragm. (one quire, preceded by the
outer bifolium of another) from a register
written (fos. 2–8r) in a 15th–16th cent.
hand with rubrics, red initials etc. Contains copies of deeds, memoranda etc. (17
entries) rel. Salton etc., with a later 16th
cent. continuation (fos. 1, 8v–14) which
adds 19 further entries. (Sir F.) M(adden) &
(J. G. ?) N(ichols), 'Abstract of a . . . Cartulary of Hexham Abbey' etc., *Coll. Top.
et Genealogica* vi (1840), 38–46.
     Fos. 14 (1, 14, vellum cover). 8¾ × 6 in.
FO: R. Thoresby, 1711; J. B. Nichols,
1833; J. G. Nichols, 1865.
¶ *Other registers etc.*
486.   **Viscount Allendale,** Bywell Hall,
Stocksfield-on-Tyne. 'The Black Book.'
Rental, 1479 etc. Ed. J. Raine, *The Priory
of Hexham* ii (Surtees Soc. xlvi, 1865 for
1864), 1–82. *FO:* Sir J. Fenwick, 1622 (*D*);
the Beaumont fam., Bretton Hall.

HICKLING   co. Norf.
Aug. Priory   *f.* 1185
487.   **Oxford, Bodl., Tanner 425.** Gen.
cartulary, mid-13th cent., with occasional
rubrication, red initials etc. and some later
13th cent. additions. Arranged apparently
topographically, with a section of papal,
episcopal, royal etc. charters at fos. 37–46.
     Fos. 54 (18th cent. pagination, 3–102, of
fos. 1–50). 8¾ × 5¾ in.

¶ *Other registers etc.*
488.   **Oxford, Bodl., Tanner 194.**
Accompts of the prior as cellarer, 1–13
Hen. VIII.

HIGHAM FERRERS   co. Northt.
Coll. of SS. Mary, Thomas and Edw.
Conf.   *f.* 1422
489.   **BM., Stowe 931.** Cartulary, 15th
cent., with an illuminated opening initial (fo. 1), containing copies of 15 charters
rel. the college's foundation, endowment
etc., 1422–37, and two deeds rel. the vicars
of Higham Ferrers, 1358, 1429.
     Fos. 83. 9 × 6½ in. *FO:* T. Astle (*P*).

HINCHINGBROOKE   co. Hunt.
Ben. Priory (Nuns)   *f.* bef. 1087
490.   **Destroyed.** 'Registra . . . penes
praehonorabilem com. Sandwicensem'
(*T*), i.e. the Montagu fam., earls of Sand-
wich (cr. 1660). Burnt in a fire at Hinchingbrooke, 1830.

HOLBORN   co. Middx.
Hosp. of St. Giles   *f.* 1101
491.   **BM., Harley 4015.** Cartulary
made, 1402, for W. Lynton, master of the
hospital of Burton Lazars (cf. No. 90).
Small blue initials, decorated with red, and
some additions. Arranged in sections by
parishes, which are listed at fos. 2v–3, with
the copies of royal charters, from *temp.*
Ric. I, at fos. 206–11.
     Fos. 214 (excl. blank leaves; post-
medieval pagination, 1–461, from fo. 5).
10½ × 7½ in. *FO:* Thomas Rawlinson.

HOLM CULTRAM   co. Cumb.
Cist. Abbey   *f.* 1150
     Nos. 492–4 are described by F. Grainger
& W. G. Collingwood, *The Register and
Records of Holm Cultram* (Cumberland &
Westm. Antiq. & Arch. Soc., Record ser.
vii, 1929), who calendar No. 492 with supplementary extracts from Nos. 493–4.
Extracts, mainly from Nos. 493–4, are
printed in *Mon. Angl.* v, 594–618.
492.   **Carlisle, D. & C.,** Muniments.
Gen. cartulary, late 13th cent., with
rubrics etc. and blue and red decorated, or
plain red, initials. Arranged in sections,
mainly topographically (pp. 157–68, royal
charters; 239–66, papal), with misc. additions *passim*. The original order of the

quires has apparently been disturbed. Transcripts, 18th cent., are in BM., Harley 1881, fos. 143–210 (*FO:* H. Todd, D.D.) and of the Scottish material etc. in NLS., Adv. 34. 1. 4 (*FO:* J. Goldie).

Fos. 3 + 142 (paginated, 1–284). 5 × 3¾ in. *FO:* W. Blenerhasset; T. Denton; Bp. W. Nicolson; J. Nicolson.

493. **BM., Harley 3911.** Gen. cartulary, 13th–14th cent. (*temp.* Edw. I), with rubrics etc., plain red or blue initials and additions down to *temp.* Edw. III. Arranged in 43 sections, mainly topographically, with the royal charters entered under topographical heads and the papal at the end (section *xxxv*), followed (*xxxvi–xliii*) by misc. gen. charters of liberties, statutes, perambulations etc. Contemp. Table, fos. 3–6. *Mon. Angl., l.c.,* nos. i–ii, xxi ff.

Fos. 196. 6 × 4¼ in. *FO:* C. Musgrave; Ld. Wm. Howard; J. Warburton.

494. **BM., Harley 3891.** Gen. cartulary, 14th cent. (*temp.* Edw. II–III), with rubrics etc., red initials and later 14th cent. additions. Arranged in 15 sections (*i* Foundation, *ii* royal, *iii–xv* topographical) followed by three others, unnumbered, containing copies of records of legal proceedings, papal privileges, gen. charters of liberties etc. Contemp. Table, fos. 8v–9, 2. *Mon. Angl., l.c.,* nos. iv–xxi.

Fos. 144. 7½ × 5⅜ in. *FO:* Ld. Wm. Howard (?).

HORNCHURCH co. Essex
Hosp. of SS. Nicholas & Bernard *f.* 1159

No cartulary recorded. H. F. Westlake, *Hornchurch Priory: a Kalendar of Documents in the Possession of New College, Oxford* (1923), calendars 547 original charters, deeds etc.

HORSHAM ST. FAITH co. Norf.
Ben. Priory *f. c.* 1190

495. **Untraced.** 'Registrum . . . penes Joannem Hobart bar.' (*T*), i.e., presumably, Sir John Hobart, 5th bart. of Blickling, succeeded 1698, cr. Baron Hobart 1728, Earl of Buckinghamshire 1746. But the 2nd and 3rd barts. (d. 1647, 1683) were also named John.

HORTON, MONKS co. Kent
v. MONKS HORTON.

HOXNE co. Suff.
Ben. Priory *f.* 1130

496. **Untraced.** Fragm. of a 14th cent. cartulary, of which the contents are noticed by F. Blomfield, *Hist. Norfolk* iii (2nd ed., 1805–10), 607 ff., and in the sale-cats. etc. of libraries of former owners.

Fos. 12 (so (*P*), but Blomefield cites fos. 14, 18). Folio. *FO:* T. Martin, 1743; J. Ives; T. Astle; C. Ord; Sir T. Phillipps (MS. 3793).

HULME, ST. BENET OF co. Norf.
Ben. Abbey *f.* 1019

497. **BM., Cotton Galba E. ii.** Gen. cartulary written (fos. 30–173) *temp.* N. de Walsham, abbot 1275–1302, with rubrics, red initials etc. Comprises sections of royal, papal, episcopal etc. charters followed by others of private deeds etc. grouped by abbots (Richerus, 1101–25, to N. de Walsham). The last section, written apparently *seriatim* in several hands, contains material down to 1301. Additions *passim* at fos. 173v ff. include an early 14th cent. index (fos. 183–8). A later 14th cent. index, added as fos. 1–27, is printed in *Mon. Angl.* iii, 66 (*e*). A modern index of persons and places is in BM., Add. 43407. Extracts, 17th cent., are in BM., Stowe 932. J. R. West, *St. Benet of Holme* 1020–1210 (Norfolk Record Soc. ii, iii, 1932) edits the 11th–12th cent. material.

Fos. 222 (30–173 with contemp. numeration, i–cxliii). 14 × 8½ in.

498. **Norwich, D. & C.,** Muniments, 'Reg. VIII'. Register, late 14th cent. (*temp.* Edw. III), of charters, 13th–14th cent., incl. some royal, papal and episcopal documents, rel. the abbey's churches. Rubrics, red and black initials etc.

Fos. 54 (contemp. foliation, ii–lv). 11¼ × 8¼ in. Paper.

HULNE by Alnwick co. Northumb.
v. ALNWICK.

HUNTINGDON co. Hunt.
Aug. Priory *f.* 1113

499. **BM., Cotton Faust. C. i,** fos. 2–65. Gen. cartulary, 14th–15th cent., written in sections in two main hands, of which one (fos. 1–17, Huntingdon etc.; 30–41, Gidding) appears to be somewhat earlier than the other. Arranged topographically,

with a custumary and other contemp. and
later misc. additions at the end (fos. 57 ff.),
and incl. copies of some royal (English and
Scottish) and episcopal charters *passim*.
Calendared, down to fo. 25, by W. M.
Noble, 'The Cartulary of . . . Huntingdon', *Trans. Cambr. & Hunt. Arch. Soc.* iv
(1930), 89–280 *passim*.

Fos. 64. $11\frac{1}{2} \times 7\frac{1}{2}$ in.

HYDE   co. Southt.
v. WINCHESTER.

IPSWICH   co. Suff.
Aug. Priory of SS. Peter & Paul   *f.* bef.
                            1189
500.   **Lexington Public Libr.,** Kentucky, U.S.A. (091–M. 313). Gen. cartulary, late 13th cent., with partial rubrication, red initials etc. Quires mainly of 8
leaves, now misbound. Appears originally
to have been arranged in alphabetical order
of places (fos. 87–92, quire *a*, wants the first
leaf; fos. 18–76, *b–j*), with sections of inquisitions and fines at the end (fos. 3–(17?),
k and (*l*?)) followed by misc. additions,
temp. Edw. I etc. A photostat copy is in
Ipswich Public Reference Libr.

Fos. 92 (wants a leaf aft. fo. 17 and occa-
sional others elsewhere). $9\frac{1}{2} \times 6\frac{1}{4}$ in. Presented by Mr. John Bobbs of Lexington,
1806.

KEELING, NUN   co. York
v. NUNKEELING.

KENILWORTH   co. Warw.
Aug. Abbey   *f.* (as a priory) *c.* 1125
v. also STONE.
501.   **BM., Harley 3650.** Parts of apparently more than one cartulary, written
in late 12th–mid-13th cent. hands with uncompleted rubrication, red initials and
occasional additions *passim*. Arranged by
grantors (founders etc., magnates, episcopal, lay), with some repetition of material. Extracts, 1637, by Sir Wm. Dugdale
are in Bodl., Dugdale 12 (*SC.* 6502), pp.
275–317, for which see P. Styles, 'Sir
Simon Clarke', *Trans. Birmingham Arch.
Soc.* lxvi (1950 for 1945–6), 24–7.

Fos. 88. $9\frac{3}{4} \times 6\frac{1}{2}$ in. *FO:* Sir Simon
Clarke, bart., 1637 (*D*); Richard Graves,
1726 (*T*); James West, 1731.
502.   **BM., Add. 47677.** Gen. cartulary,

16th cent. (aft. 1514), with bold headings
in black. Arranged mainly topographically,
with an index of places at fos. 1–3, and incl.
series of episcopal and papal charters at fos.
93v–109, and of royal ones at fos. 376v–370,
with copies of others *passim*. Extracts,
1596, are among the records of Lord
Aylesford at Packington.

Fos. iii + 370 (contemp. foliation, i–
ccclxii, from fo. 6). $11\frac{1}{2} \times 7\frac{3}{4}$ in. (cropped).
FO: Robert Dudley, earl of Leicester;
Sir Christopher Blount, 1596; the Coke
fam., earls of Leicester, Holkham.
503.   **Untraced.** Register *penes* Henry
Clinton *al.* Fiennes, 2nd earl of Lincoln,
1589. An extract by Ld. Wm. Howard of a
charter of G. de Clinton, 1269, is in Bodl.,
Top. Devon b. 5, fo. 51. Possibly identical
with No. 501 or No. 502.
504.   **Untraced.** Register *penes* E. Gres-
wold of Cubbington, 17th cent. Cited by
Dugdale, *Antiq. Warwickshire* (2nd ed.,
1730), 507–832 *passim*.
¶ *Other registers etc.*
505.   **Untraced.** Register of W. Wall,
abbot 1516–37, cited by Dugdale, *op. cit.*,
12–1036 *passim*. *FO:* Sir Simon Clarke,
bart. (?) (cf. Styles, *l.c.*, 26–7).

KERSEY   co. Suff.
Aug. Priory   *f. c.* 1218
     v. also No. 1212 below.
506.   **Cambridge, King's Coll.,** Muniments (O. 34). Quire from a 13th cent. cartulary (*temp.* Edw. I?), with red paragraphs and uncompleted rubrication. Contains copies of about 40 deeds rel. Kersey,
beginning and ending in the middle of
entries.

Fos. 12. $9 \times 6\frac{3}{8}$ in.
507.   **Ditto** (O. 33, 37). Cartulary, 1343–
4, rather roughly written, with a limp
vellum cover, and arranged topographically. O. 37 is a detached leaf.

Fos. 22 + 1. $11 \times 7\frac{1}{2}$ in.
¶ *Pitanciarius*
508.   **Ditto** (O. 39). 'Rotulus de cartis
pittancie.' Copies, 13th cent. (*temp.* Hen.
III) of about eleven deeds etc., with five
others added in later 13th cent. hands,
Rubrics and small red initials.

Roll of 1 membr. $24\frac{1}{2} \times 8$ in.
¶ *Other registers etc.*
509–511.   **Ditto** (O. 35, 36, 38). Three
rolls containing copies of misc. charters of

the priory, 13th–14th cent. O. 35 includes numerous episcopal etc. documents and one papal bull. O. 36, 38, contain 6–7 entries apiece.

KEYNSHAM co. Som.
Aug. Abbey *f.* 1167–72
512. **Untraced.** 'Register of Keinsham Abbey and Tewkesbury' cited in P. Holland's translation of Camden's *Britannia* (1637), 368, as a source of information about Robert, earl of Gloucester (cr. 1122).

KINGS LYNN co. Norf.
v. LYNN.

KINGSWOOD co. Glouc.
Cist. Abbey *f.* 1139
513. **Untraced.** Cartulary *penes* John Smith of Nibley, 1651 (*D*), from which extracts, beginning with a narrative account of the abbey's foundation, are printed in *Mon. Angl.* v, 425 ff. Perhaps the 'Liber Donationum' cited in Leland's *Itinerary* (ed. T. Hearne, 1744) vi, 41 ff. For other material removed from Nibley to Condover Hall, incl. some of the abbey's original charters, see A. J. Horwood, *HMC. Fifth Report* (1876), App., 333 ff.

KINGTON ST. MICHAEL co. Wilts
Ben. Priory (Nuns) *f.* bef. 1155
514. **Untraced.** 'Cartularium olim penes dom. Robertum Long, penes Joannem Aubrey arm. penes magistrum Rogers de Chippenham' (*T*).
¶ *Other registers etc.*
515. **Cambridge U.L., Dd. 8. 2,** art. 1. Obit-book, late 15th cent. *FO:* Bp. J. Moore.

KIRBY BELLARS co. Leic.
Aug. Priory *f.* (as a Coll.) 1316
516. **Comdr. Sir Michael Culme-Seymour, bart.,** Rockingham Castle (Library). Cartulary, late 14th cent., arranged topographically with a few additions on the last 10 leaves. Imperf. at the beginning and lacks other leaves *passim*. Includes copies of some royal grants of pardon, wills etc.
Fos. iv + 66. 11¼ × 7⅜ in. *FO:* the Watson fam., earls of Rockingham etc.

KIRKHAM co. York
Aug. Priory *f. c.* 1122
517. **Oxford, Bodl., Fairfax 7** (*SC.* 3887). Abstract, late 15th cent., of the priory's charters, with rubrics and a few misc. additions on the end fly-leaves etc. Arranged mainly topographically, with notes of royal charters at fos. v–vii and of papal ones, fines, *sentencie iudicum* etc. at fos. lxxxx–c, followed (fos. ciᵛ–cii) by an index of places etc. Omits names of witnesses and dates. Extracts, 1644, are in Bodl., Dodsworth 95 (*SC.* 5036), fos. 1–28.
Fos. ii + 105 (contemp. foliation, i–c). 11¾ × 8½ in. *FO:* R. Dodsworth, 1632; salvaged by Col. Charles Fairfax from St. Mary's Tower, York, 1645.

KIRKSTALL co. York
Cist. Abbey *f.* 1147
518. **PRO., Duchy of Lanc.** (Misc. Bks. 7). 'Liber Niger.' Gen. cartulary (fos. 17–78), early 13th cent. (aft. 1210), with rubrics etc. Arranged mainly topographically, with copies of gen. charters (*de humagiis*, royal, compositions) at fos. 60–75 and misc. additions *passim* and on added leaves at the beginning and end, incl. (fos. 2–6) a section of fines. A detached bifolium (fos. lxxxviii, xci, in the medieval foliation, of which the first contains part of an added index, continued on the modern fos. 86–7) is now **BM., Add. Ch. 17119,** among deeds of the Calverley fam. presented, 1866, by Sir W. C. Trevelyan. Ed. W. T. Lancaster & W. P. Baildon, *The Coucher Book of . . . Kirkstall* (Thoresby Soc. viii, 1904.
Fos. 115 (medieval roman and 17th cent. foliations; wants two leaves aft. fo. 75 in addition to Add. Ch. 17119). 8½ × 6½ in.

KIRKSTEAD co. Linc.
Cist. Abbey *f.* 1139
519. **BM., Cotton Vesp. E. xviii.** Cartulary, 13th cent., made up of topographical sections, in hands of varying date, put together aft. 1259, when Tables, where not already present, were added at the beginning of each, with some other connecting etc. material. The latter includes (fos. 209–13) lists of *cyrographa perpetua, carte Refectorarii, carte Lundon, confirmationes et libertates Regum,* and *Superhabundantia cartarum* (duplicates etc.),

for the most part not copied in full elsewhere in the volume. Further additions have subsequently been made *passim*. Extracts, 1643, by Gervase Holles, are in BM., Lansdowne 207E, fos. 75–199. A 20th cent. transcript and rotographs are in Lincolnshire Archives Office (Foster Libr.). *Mon. Angl.* v, 417 (*t*) etc., lists the heads of the sections, with extracts. Described, with further extracts, by F. M. Stenton. *Documents Illustrative . . . of the Danelaw* (London, 1920), 103 ff.

Fos. 230 (post-medieval pagination, 1–434, excl. some insertions). $11 \times 7\frac{3}{4}$ in. (cropped). *FO*: Christopher, baron Hatton, 1643.

¶ *Inventories*

520. **BM., Harley Roll G. 21.** Inventory, 12th cent., of deeds rel. Gayton-le-Wold etc., with some 13th cent. and a few 14th cent. additions. A 13th cent. copy is in No. 519, fos. 77–8.

Roll of 2 membrs. $45\frac{1}{4} \times 6\frac{1}{8}$ in.

521. **BM., Harley Roll O. 5.** Inventory, early 13th cent., with additions, of deeds arranged and numbered by places.

Roll of 2 membrs. $27\frac{1}{2} \times 5$ in.

KNIGHTS HOSPITALLERS
v. ST. JOHN OF JERUSALEM.

KNIGHTS TEMPLARS
v. TEMPLARS.

KNOWLE co. Warw.
Guild of St. Anne *f.* 1412
No cartulary recorded.

¶ *Other registers etc.*

522. **Birmingham, Reference Libr.** Register of confraternity, 1451–1535. Ed. W. B. Bickley, *Register of the Guild of Knowle* (Walsall, for the Birmingham & Midland Inst., 1894). *FO*: Sir Simon Archer (*D*); T. Caldecott (from Vanderberg, bookseller, Westminster, *c.* 1790); W. Hamper, 1822; W. Staunton.

LACOCK co. Wilts
Aug. Abbey (Canonesses) *f.* 1230–2
A report by N. R. Ker, 1944, on material at Lacock, is with the Hist. MSS. Commission (Unpublished Material, 85). An edition of Nos. 523–4 is in preparation by Miss Joan Gibbs.

523. **Mrs. A. D. Burnett-Brown,** Lacock Abbey. Gen. cartulary, 13th cent.,

6—M.C.

in two parts: (1) fos. 7–20, aft. 1242, with red initials and spaces for titles, copies mainly of charters of the foundress and first abbess, Ela, countess of Salisbury; (2) fos. 21–72, aft. 1268, in similar format, copies of some 130 further charters, partly repeating pt. i, and (fos. 45–57, 72) rentals and custumaries. Includes copies of royal and one or two episcopal charters *passim*, with misc. additions, fos. 1–6, 72v ff. The custumaries are edited by W. G. Clark Maxwell, 'The Customs of four Manors of the Abbey of Lacock', *Wilts. Arch. & Nat. Hist. Mag.* xxxii (1901–2), 311–46.

Fos. i + 93 (90–3, binding leaves, parts of a 14th cent. roll of accompts etc.). $10\frac{3}{8} \times 7\frac{1}{4}$ in. *FO*: the Sherington and Talbot fams., Lacock.

524. **Ditto.** Gen. cartulary, early 14th cent. (aft. 1304), with spaces for initials and titles. Arranged topographically and incl. copies of some royal and one or two episcopal charters *passim*, with misc. additions, fos. 136 ff. etc. An abstract in J. Stevens, *Hist. Ancient Abbeys* etc. ii (1723), App., 355–66, is reprinted by W. L. Bowles & J. G. Nichols, *Annals . . . of Lacock Abbey* (1835), App., viii–li, and extracts are given in *Mon. Angl.* vi, 502–9.

Fos. iv + 147 (i–iv, 144–7, binding leaves, are from the same roll as in No. 523). $10\frac{1}{2} \times 6\frac{3}{4}$ in. *FO*: as No. 523.

LANCASTER co. Lanc.
Ben. Priory *f.* 1094
525. **BM., Harley 3764.** Gen. cartulary, 15th cent. (*c.* 1428, when the priory was granted to Syon Abbey?), with blue initials and uncompleted rubrication. Arranged mainly topographically with copies of the foundation, royal, papal and other general charters at the beginning (fos. 1–20), of episcopal etc. charters *passim*, and of documents rel. litigation at the end (fos. 67 ff.). Ed., with translation, W. O. Roper, *Materials for the History of the Church of Lancaster* (Chetham Soc., New ser. xxvi, xxxi, 1892–4).

Fos. 83. $10\frac{3}{4} \times 7\frac{1}{2}$ in. Signatures (notarial?), 16th cent., of John Mabancke and Thomas Cole *passim*.

LANERCOST co. Cumb.
Aug. Priory *f.* 1165–9
526. **Untraced.** Cartulary formerly

belonging to Ld. Wm. Howard and the earls of Carlisle, Naworth Castle. An abstract of a 17th–18th cent. transcript in Carlisle, D. & C. Muniments, showing the material to have been arranged in 15 parts with a Table before pt. 15, is printed by M. E. C. Walcott, 'Breviate of the Cartulary of Lanercost', *Trans. Royal Soc. of Literature*, Second ser. viii (1866), 434–524.

LANGDON co. Kent
Praem. Abbey *f.* 1189
527. **PRO., Exch., K.R.** (Misc. Bks. i. 29). Cartulary, early 14th cent. (*temp.* Edw. I–II), with red (or occasionally blue) initials, page-headings, underlining of titles etc. Arranged topographically in sections with copies of some episcopal charters included in the first section, for Langdon, and a few royal ones among additions *passim.*
Fos. 181. 11⅞ × 8⅛ in. *FO:* H. Dineley al. Dingley, 1574; delivered into Court, 1596.

LANGLEY co. Norf.
Praem. Abbey *f.* 1195
528. **BM., Add. 5948.** Fragms. of a register begun (fo. 12) in a good 13th cent. hand, with red and green initials (sometimes decorated) and occasional red titles, and continued without decoration in other 13th cent. hands. Contains notes of grants to the abbey arranged under 43 topographical heads (*i*, incomplete; *vii–xvi, xxxii–xliii*, wanting), with an added 13th–14th cent. Table at fo. 2, printed in *Mon. Angl.* vi, 930 (*b*). Inserted at the beginning are: (*a*) fos. 3–11 (apparently part of another register), copies of 13th cent. grants by the abbots, in a series of contemp. hands; (*b*) fos. 15–19, five non-consecutive leaves, apparently from the missing quires *i–ii* of No. 529, containing copies and abstracts of grants rel. Langley and Hardley. Other misc. additions, incl. copies of charters, have been made on blank and added leaves, *passim.*
Fos. 58. 13¼ etc. × 8¾ in. *FO:* A. Hobart, 17th–18th cent.; purchased, 1806.
529. **Oxford, Bodl., Bodley 242** (*SC.* 27695). Composite register. Fos. 51–119 (bound in disorder) form quires *iii, v–ix*, of a 13th–14th cent. cartulary with red and blue decorated initials, paragraphs etc., containing copies and abstracts of deeds which

are shown by a Table at fo. v originally to have been arranged topographically. For five other leaves see No. 528. The rest of the volume consists of surveys and rentals, with misc. additions, apparently from another compilation of slightly later date.
Fos. v + 156. 13½ × 8¾ in. *FO:* Bp. J. Moore; Cambridge U.L., 1715; Bp. T. Tanner.

LANTHONY co. Glouc.
Aug. Priory *f.* (from co. Monm.) 1136
The cartularies are listed by W. Holtzmann, *Papsturkunden in England* (Göttingen, 1930–52) i, 59–63; iii, 74. Extracts by R. Furney, *c.* 1747, are in Bodl., Top. Glouc. c. 5 and a description by M. Gibson, 1728, is in *ib.*, Tanner 342, fos. 32–7.
530. **PRO., Chancery** (Masters' Exhibits, C. 115 A. 9). Cartulary, 13th cent. (aft. 1244), with rubrics. Arranged topographically and incl. copies of episcopal and occasional royal charters *passim.* Misc. 13th–14th cent. additions include (fos. i–xi) a 13th cent. repertorium of the muniments, preceded on three unnumbered leaves by a 15th cent. Table. Post-medieval title, 'Registrum Antiquum'.
Fos. *c.* 180 (medieval foliation, i–clxxv, omitting a few preliminary leaves). 11½ × 8 in. *FO:* the Porter fam., Lanthony by Gloucester; the Scudamore and Fitzroy-Scudamore fams., Holme Lacy; Frances, duchess of Norfolk (d. 1820).
531. **Ditto** (C. 115/A. 1, 2). Gen. cartulary, *c.* 1350, in two vols., with rubrics, red initials decorated mauve etc., and additions down to the 15th cent. Arranged in twenty-eight sections or parts (vol. i, pts. *i–xvii*) by pressmarks, mainly topographically (*xxvi* royal and papal charters, *xxvii Compositiones inter domos Lanth. et Wallie, xxviii* charters rel. Ireland). Includes an elaborate Table of pts. *i–xxv* at the beginning of vol. i, and an added list of books bequeathed by Mag. J. de Lech, late 14th cent., in vol. ii, fo. 281. Post medieval title, 'Registrum Magnum'.
Fos. (vol. i) *c.* 330 (unnumbered); (vol. ii) 288. 15 × 9¾ in. *FO:* as No. 530.
532. **Ditto** (C. 115/A. 8). Cartulary, 1408, of lands in Ireland, made by A. Elmely and W. Temset. Rubrics, plain red initials and red quire numbers. Includes a contemp. Table on three leaves at the be-

ginning; an extent of the lands, 1408, on seven at the end; and copies of some royal, episcopal etc. charters *passim*. Ed., with pts. *xxvii, xxviii*, of No. 531, E. St. J. Brooks, *The Irish Cartularies of Llanthony Prima & Secunda* (Irish MSS. Comm., 1953).

Fos. *c.* 70 (unnumbered). 12 × 8¼ in. *FO:* as No. 530.

533. **Ditto** (C. 115/A. 6). Cartulary, 1440, of lands in Gloucester etc., with rubrics, plain red initials etc. Arranged by pressmarks *in novo scrinio* and the deeds numbered, *i–cccclvii*, consecutively throughout. An elaborate Table at fos. 1–20, followed (fos. 22–5) by an index, is stated to be based on one compiled by R. Steymus (cf. No. 534), and here copied by R. Cole, *rentarius*, and J. Machyn, *coquinarius*.

Fos. 213 (contemp. foliation, i–clxxix, from fo. 28). 11 × 8½ in. *FO:* as No. 530.

534. **Ditto** (C. 115/A. 4, 5). Gen. cartulary, 1449, in two vols., made by R. Steymus (cf. No. 533), with occasional additions. Finely written with rubrics, blue initials decorated with red (illuminated, with borders, in vol. i, fos. 1, 15) etc. Arranged mainly topographically (vol. i, places other than Gloucester, incl. copies of baronial etc. charters at the beginning, under Lanthony, and of papal, episcopal and royal ones at the end (fos. 196–225); vol. ii, Gloucester and suburbs), each vol. being preceded by an elaborate Table in red.

Fos. (vol. i) 225 (contemp. foliation, i–ccii, from fo. 15); (vol. ii) 139 (contemp. foliation, i–cxiiii, from fo. 17). 15½ × 11 in. *FO:* as No. 530.

535. **Lady Vestey**, Stowell Park, Northleach. Abstract of charters (fos. 2–32) made, 1458, by R. Cole, 'ad edificationem omnium fratrum suorum', with instructions (fo. 2) that it was to be kept in the custody of the precentor. Rubrics, blue initials decorated with red etc. Apparently based on No. 534, vol. i, opening with a short contemp. account of the priory's foundation (fo. 1). Also contains copies of misc. pleas, charters, writs etc., *temp.* W. Cheriton, prior 1377–1401, in later 15th cent. hands (fos. 33–58); and copies, 15th–16th cent., of Wills of citizens of Gloucester, 14th–15th cent. (fos. 59–71).

Fos. 71 + 8 blank fly-leaves. 11⅜ × 8 in. *FO:* as No. 530 (Holme Lacy press-mark,

A. 13); Sir T. Phillipps (MS. 65, from T. Thorpe, bookseller).

¶ *Other registers etc.*

536. **PRO., Chancery** (Masters' Exhibits, C. 115/A. 12). Register of S. Brockworth, prior 1362–77. *FO:* as No. 530.

537. **Ditto** (C. 115/A. 7). Register of W. Cheryton, prior 1377–1401. *FO:* as No. 530.

538. **Ditto** (C. 115/A. 3). Register of J. Wyche, prior 1408–36. *FO:* as No. 530.

539. **Ditto** (C. 115/A. 11). Register of J. Hayward, prior 1457–65. Wants fos. xxvi–lii. *FO:* as No. 530.

540. **Ditto** (C. 115/A. 14). Register, 1501–25, of prior E. Forest. *FO:* as No. 530.

541. **Ditto** (C. 115/A. 13). Rental for Gloucester etc., *c.* 1449. *FO:* as No. 530 (Holme Lacy pressmark, A. 10 ?).

LAUNCESTON co. Cornw.
Aug. Priory *f.* 1127

542. **London, Lambeth Palace, MS. 719.** 'Regestrum Munimentorum.' Cartulary, 15th cent. (*temp.* Hen. VI ?), with large black decorated initials and titles, and occasional additions. Arranged topographically and incl. copies of a few royal documents, the material being mainly 14th–15th cent. Contemp. inscription, 'Liber Johannis Legh', on the verso of a blank leaf at the end. A modern transcript is at Truro, Royal Inst. of Cornwall. M. R. James, *Cat. Lambeth MSS.* (Cambridge, 1932), 797–9.

Fos. 236 + vii. 11⅛ × 8⅜ in. Paper. *FO:* R. Escott (?) (*D*); W. Griffith, 1678.

¶ *Other registers etc.*

543. **Oxford, Bodl., Tanner 196.** Formulary etc., 14th–15th cent.

LEEDS co. Kent
Aug. Priory *f.* bef. 1119

544. **Maidstone, Kent R.O.** (Acc. No. 154). Quire from a 14th cent. cartulary (aft. 1328), with spaces for initials and titles. Contains copies of part of a royal charter of *Inspeximus*, 1328, followed by 8 archiepiscopal and other confirmations etc., 12th–13th cent., reciting further charters mainly rel. tithes, churches etc. Transcripts, 18th cent., are in Bodl., MS. Eng. hist. c. 313, pp. 213–58, and London, Soc. of Antiquaries MS. 194. L. Sherwood, 'The

Cartulary of Leeds Priory', *Arch. Cantiana* lxiv (1951), 24–34 (abstract).

Fos. 12. 12 × 8¼ in. *FO:* Sir E. Filmer, 3rd bart., 1724; Sir B. Filmer, 5th bart., 1798; presented anonymously, 1947.

❡ *Inventory*

545. **London, Lambeth Palace** (Carte Misc. v, art. 111). Inventory, 13th cent., of the priory's charters, to a total of 346, incl. references to papal, royal and episcopal documents. Written mainly in double columns and arranged by grantors.

Roll of 3 membrs. (now mounted singly). 21 × 8 and (membr. 3) 13¾ × 6½ in.

❡ *Other registers etc.*

546. **BM., Add. 19772,** fo. 2. Abstracts, *c.* 1330, of deeds rel. grants of rents, written on the back of a rent-roll. *FO:* the Rev. B. Faussett.

LEGBOURNE co. Linc.
Cist. Priory (Nuns) *f. c.* 1150

547. **Untraced.** Cartulary *penes* Sir George Heneage, knt., 20 Dec. 1649. Eighteen deeds (one dated 1304) from fos. 2–32 are copied in Bodl., Dodsworth 75 (*SC.* 5017), fos. 23–7.

LEICESTER co. Leic.
Aug. Abbey *f.* 1143

M. R. James and A. Hamilton Thompson, 'Catalogue of the Library of Leicester Abbey' (ctd.), *Trans. Leic. Archit. & Arch. Soc.* xxi (1940–1), 53 ff., print a late medieval list of the abbey's 'chartwaries' and other registers from Bodl., Laud. misc. 623, fos. 49v–50. None of the former is known to survive.

❡ *Other registers etc.*

548. **Oxford, Laud misc. 625.** 'Rentale . . . generale . . . per Willm. Charyte quondam priorem . . . renovatum 1477.' An early 16th cent. revision of Charyte's work, incl. notes of donors of lands etc. and of royal (fos. 6v–7, 8v–9), papal and episcopal (fos. 182–3v) and other charters etc. Sec. folio 'Habemus'. J. Nichols, *Hist. Leicester* ii, pt. 1 (1795), App. xvii, 53–100 (large extracts).

Fos. ii + 219. 13¾ × 9 in.

549. **BM., Cotton Vit. F. xvii.** A similar but apparently abridged compilation, 15th–16th cent. Damaged by fire, 1731, and now comprises fragms. of 42 leaves.

LEISTON co. Suff.
Praem. Abbey *f.* 1183

550. **BM., Cotton Vesp. E. xiv.** Gen. cartulary, first half of the 13th cent., with some rubrication etc. and misc. additions, mainly at the end. The papal, episcopal, royal etc. charters are now grouped mainly at the beginning (fos. 1–43), but fos. 29–39 (royal) appear originally to have followed fo. 76 as quire *viii*. A transcript, 1815, by H. Jermyn is in BM., Add. 8171, fos. 61–84.

Fos. 83. 7½ × 5½ in.

LENTON co. Nott.
Clun. Priory *f.* 1102–8

551. **Destroyed.** A former Cotton MS. Otho B. xiv (fos. ix + 174, folio), which was burnt in 1731, is described by T. Smith, *Cat. Bibl. Cotton.* (Oxford, 1696), *ad loc.*, as 'Chartularium Prioratus de Lenton . . . cum syllabo maneriorum, advocationum Ecclesiarum, portionum garbarum, et foeni, pensionum, terrarum, et reddituum, ad ejusdem Priorem et Conventum spectantium'. Formerly belonged to Samuel Roper of Heanor (*D*) and, like No. 988, was probably put into the Cotton. Libr. in the late 17th cent. The present BM., Cotton Otho B. xiv (No. 891 below) was so numbered in 1639 (Bodl., Dodsworth 78 (*SC.* 5019), fo. 41) and reacquired after long absence in 1787.

LEOMINSTER co. Heref.
Ben. Priory *f.* aft. 1123
v. also READING.

552. **BM., Cotton Domit. A. iii,** fos. 40–254. Gen. cartulary, 13th cent. (aft. 1234), with rubrics, red and blue initials, and misc. additions *passim*. Arranged apparently by grantors with the copies of royal and episcopal charters, preceded by a contemp. Table, at the beginning and the papal ones included *passim*. Followed by two supplements: (*a*) fos. 137–79, early 14th cent. (aft. 1305), with rubrics, red initials, and (fos. 137–9) a Table; (*b*) fos. 183–247, 15th cent., with rubrics and red and blue decorated initials. *Mon. Angl.* iv, 52 (*d*) (partial list of contents).

Fos. 215 (earlier foliation, 38–250). 8¼ × 5¾ in.

553. **Untraced.** 'Cartularium penes Thomam Blount de Orleton arm. A.D. 1669' (*T*).

554. **Untraced.** 'Registrum penes Thomam comitem Conyngesby A.D. 1719' (*T*).

LESNES (*al.* **WESTWOOD**) co. Kent
Aug. Abbey *f.* 1178
555. **PRO., Exch., T.R.** (Ancient Deeds, AA. 235). Abstracts, early 14th cent., of deeds rel. rents etc., mainly in Dartford, with later 14th cent. additions. Roll of 5 membrs. *c.* 100 × 7¾ in.
556. **Untraced.** 'Chartularium domini abbatis de Lesny.' Extracts from fos. 1–32 by J. Blackbourne (1683–1741) are in Bodl., Rawlinson B. 461, fos. 50–77. Fos. 1–7 contained a copy of letters patent of Henry VIII.

LEWES co. Suss.
Clun. Priory *f.* 1078–81
557. **BM., Cotton Vesp. F. xv.** (Part of a?) cartulary made, 1444, for Prior R. Auncell. Red tricking of initials, underlining of titles etc. and a few misc. additions at the end. Arranged mainly topographically by counties (fos. 1–8, 320–6, earlier drafts of the sections for E. Grinstead, Southover etc. (fos. 43 ff.); fos. 9–42, foundation (earls of Warenne etc.); fos. 307–13, properties assigned to the *Magister Operum*). Omits the main papal, royal and episcopal sections of the priory's muniments and those for properties assigned to other obedientiaries. *Mon. Angl.* v, 7 (*d*) (partial list of contents). Ed., in translation, L. F. Salzman, *Chartulary of . . . Lewes*, 2 vols. (Sussex Record Soc. xxxviii, xl, 1932–4), with an extra vol. (1943) comprising reprints of C. T. Clay, 'The Yorkshire Portion' etc., *Yorks. Arch. J.* xxxi (1931–4), 290–319; D. Harrison, 'The Surrey Portion' etc., *Surrey Arch. Coll.* xliii (1935), 84–112; J. H. Bullock, *The Norfolk Portion* etc. (Norfolk Record Soc. xii, 1939); *Id.* and W. M. Palmer, *The Cambridgeshire Portion* etc. (Cambr. Antiq. Soc., 1938); with a fifth part added (ed. L. F. Salzman and W. Budgen) for the Wilts, Devon, Dors., London and Essex material, see also V. H. Galbraith, 'Pressmarks on Deeds of Lewes Priory', *Sussex Arch. Coll.* lxv (1922), 196–205.

Fos. 326 (9–313 with contemp. foliation, 1–351). 13¾ × 10 in. *FO:* J. Strange-

man, 1590 (?) (fo. 326); Edward Sackville, 4th earl of Dorset, 1629 (*D*); (Sir) E. Bysshe, 1648 (*D*); John Selden, 1649 (*D*); M. Hutton, D.D.

¶ *Other registers etc.*
558. **PRO., Exch., K.R.** (Eccl. Docs., E. 135/2/40) + **BM., Cotton Vesp. E. ii,** fos. 106–7. Four consecutive leaves (bifolia) from a 12th cent. rental rel. the 'Decania de Norfulch.' etc. *Mon. Angl.* v, 9 (*a*), prints the inner (BM) bifolium. Galbraith, *l.c.*, 197.
559. **PRO., Duchy of Lanc.** (Misc. Bks. 10). Abstracts etc., 16th cent., of court rolls, 15th–16th cent., for Langney and Willingdon, and (pp. 1–12) of deeds rel. Langney.

LEWISHAM co. Kent
Ben. Priory *f. c.* 1044
v. also No. 891 below. For other cartularies of St. Peter's Abbey, Ghent, incl. some English material, see J. de Saint-Genois, 'Notice sur les Archives . . . de la Flandre Orientale', *Messager des Sciences historiques de Belgique*, Année 1841 (Ghent), 184–93.
560. **Ghent, State Archives** (St. Peter's Abbey at Ghent, 1st ser., No. 7, pt. i). Cartulary, mid-13th cent., with the opening title and initials in red. Contains copies (fos. 10–21r) of 19 charters of English kings, bishops and others, 918–1222, rel. the English lands of St. Peter's, with misc. 14th cent. additions (fos. 7–9, 21–7) in Latin, French and Flemish. Formerly bound at the end of a larger cartulary (fos. clxxxviii), written in the same hand (aft. 1254) and now in the archives of the See of Ghent (deposited *ib.*), to which a contemp. Table at the beginning refers; now bound (18th cent.) with unrelated material. Mainly transcribed and the contents listed, 19th cent., in PRO., Record Commission Transcripts, ser. ii, vol. 142, fos. 384 ff. and vol. 163, art. 2. Saint-Genois, *l.c.*, 188–9 (description). *Id.*, 'Précis analytique des Documents historiques etc.', *ib.*, Année 1842, 238–61 (extracts).

Fos. 27 (numbered, *c.* 1400, clxxxix–ccv from fo. 10). 12½ × 8⅝ in.
¶ *Other registers etc.*
561. **Ghent U.L., MS. 536** (58). Register, 14th–15th cent., of misc. evidences,

incl. copies of charters etc., rel. the English lands of St. Peter's. Written apparently as a manual for use in legal proceedings. Saint-Genois, *Cat. MSS. Bibl. de la Ville et de l'Université de Gand* (Ghent 1849–52), 77–9.

LICHFIELD co. Staff.
Cath. Church (Secular Canons) *f. c.* 656
  For a general account of the registers see H. E. Savage, *Magnum Registrum Album* (Wm. Salt Arch. Soc., *Coll. Hist. Staffordshire*, 1926 for 1924), who edits No. 563. For a more detailed account of those at Lichfield see J. C. Cox, *Cat. of the Muniments* etc. (*ib.* vi, pt. ii, 1886), supplemented and amended by R. L. Poole, *HMC. Fourteenth Report*, App. viii (1895), 205–36.
562.   **BM., Harley 3868.** Three quires, early 14th cent. (*temp.* Edw. II?), with spaces for titles, containing copies of papal, royal, episcopal and other documents (*Exhibita*), 12th–13th cent., rel. the appropriation to religious houses of churches in the diocese. Arranged by houses. Bound, 15th cent., with No. 564 and other material, and in this form apparently known as the 'Reg. Rubrum' *al.* 'Tertium'. *BM., Cat. Harl. MSS.* iii, 88–9. Savage, *op. cit.*, xviii–xx. W. Holtzmann, *Papsturkunden in England* (Göttingen, 1930–52) i, 133–4; ii, 28.
  Fos. 36 (15th–16th cent. foliation, 275–310)+2. $11\frac{3}{8} \times 8$ in. Alienated by W. Whitlock, 1583. *FO:* P. Le Neve, 1704 (who added a Table, fos. 37–8).
563.   **Lichfield, D. & C.,** Muniments, 'Magnum Registrum Album'. Register (fos. 83–298), *c.* 1317–29, of evidences rel. the rights, privileges, churches and other possessions of the cathedral, incl. copies of royal, papal, episcopal and other charters. Written in double columns, with rubrics etc. and a few additions. Preceded by texts of the Chester and Burton Annals, between which (fos. 5v–11 of twelve preliminary leaves) is a contemp. Table. Eight smaller leaves at the end contain an added 16th cent. Table, with others of a 'Parvum Registrum cum Takys al. Taggis' (fos. 43) and the 'Registrum Tertium' (cf. No. 562). Ed. Savage, *op. cit.*
  Fos. viii+310 (12+298). $11\frac{1}{2} \times 8\frac{1}{4}$ in.
564.   **BM., Harley 4799.** Cartulary (fos. 5–74), written in the hand of the last two

quires of No. 563 (bef. 1329?), in similar format, and containing copies of deeds etc. rel. the cathedral's parishes in the High Peak. Bound, 15th cent., with No. 562 and other matter (fos. 2–4, 75–86 etc.), with a collective index by J. Yotton, late 15th cent., at fo. 87.
  Fos. 87 (5–74 with contemp. foliation, 1–72; 75–86 numbered, 311–22, in the later foliation of No. 562). $11\frac{1}{2} \times 8$ in. *FO:* as No. 562.
565.   **Oxford, Bodl., Ashmole 1527.** Gen. cartulary, early 15th cent. (aft. 1402), arranged mainly topographically (but the original order of the quires is apparently disturbed). An added section of papal bulls at the beginning (fos. 1–14; 1–4 should follow 14) precedes copies of royal and episcopal charters, and there are further copies of royal charters (fos. 96–103), with an added 17th cent. index, at the end. W. H. Black, *Cat. MSS. Bibl. Bodl.* x (i) (Oxford, 1845), 1439–41.
  Fos. 103. $12\frac{1}{4} \times 8$ in.
566.   **Lichfield, D. & C.,** Mun., 'Reg. XXIII'. Register, late 15th cent., of grants to the cathedral of pensions from churches, 13th–15th cent. Arranged in alphabetical order of places, with blank leaves *passim* on which a few 16th cent. additions have been made. Cox, *op. cit.*, 98–9.
  Fos. 47+xx. $14\frac{1}{4} \times 9\frac{1}{4}$ in.
¶ *Vicars Choral*
567.   **Ditto,** 'Reg. XXIV (a)'. Register of grants to the Vicars Choral, ordinations of obits, lists of properties, leases, and other misc. documents, written in number of 14th and 15th cent. hands.
  Fos. 60. $12 \times 8\frac{3}{4}$ in. Paper.
568.   **Ditto,** 'Reg. XXV'. Similar to No. 567, 15th cent.
  Fos. 42. $15\frac{1}{2} \times 11$ in. Paper.
569.   **Stafford, Wm. Salt Libr., MS. 228.** Quire from another similar 15th cent. register, with spaces for initials.
  Fos. 7. $11\frac{1}{8} \times 8$ in. *FO:* R. Wright, 1806; Wm. Salt.
570.   **Lichfield, D. & C.,** Mun., 'Evidence Book of the Vicars'. Similar register, *c.* 1535. Cox, *op. cit.*, 163–7.
  Fos. 116. $6\frac{3}{4} \times 5\frac{1}{4}$ in.
¶ *Chantries*
571.   **Ditto,** 'Reg. XXVI'. Register, 15th–16th cent., with rubrics, of ordinations and other documents rel. the founda-

tion of chantries of SS. Blasius, Saviour and Anne.

Fos. 45. $11\frac{1}{2} \times 7\frac{1}{2}$ in.

572. **Ditto**, 'Reg. XXVII'. Similar to No. 571.

Fos. 37. 12×8 in.

573. **Ditto**, 'Reg. XXVIII'. Similar to No. 571.

Fos. 63. $11 \times 7\frac{1}{4}$ in.

574. **Ditto**, 'Reg. XXIX'. Similar to No. 571, with blue and red initials.

Fos. 21. $15\frac{1}{2} \times 10\frac{1}{4}$ in.

¶ *Other registers etc.*

For other registers at Lichfield see also Cox and Poole, *ll. cc.*

575. **Ditto** (O. 3). 'De munimentis in custodia m(ag.) W. de Brunalston London. existentibus.' Inventory, 1340, of about 20 documents produced in the court of Arches. Poole, *l.c.*, 233–5.

576. **Oxford, Bodl., Ashmole 794,** fos. 1–201. Chapter Act-Book, 1321–1384.

LILLESHALL co. Salop
Aug. Abbey *f.* 1144–8
577. **The Duke of Sutherland,** and his Trentham Trustees, deposited in the British Museum (MSS. Loans No. 39). Gen. cartulary, 13th cent. (aft. 1236), with rubrics etc. and misc. additions (pp. 1–43, 95 ff., and *passim*). The royal, episcopal etc. charters are placed at the beginning of the original compilation (pp. 44–9), and fines, papal charters (which have small red or blue initials) and a rental at the end (pp. 80 ff.). Pp. 2–25 are a quire from a register of Wenlock Priory (No. 1008 below). A transcript, 1855, by R. W. Eyton in Bodl., Top. Salop. d. 3 was used by him in his *Antiq. Shropshire* (1854–60).

Fos. xxv + 143 (paginated, 1–186). $14\frac{1}{4} \times 10\frac{1}{2}$ in. *FO:* Sir R. Leveson, 1604 (*D*); stated by Eyton (Bodl., Top. Salop. d. 2) to have been exchanged, 1638, with Sir R. Lee, bart., for the Shrewsbury cartulary (No. 895 below); John Smith of Acton Burnell, 18th cent. (Stevens); the Leveson-Gower fam., dukes of Sutherland, 1838 (*P*).

LINCOLN, See of *f.* 1072
No cartulary found.
¶ *Other registers etc.*
578. **Lincoln, D. & C.,** Muniments, 'Liber de Cartis Pensionum' (B. i/5/17/1). Copies, *c.* 1330–50, of 44 charters rel. grants of pensions to the bp., *temp.* Edw.

III, with accompts rel. pensions etc. received on his behalf, 1335–40, 1347–8. Noticed by C. W. Foster, *Registrum Antiquissimum* ii (Lincoln Record Soc. xxviii, 1933 for 1931), xxxi.

579. **Oxford, Queen's Coll., MS. 366.** Rentals, lists of fees, surveys etc. rel. the bp.'s lands, 14th cent. H. O. Coxe, *Cat. MSS. Oxon.* i (Oxford, 1852), *ad loc.*

LINCOLN co. Linc.
Cath. Church *f. c.* 1075
C. W. Foster, *Registrum Antiquissimum* (Lincoln Record Soc., 1931 etc., in progress; vol. iv ed. with and v ff. by Kathleen Major), describes the cartularies (i, pp. xiii–xlviii; ii, p. xxxi), and edits all the cathedral's early charters, using No. 583 as a basis. For material at Lincoln, see also J. A. Bennett, *HMC. Twelfth Report*, App. ix (1891), 553–72.

580. **Lincoln, D. & C.,** Muniments, 'Reg. Superantiquissimum' (A/1/4/1). Unbound fragm. of a 12th–13th cent. cartulary containing copies of 59 royal charters, Hen. I–II, and papal bulls, Honorius II–Innocent II. Written in book-hand, with spaces for titles and marginal annotations in a minute and slightly later charter-hand.

Fos. 16. $10\frac{1}{4} \times 6\frac{1}{2}$ in.

581. **BM., Cotton Vesp. E. xvi,** fos. 2–25. The first four sections of a 12th–13th cent. cartulary, written without uniformity in several book-hands and containing copies of royal charters, Will. I–Hen. II, and papal bulls, 1061–1148. Sections *i* & *iv* have red and green decorated initials, and *ii–iii* occasional plain red ones. Intended rubrication is executed only down to fo. 2v. Marginal annotations as in No. 580.

Fos. 25 (fo. 5 duplicated). $8\frac{1}{2} \times 6$ in.

582. **Lincoln, D. & C.,** Mun., 'Reg. Praeantiquissimum' (A/1/4/2). Two unbound fragms., apparently from the same compilation as No. 581. Fos. 1–4 contain copies of royal (Hen. II), episcopal and decanal charters; fos. 5–9 (mutilated), parts of two papal bulls, 1146, 1153.

Fos. 9. $9\frac{1}{2} \times 6\frac{3}{4}$ in. etc.

583. **Ditto,** 'Reg. Antiquissimum' (A/1/5). Gen. cartulary, *c.* 1225, written in a small book-hand with uncompleted rubrication, marginal annotations in the hand of the text and additions down to the 16th cent. *passim* and at fos. 177 ff. Arranged

in sections, mainly topographically (by ridings in Lincolnshire), with the royal, papal, baronial and episcopal material placed at the beginning. Ed. Foster & K. Major, *op. cit.*

Fos. iv + 250. $12\frac{1}{2} \times 8\frac{1}{2}$ in. The name 'Cha. Smithson' (prebend, 1700–14) deleted on the front fly-leaf. Restored to the cathedral, 1712, by Bp. W. Wake, but again in his hands, 1717 (*T*); finally restored, 1764, by Christ Church, Oxford, which received it, in 1737, with Wake's MSS.

584.   **Ditto**, 'The Registrum' (A/1/6). Gen. cartulary, *c.* 1350, with uncompleted rubrication, initials touched with red, and some additions *passim* and at the end. Arranged in three parts: (1) fos. 1–76, royal and other charters; (2) fos. 78–152, city of Lincoln; (3) fos. 153–264, other places (indexed at fo. 252v).

Fos. 272 (earlier foliation by parts). $16\frac{1}{4} \times 9\frac{3}{4}$ in.

585.   **Ditto** (A/1/4/5). Two leaves from a mid-14th cent. cartulary (the outer bifolium of quire *xi*), written in a small charter-hand with headings, marginal titles and elongated paragraphs against each entry in the hand of the text. Copies of seven deeds rel. the wapentake of Calceworth and eight rel. the soke of Bolingbroke. K. Major, *op. cit.* vi, nos. 1751–7, 1792–9.

Fos. 2. $14\frac{1}{4} \times 9$ in.

586.   **Ditto** (D. ii/86/1/52). Leaf from a 14th cent. register containing copies of four episcopal etc. charters rel. the appropriation of Rushden church, co. Hertf., 1319–28.

Fos. 1. $11 \times 9\frac{3}{4}$ in.

¶ *Deanery*

587.   **Ditto** (A/1/7). 'Carte tangentes Decanatum beate Marie Lincoln' (fo. 1), 14th cent. (aft. 1330). Cartulary of deeds, arranged in topographical sections, rel. the rectories and other property of the deanery in cos. Derby and Nott. Foster, *op. cit.* iii, pp. viii, 38–135.

Fos. 94. $14\frac{1}{2} \times 9$ in.

¶ *Vicars Choral*

588.   **Lincoln, the Vicar Choral.** Cartulary, 14th cent. (*temp.* Edw. II–III), of the vicars choral, with uncompleted rubrication etc. Arranged topographically and incl. copies of some royal, papal and epis-

copal documents. Misc. additions on added etc. leaves towards the end include a post-medieval repertorium on paper.

Fos. 74. $14\frac{1}{4} \times 10$ in.

¶ *Choristers*

589.   **Lincoln, D. & C.**, Mun., 'Reg. Choristarum III' (A/2/10/1). Quire from a 14th cent. register of the choristers (*temp.* Edw. II ?), written in double columns with rubrics and misc. additions *passim*. Contains ordinations of the *Pueri de Choro* followed by copies of misc. documents rel. Ashby Puerorum etc., largely as printed by Foster, *op. cit.* ii, 137–53, from No. 591. Condition decayed.

Fos. 8 (bound as 9). 12×8 in.

590.   **Ditto**, 'Reg. Choristarum I' (A/1/4/3). Two further quires (8 and 4 leaves) from the same register as No. 589, which they apparently complete. Copies of deeds and other memoranda arranged by places. Limp medieval binding. Foster, *op. cit.* ii, 153–86.

Fos. 12. 12×8 in.

591.   **Ditto**, 'Reg. Choristarum II' (A/2/4). A late 14th cent. revision of Nos. 589–90, with a few additions at the end. Written continuously with rubrics, red paragraphs at the beginning of each entry and initials touched with red. Foster, *op. cit.* ii, 137–91.

Fos. 16. $11\frac{3}{4} \times 8\frac{1}{4}$ in.

¶ *Chantries*

592.   **Ditto**, 'Liber de Ordinationibus Cantariarum' (A/1/8). Abstracts of the ordinations of chantries (fos. 1–77), followed by a cartulary arranged in sections, by chantries. Written in a number of 14th (and towards the end occasionally 15th) cent. hands with rubrics and in some sections red, or red and blue decorated, initials.

Fos. 385. $12\frac{1}{2} \times 8\frac{1}{4}$ in.

593.   **Ditto** (A/1/10). Cartulary, 1382, of deeds etc. rel. lands of the chantries of J. de Welbourne (d. 1381) and Henry, duke of Lancaster (d. 1361). Blue initials decorated with red. Contains copies of deeds arranged topographically, followed (fo. 76v) by ordinations of the chantries and other misc. material.

Fos. 86. $12\frac{1}{2} \times 9\frac{1}{4}$ in.

¶ *Other registers etc.*

For other registers at Lincoln see Bennett, *l.c.*

LLANCARFAN   co. Glam.
Monastery of St. Cadoc   *f.* 6th cent.
Notes of 14 early grants to this house
found in texts of the late 11th cent. 'Vita
Cadoci' (ed. A. W. Wade-Evans, *Vitae
Sanctorum Britanniae et Genealogiae* (Cardiff,
1944), 124–41 (capp. 55–68)) are con-
cluded by H. D. Emanuel, 'An Analysis of
the Composition of the "Vita Cadoci"',
Nat. Libr. of Wales J. vii (1951–2), 217–27,
to have been interpolated from other
sources when the earliest extant MS. (BM.,
Cotton Vesp. A. xiv, fos. 17–43v), was
compiled, *c.* 1200.

LLANDAFF   co. Glam.
Cath. Church   *f.* 6th cent.
594.   **Aberystwyth, NLW., Gwysaney 1.** 'Liber Landavensis.' An account of
the cathedral's foundation with lives of
early bishops and other connected saints,
incorporating notes and copies of grants
down to *temp.* Bp. Herwald and copies of
12th cent. papal bulls and other memoranda rel. its privileges. Written in double
columns, in hands of the middle and
second half of the 12th cent., with rubrics
and red initials. Bound in at the beginning,
apparently at a later date, is a version of St.
Matthew's Gospel, early to mid-12th cent.
(except the first quire, replacing an original
now lost, 15th cent.). Ed. J. G. Evans & J.
Rhys, *The Text of the Book of Llan Dâv*
(Oxford, 1893). Analysed by E. D. Jones,
'The Book of Llandaff', *Nat. Libr. of
Wales J.* iv (1945–6), 123–57.
Fos. 128. 12¼ × 8½ in. *FO:* John Selden
(by loan of Bp. T. Field); Sir J. Vaughan;
Robert Davies, *c.* 1696.

LLANTHONY   co. Monm.
v. LANTHONY, co. Glouc.

LODERS   co. Dors.
Ben. Priory   *f. temp.* Hen. I
595.   **Destroyed.** Gen. cartulary, 14th
cent., formerly at St. Lo, Archives departe-
mentales de la Manche, which were
bombed, 6 June 1944. Rubrics, red initials
etc. Arranged mainly topographically, and
incl. copies of royal, papal, episcopal etc.
charters. A 19th cent. transcript was
formerly owned by Sir T. Phillipps (MS.
10557, untraced). Ed. L. Guilloreau,
Cartulaire de Loders (Evreux, 1908). J. H.

Round, *Cal. Documents preserved in France* i
(1899), 313–22 (extracts).
Fos. 71 (incomplete at the end). 11¾ × 7⅞
in.

LONDON
Cath. Church of St. Paul   *f.* 604
An account of the muniments of the
Dean & Chapter by H. C. Maxwell Lyte,
HMC. Ninth Report, pt. i (1883), App.,
1–72, is supplemented by W. Holtzmann,
Papsturkunden in England i (Göttingen,
1930), 177–82, and Marion Gibbs, *Early
Charters of St. Paul's Cathedral* (Camden
Third ser. lviii, 1939), who refer also to
material now lost and cite further bibliography.
596.   **London, St. Paul's Cathedral,**
Muniments, 'Liber L' (W.D. 4). Composite register, 12th cent., with additions,
comprising: (1) fos. 1–26 (four quires
written in a large book-hand with rubrics
and red or green initials), copies of royal
charters down to *temp.* Hen. I and a bull of
Pope Agatho, 680, followed (fo. 16) by
early deeds etc. rel. London; (2) fos. 27–56
(five quires written in a smaller book-hand
with headings in the hand of the text and
red or green initials), copies of early deeds
rel. churches and other lands, leases of
manors, a survey (fos. 47–50) of lands in
the city of London etc., with a few additions in the margins etc. *passim*; (3) similar
sections, in various formats, containing
statutes of the cathedral, inventories, lists
of rents etc. Index, 15th cent. (*temp.* Dean
Lyseux), on three preliminary leaves.
Maxwell Lyte, *l.c.*, 60–9.
Fos. iii + 149. 11¼ × 7½ in.
597.   **Ditto,** 'Liber A' *al.* 'Pilosus'
(W.D. 1). Gen. cartulary begun in 1241
and continued (aft. fo. 37), and enlarged
(aft. fo. 40), in a series of hands, down to
1340. The original compilation (ed. M.
Gibbs, *op. cit.*), with uncompleted rubrication and red marginal pressmarks, has the
royal charters grouped mainly at the beginning. Seventeen unnumbered preliminary
leaves contain a 15th cent. index (*temp.*
Dean Lyseux) followed by 14th and 13th
cent. Tables, both with later additions.
Fos. xvii + 106 (medieval foliation by
openings). 15¼ × 10¾ in.
598.   **Ditto** (A Box 69). 'Carte liber-
tatum ecclesie Sci. Pauli.' Copies of some

thirty 11th–12th cent. royal writs etc. (a few in Old English), ornately written in a hand reminiscent of the 12th but in fact late 13th cent., with pen-decorated initials and pressmarks. M. Gibbs, *op. cit.*, xliii *n*.3 etc.

Roll of 3 membrs. 82 × 8⅜ in. (overall).

599.   **Oxford, Bodl., Ashmole 801,** fos. 50–73. Fragm. (fos. lviii–lxxxi) of a late 14th cent. register (aft. 1382) containing abstracts of charters, leases etc. arranged and numbered by parishes, with notes of rents in the margin. W. H. Black, *Cat. MSS. Bibl. Bodl.* x (Oxford, 1845), 442, lists the parishes.

Fos. 24. 12 × 8½ in. Paper.

❡ *Inventories*

600.   **London, St. Paul's Cathedral, Muniments** (W.D. 11a). 'Tabula extracta de evidenciis in Thesauraria . . . per m(agistrum) Thomam Lyseux decanum 1447.' Inventories of deeds, with red indicator letters at the head of pages and red underlinings *passim*, arranged: (*a*) alphabetically by subject matter, with pressmarks; (*b*) by pressmarks (*armariola* etc.); (*c*) by chantries, obits etc.; with contemp. and later additions and corrections.

Fos. i+82. 12 × 8¾ in. Paper.

601.   **Ditto** (W.D. 11). An apparently contemp. fair copy of No. 600, with rubrics, red and blue indicator letters, paragraphs etc., the final section being somewhat elaborated. Followed (fo. 78) by Tables, in alphabetical order of subjects, of a number of registers (listed by Holtzmann, *l.c.*, 178–80), now mostly lost.

Fos. 140+15 blank leaves. 12¼ × 8½ in.

❡ *Elemosinarius*

602.   **Untraced.** Register of the almoner formerly at St. John's Coll., Cambridge, containing copies of deeds, statutes, leases, wills, a rental and other misc. material, the latest dated entry being of 1360. Ed., from a 17th–18th cent. transcript in BM., Harley 4080, (Maria Hackett), *Reg. Eleemosynariae D. Pauli Londonensis* (1827).

Fos. 76. 8¼ × 6 in. Paper.

❡ *Other registers etc.*

For other registers at St. Paul's see also Maxwell Lyte, *l.c.*; and for Nos. 603–5, W. D. Simpson, *Registrum Statutorum et Consuetudinum . . . Sancti Pauli Londonensis* 1873).

603.   **London, St. Paul's Cathedral, Muniments** (W.D. 9). 'Statuta Majora,' late 14th cent., incl. lists and inventories of the cathedral's possessions etc.

604.   **Ditto** (W.D. 10). 'Statuta Minora,' 15th cent.

605.   **Cambridge U.L., Ee. 5. 21.** 'Liber Statutorum,' 1450 etc. *Cambr. U.L. Cat. MSS.* ii, 179–83. *FO:* Bp. J. Moore.

606.   **BM., Harley Roll I. 1.** Copy, 15th cent., of an *Inspeximus* of Henry IV, 1400.

LONDON

Ben. Abbey of St. Peter, Westminster
    v. WESTMINSTER.

LONDON

Charterhouse   *f.* 1371

607.   **PRO., Exch., L.R.** (Misc. Bks. 61). Cartulary, 15th cent., of lands in London and cos. Middx., Essex, Hertf., Wilts etc., *temp.* Edw. III–Hen. VI. Arranged topographically, with a section rel. the foundation at the beginning and some additions at the end, and incl. copies of some royal documents.

Fos. *c.* 210 (unnumbered). 16¼ × 12¾ in.

❡ *Other registers etc.*

608.   **PRO., Exch., K.R.** (Ancient Deeds, DD. 250). List of 162 charters etc. rel. the manor of St. Pancras, delivered to the prior 1404–5. Sealed and indented roll.

LONDON

Ben. or Aug. Priory (Nuns), Clerkenwell
    v. CLERKENWELL.

LONDON

Aug. Priory (Nuns), Haliwell, Shoreditch
                                        f. bef. 1127

609.   **Untraced.** Cartulary *penes* Edm(und) B(olton?), 17th cent., from which extracts are in BM., Add. 5937, fos. 74–5, and Bodl., Dodsworth 102 (*SC.* 5043), fos. 92–3.

LONDON

Aug. Priory of the Holy Trinity (*al.* Christ Church), Aldgate   *f.* 1107–8

610.   **Glasgow U.L., Hunter U. 2. 6** (*al.* S. 2. 9). Gen. cartulary, early 15th cent. (*temp.* W. Haraday?, prior 1408–20), with red and blue initials (in some sections illuminated), paragraphs etc. Contains

copies of title-deeds, leases, notes of rents and other memoranda arranged in *capitula* by parishes, preceded (fos. 1–7) and followed (fos. 149–200) by sections rel. the foundation etc., the *Soca extra Algate*, St. Katharine's Hospital, and *Carte de pluribus parochiis*, which include a list of priors and copies of royal, papal and episcopal charters *passim*. Misc. additions at the end include (fo. 206) a 15th cent. list of parishes. A 19th cent. transcript is in London, Guildhall Libr. Muniment Room (MS. 122). J. Young & P. Henderson Aitken, *Cat. Hunterian MSS.* (Glasgow, 1908), no. 215.

Fos. 208. 13½ × 9¼ in. *FO:* John Stow (?); S. Batman, D.D.; J. Anstis; T. Astle.

611. **BM., Lansdowne 448.** Cartulary, similar in date and format to No. 610, with spaces for initials. Contains copies and notes of royal, papal, episcopal and some other ecclesiastical etc. charters and documents rel. the priory's foundation etc. (fos. 3–4, written in double columns) and the appropriation etc. of its churches (fos. 5–12). Perhaps unfinished. The churches are listed in *Mon. Angl.* vi, 151.

Fos. 16. 13¾ × 9¼ in. *FO:* James West.

❡ *Other registers etc.*

612. **PRO., Exch., K.R.** (Misc. Bks. i. 18). Rentals and custumaries, 14th cent.

LONDON

Aug. Priory of St. Bartholomew *f.* 1123
No cartulary recorded. For the Hosp. of St. Bartholomew, independent from the early 13th cent., see also Nos. 617–9 below.

❡ *Other registers etc.*

613. **BM., Cotton Vesp. B. ix.** 'Liber Fundationis', 15th cent. An account of the foundation etc. in Latin, with English translation. *FO:* T. Otwell; T. Powell; R. St. George.

614. **BM., Add. 34768.** A collection of medieval and other charters made, 1663–73, to show the title of Robert Rich, 2nd earl of Holland and (1673) 5th earl of Warwick. E. A. Webb, *Records of St. Bartholomew's, Smithfield* i (1921), xxix–xxx. *FO:* Sir T. Phillipps (MS. 40).

LONDON

Coll. of St. Martin le Grand *f. c.* 1068
615. **Westminster Abbey** (Muniment Bk. 5). Register, 15th cent. (*temp.* Hen. VI), of rights, privileges etc., incl. copies of

royal, papal and episcopal documents but no private deeds. The original compilation (fos. 1–64), with rubrics, blue initials decorated with red and occasional illumination, is followed by misc. added quires etc. Incomplete Table, fos. 1–6. L. E. Tanner, *Trans. Royal Hist. Soc.*, Fourth ser. xix (1936), 80 (note of contents).

Fos. ii + 112. 12¼ × 8½ in.

LONDON

The Temple.
v. TEMPLARS.

LONDON

Hosp. or Fraternity of St. Augustine Papey *f.* 1442
No cartulary recorded.

❡ *Other registers etc.*

616. **BM., Cotton Vit. F. xvi,** fos. 113–23. Fragm. (much mutilated) of a 15th–16th cent. register of statutes, members etc., incl. copies of one or two grants to the fraternity. Extracts are in BM., Harley 604, fo. 12. *FO:* John Stow (?).

LONDON

Aug. Hosp. of St. Bartholomew, Smithfield. *f.* 1123
v. also Nos. 613–4 above.

617. **London, St. Bartholomew's Hospital,** Archives, 'Cok's Cartulary'. Gen. cartulary, 15th cent. (*temp.* Hen. VI–Edw. IV), compiled by John Cok in four parts: (1) royal, papal etc. charters rel. the foundation and site, fos. 32–87; (2) London, fos. 88–430; (3) Middlesex, fos. 431–56; (4) Country, fos. 464–584. Preceded (fos. 1–32) by a rental, 1456, of the London properties and followed by a contemp. index and Table (fos. 585–625), and copies of further misc. deeds. Pt. 2 is rubricated and pt. 4 has initials decorated with pen-drawn grotesques. Fos. 88, 464, have illuminated borders and initials by Walter Abel. An edition by Gweneth Whitteridge is in preparation.

Fos. 637 (medieval foliation, from fo. 88). 15¼ × 10 in.

❡ *Other registers etc.*

618. **Ditto,** 'The Little Cartulary'. Register, 15th cent., of leases, 13th–15th cent. Also apparently made by J. Cok.

619. **Ditto,** 'The Repertory Book'. Cartulary, 16th–18th cent., of lands acquired aft. 1547, incl. copies of some medieval deeds.

LONDON
Hosp. of St. Giles-in-the-Fields.
v. HOLBORN.

LONDON
Aug. Hosp. of St. Katharine-by-the-Tower
f. 1148
v. No. 610 above.

LONDON
Aug. Hosp. of St. Mary-without-Bishops-
gate *f.* 1197
620. **PRO., Exch., T.R.** (Misc. Bks.
265). Cartulary, 14th cent., with occasional
additions *passim*, arranged by parishes, of
which there is an added list at fo. 1.
Severely mutilated and faded, and now
almost entirely illegible to the naked eye.
Fos. 104 (originally upwards of 207).
$15\frac{1}{2} \times 11$ in. Paper.

LONDON
Hosp. of St. Thomas of Acon *f.* bef. 1191
621. **London, Mercers' Company,**
'Register of Writings, Vol. I'. Vol i of a
late 15th cent. gen. cartulary (*temp.* Edw.
IV), with spaces for rubrics and initials,
incl. copies of some royal and papal
charters *passim*. Contains material for the
City of London, calendared by R. R.
Sharpe in J. Watney, *Some Account of the
Hospital of St. Thomas of Acon* (1892), 237–
97.
Fos. 190. $13\frac{1}{4} \times 9\frac{1}{4}$ in.
622. **BM., Cotton Tib. C. v,** fos. 152–
287. Vol. ii (cf. No. 621), containing material for Wapping and Stepney, Plum-
stead, Coulsdon, Doncaster (Hosp. of St.
James), Ireland and Cyprus.
Fos. 136. $11\frac{1}{4} \times 8\frac{1}{4}$ in. (cropped). *FO:*
J. Povey.
623. **PRO., Exch., K.R.** (Eccl. Docs.,
E. 135/2/57). Cartulary, 16th cent. (aft.
1516), of deeds, wills etc., 15th–16th cent.,
rel. grants to the hospital in the City of
London. Preceded on two unnumbered
leaves by a *Status*, 1518, of its revenues,
outgoings etc. Presumably intended as a
supplement to Nos. 621–2.
Fos. 2+91. $13\frac{3}{4} \times 9\frac{1}{2}$ in. Paper.
¶ *Other registers etc.*
624. **Ditto** (Eccl. Docs., E. 135/20/2).
Fragm. (fos. 23) of a register of leases and
other *acta*, 1510–9 (*temp.* J. Yonge,
master).

LONDON
Par. Church of St. Botolph-without-
Aldersgate.
625. **BM., Add. 37664.** Guild-Book of
the fraternity of the Trinity and SS.
Fabian & Sebastian, 15th cent. (aft. 1454),
with partial rubrication and red and blue
decorated initials. Includes a kalendar,
rules, lists of members, accompts etc. and
(fos. 36–89) a cartulary of deeds, wills etc.
rel. property in London. *BM. Cat. Add.
MSS.* 1906–1910, 95–6.
Fos. i+98 (excl. blank leaves; contemp.
foliation, i–cxlviii, from fo. 9). $11\frac{1}{2} \times 8\frac{1}{4}$ in.
Paper (except fos. 1–8, 98, vellum). *FO:*
C. Ord; Sir T. Phillipps (MS. 3795).

LONDON
Par. Church of St. Botolph-without-
Aldgate.
626. **BM., Cotton App. xix.** Cartulary, 15th–16th cent., of deeds, wills etc.,
14th–16th cent., arranged by properties, in
London.
Fos. 63 (lacks material at the end).
$11\frac{1}{4} \times 8\frac{1}{2}$ in.

LONDON
Par. Church of St. Botolph-by-Billings-
gate.
627. **London, Guildhall Libr.,** Muniment Room (MS. 59). Register of deeds,
wills etc. (incl. royal letters patent, *temp.*
Edw. III–Ric. II etc.), begun in 1418 and
continued (from fo. 15) in a succession of
hands down to 1530. T. Thorpe, *Sale-Cat.
of Ancient MSS.* (1844), item 274 (partial
list of contents).
Fos. 48. 13×9 in.

LONDON
Par. Church of St. Margaret, Bridge St. *al.*
New Fish St.
628. **London, Guildhall Libr.,** Muniment Room (MS. 1174). Cartulary (fos.
32–92), late 15th cent. (*temp.* Edw. IV ?), of
deeds, wills etc. rel. property in London,
arranged by grantors. Preceded (fos. 16–
31) by an abstract of the contents and (fos.
8–14) inventories, 1472, of plate, vestments, service-books etc.; with misc.
additions on blank leaves at the beginning
and end.
Fos. 122. $12\frac{1}{4} \times 8\frac{3}{4}$ in.

LONDON
Par. Church of St. Martin, Ludgate.
No cartulary recorded.
¶ *Other registers etc.*
629. **London, Guildhall Libr.**, Muniment Room (MS. 1311 (1)). Record Book begun in 1410 and continued down to the 18th cent., incl. copies of a few deeds, wills etc. in the medieval part (fos. 4–76).

LONDON
Par. Church of St. Mary, Woolnoth.
630. **BM., Harley 877.** Register, in a series of 15th–16th cent. hands, of deeds, wills etc. (five documents in all) rel. benefactions etc. 1396–1498. *BM. Cat. Harl. MSS.*, *ad loc.*, lists the contents.
Fos. 35. 10½ × 7 in.

LONDON
Par. Church of St. Pancras, Soper Lane.
631. **London, Guildhall Libr.**, Muniment Room (MS. 5020). Evidence-Book, begun early 16th cent. and continued down to the 19th cent., of charters, wills etc., from *temp*. Edw. II.
Fos. 115. 14⅞ × 10 in.

LONDON
Par. Church of St. Peter-upon-Cornhill.
632. **London, Guildhall Libr.**, Muniment Room (MS. 4158). Cartulary, 1425–6, of deeds, wills etc. rel. properties in London of the fraternity and guild of St. Peter. Blue initials decorated with red. Arranged by grantors with a contemp. Table on 11 preliminary leaves. Fos. 131–45 (copies of a charter of Henry IV and statutes) were perhaps originally bound at the beginning. A. J. Horwood, *HMC. Sixth Report* (1877), App., 407–18, prints the Table and other extracts.
Fos. 13 + 309. 8½ × 6¾ in. *FO:* Sir G. W. Dasent; E. H. Freshfield.

LONDON
Par. Church of St. Stephen, Coleman St.
No cartulary recorded.
¶ *Other registers etc.*
633. **London, Guildhall Libr.**, Muniment Room (MS. 4456). Record Book, 1466–1832.

LUFFIELD
Ben. Priory   co. Northt.
     f. 1116–18
634. **Westminster Abbey** (Muniment Bk. 10). Gen. cartulary, late 15th cent.,

with rubrics etc. and blue initials decorated with red (illuminated at the beginning of sections, with coloured borders). Arranged topographically with copies of the founder's, papal, episcopal and royal charters at the beginning, preceded (fos. 1–13v) by an incomplete Table, and with misc. rentals etc. at the end. L. E. Tanner, *Trans. Royal Hist. Soc.*, Fourth ser. xix (1936), 79 (note of contents etc.).
Fos. 257. 13¾ × 10¼ in.
¶ *Other registers etc.*
635. **Cambridge U.L., Ee. 1. 1.** A collection of misc. legal material, incl. copies of a few charters (royal and private) at the end (fos. 273v–275). *Cambr. U.L. Cat. MSS.* ii, 1–4. *FO:* Francis Tate; Bp. J. Moore.

LYNN, KING'S
co. Norf.
Carmelite Friary   *f.* bef. 1261
636. **PRO., Exch., K.R.** (Eccl. Docs., E. 135/2/50). Part (apparently the second half) of a late 14th cent. cartulary (aft. 1370), with spaces for initials and a few additions, mainly at the beginning and end. Includes copies of some episcopal, royal and papal charters etc., with an incomplete list of benefactors on the first leaf and part of a contemp. Table on the second.
Fos. 2 + 19 (medieval foliation, 17–35) + vii. 11 × 7½ in.

LYNN, KING'S
co. Norf.
Gaywood Hosp. by   *f.* (?)
No cartulary recorded.
¶ *Other registers etc.*
637. **H. L. Bradfer-Lawrence Esq., F.S.A.**, Sharow End, Ripon. Bead-roll, 14th cent. *FO:* J. Ives; G. Brander; W. Bentham; Sir T. Phillipps (MS. 7427).

LYTHAM
co. Lanc.
Ben. Priory   *f.* 1189–94
638. **Untraced.** Register *penes* Thomas Clifton of Lytham, 17th cent. (*D*).

MAIDEN BRADLEY
co. Wilts
Aug. Priory   *f.* 1190
639. **BM., Add. 37503.** Register, 14th cent., rel. lands etc. mainly in Kidderminster, with some rubrication etc. and additions. Comprises: (*a*) fos. 6–29, three quires of a cartulary, *temp*. Edw. II, the

first three leaves relating to Bristol and Tothill (in Westminster), and the rest to Kidderminster; (*b*) fos. 30–56, 'Processus ecclesie de Kyderm(inistre)', i.e. copies, *temp*. Edw. III, with connecting narrative, of charters etc. (incl. royal, papal and episcopal documents) down to 1340 rel. the advowson; (*c*) fos. 1–5, 56–62, misc. additions down to 1492. Collation and binding, 15th cent. Extracts, 1736, by the Rev. G. Harbin from a transcript by H. Wanley, then with the original, are (1957) the property of David Rogers Esq., c/o the Bodleian Libr., Oxford (part of Phillipps MS. 4811).

Fos. v + 62 (with 33 blank unnumbered leaves at the beginning and end). $7\frac{1}{4} \times 4\frac{3}{4}$ in. *FO:* Thomas, 2nd baron Foley, 1736; Sotheby's sale-cat., 31 May 1907, lot 320 (property of a lady).

⁋ *Other registers etc.*

640.   **The Marquess of Bath,** Longleat (MS. 38a, formerly Muniments E. 13). Terriers, rentals, compotuses etc., 14th–17th cent.

MALMESBURY   co. Wilts
Ben. Abbey   *f.* 7th cent.

J. S. Brewer & C. T. Martin, *Registrum Malmesburiense*, 2 vols. (Rolls ser. 1879–80), edit No. 644 and describe the other cartularies, ii, pp. xxiii ff.

641.   **Oxford, Bodl., Wood empt. 5** (*SC.* 8593). Copies (fos. 9–60), 13th cent., of royal charters to the abbey, down to *temp*. Stephen, with one bull of Pope Sergius I; followed by a text of J. de Salisbury, 'Vita S. Thomae Cantuar.', two treatises on the book of Genesis etc. Uniformly written in a large book-hand with rubrics and red and green decorated initials. Contemp. white leather binding. A late 14th cent. Table of the entries, which correspond to Brewer & Martin, *op. cit.*, nos. xii–xlvi, lxiiii, is added at fo. 169.

Fos. i + 176. $9 \times 6\frac{1}{2}$ in. (cropped).

642.   **BM., Add. 38009.** Preliminary etc. leaves from a composite 13th cent. cartulary (continued in No. 643), containing copies of misc. evidences etc. rel. the abbey's lands, incl. (fos. 7–8, double columns, with red and blue initials etc.) an incomplete late 13th cent. Table to a gen. cartulary, of which fos. 1–7 of No. 643 apparently formed part. *BM. Cat. Add.*

MSS. 1906–1910, 206–7, lists other contents.

Fos. 16 (post-medieval foliation, 1–16, disarranged). $10\frac{3}{4} \times 7\frac{3}{4}$ in. *FO:* Sir T. Phillipps (MS. 24358).

643.   **BM., Add. 15667.** Continuation of No. 642, comprising: (*a*) fos. 1–7, fragm. of a mid-13th cent. cartulary with marginal rubrics, red initials (occasionally decorated with blue) etc., the entries being numbered *clxiii–clxxxii*, with later 13th cent. additions, *clxxxiii–clxxxvi*, corresponding to Brewer & Martin, *op. cit.*, nos. ccii–ccxxiii etc.; (*b*) fos. 18–39 (two interpolated late 13th cent. quires), statutes, bounds etc.; (*c*) fos. 40–120, cartulary written in a succession of late 13th cent. charter- and (towards the end) book-hands with rubrics, red and blue initials etc. and (fos. 8–9, 13v–15) a contemp. Table of the entries, which are numbered *ii–ccliii* in red, broadly corresponding to those in the latter part of No. 644, see Brewer & Martin, *op. cit.* ii, pp. lviii–lxv; (*d*) intermediate etc. leaves with misc. contemp. and later additions. *BM. Cat. Add. MSS.* 1841–1845, 54–5.

Fos. 124 (post-medieval foliation, 27–149, in the same hand as that of No. 642). $10\frac{3}{4} \times 8$ in. *FO:* Evan Seys, 17th cent.; the Jones fam., Fonmon castle.

644.   **PRO., Exch., K.R.** (Misc. Bks. i. 24). Gen. cartulary, late 13th cent. (*temp*. Edw. I), written in book-hand with rubrics, blue initials decorated with red, red numeration of the entries (*i–ccclxii*) etc. Opens with copies of general charters of liberties, statutes etc., followed without break (fo. 121v) by the foundation, royal, papal, episcopal etc. charters; lacks obvious subsequent arrangement. Contemp. Table, fos. 20–6; and misc. contemp. and later additions, fos. 1–19, 27, 307–9. Ed. Brewer & Martin, *op. cit.*

Fos. 309. $12\frac{1}{8} \times 7\frac{1}{4}$ in.

645.   **BM., Lansdowne 417.** Gen. cartulary, 14th–15th cent. (aft. 1393), written in book-hand with rubrics, blue initials decorated with red, red numeration of the entries (*i–ccclxvii*) etc. Omits the general charters, statutes etc., but is otherwise similar in contents to No. 644. Incomplete Table, in disorder, fos. 2–7. Brewer & Martin, *op. cit.* ii, pp. xlv–lvi.

Fos. 220 (wants a few leaves *passim*).

12 × 7 in. *FO:* Charles Danve(r)s, 16th
cent.; James West, 1763.

¶ *Pitanciarius*

646. **Oxford, Bodl., Bodley 191** (*SC.*
27642). Cartulary, 13th–14th cent., of
lands etc. assigned to the pittancer, written
in book-hand, changing at fo. 74 into contemp. charter-hand, with rubrics and blue
initials decorated with red. Contains copies
of private deeds, without obvious arrangement, numbered consecutively, *i–clxxxxvii*,
with a further 40–50 unnumbered 14th–
15th cent. etc. additions at the beginning
and end. Preceded by a rental (fos. 2–12)
and incomplete Table (fos. 12v–18). An
abstract, 1697, is in *ib.*, Tanner 342, fos.
165–73.

Fos. iii + 99 (lacks single leaves bef. fos.
12, 20, 86). 10¼ × 7¼ in. *FO:* W. Brewster,
M.D.

¶ *Sacristarius*

647. **BM., Cotton Faust. B. viii,** fos.
128–265. Cartulary (fos. 128–91), 14th
cent. (aft. 1367), of lands assigned to the
sacrist and chapel of the BVM. Written in
a rather heavy book-hand with rubrics,
blue initials decorated with red and red
numeration of the entries (*i–clxx*), and
arranged mainly by properties. Followed,
after a few intermediate additions, by a
supplement (fos. 199–248) in 14th–15th
cent. charter-hand with similar initials, red
underlining of headings, red and blue
paragraphs etc., which continues the
numeration of the entries down to *cclxxv*.
Fos. 250–6 are part of an added rental,
1399, of the chapel of the BVM. Fos. 257–
65 contain an incomplete contemp. Table,
printed with some abbreviation by Brewer
& Martin, *op. cit.* ii, pp. lxv–lxxxvii.

Fos. 138 (wants one or two leaves aft.
fo. 248). 10¼ × 7½ in. *FO:* R. Starkey,
1602.

MALTON co. York
Gilb. Priory *f. c.* 1150

648. **BM., Cotton Claud. D. xi.** Gen.
cartulary, 13th cent. (*c.* 1250 ?), with rubrics,
red and blue initials etc. and misc. additions
passim. Arranged in 70 sections, mainly
topographically (*i–iv* papal, royal, founders'
(Vescy) and episcopal charters; *xlvii* charters of the almoner; *lxii* ff. miscellaneous),
of which a contemp. list at fo. 2 is printed

with other extracts in *Mon. Angl.* vi, 970
(*a*) etc.

Fos. 297. 13½ × 9¼ in. *FO:* Christopher,
baron Hatton.

MAPLESTEAD, LITTLE co. Essex
Preceptory of Knts. of St. John *f.* bef.
1186

v. also ST. JOHN OF JERUSALEM,
SAMPFORD.

649. **Cambridge, Peterhouse, MS. 62**
('Summa Confessorum'). A paste-down at
the back of the 18th cent. binding is part
of a leaf from an early to mid-13th cent. cartulary, written in double columns with
rubrics and spaces for initials. On the recto
are copies of five private grants to the
hosp. of St. John of Jerusalem in co. Essex,
presumably for this preceptory. The verso
is invisible. M. R. James, *Cat. MSS.
Peterhouse* (Cambridge, 1899), 81–2 (calendar).

Fos. 1. 14¾ × 8 in. (cropped).

MARHAM co. Norf.
Cist. Abbey (Nuns) *f.* bef. 1249

650. **Mrs. Charles Howard,** deposited
in Norwich Central Libr. (Hare MSS.).
Composite gen. cartulary, incl. copies of
royal and episcopal charters *passim.* The
earliest elements (fos. 18–74 *passim*), written in several early 14th cent. hands with
rubrics, red initials etc., are arranged in
sections topographically with some repetition of material. Additions and accretions,
partly miscellaneous, at the beginning and
passim include: (*a*) an added 15th cent.
quire, incl. copies of papal privileges to the
Cistercian order, fos. 1–8; (*b*) a 14th cent.
inventory of the muniments, fos. 13–16.
Marginal annotations by Sir S. D'Ewes.
Medieval binding (restored). A. J. Horwood, *HMC. Third Report* (1872), App.,
251; W. Holtzmann, *Papsturkunden in
England* iii (Göttingen, 1952), 86–7 (descriptive notes).

Fos. 75. 11⅝ × 9 in. *FO:* the Hare fam.,
barts., Stow Hall.

MATTERSEY co. Nott.
Gilb. Priory *f. c.* 1185

651. **Untraced.** Register ascribed to
James Neville by a 17th cent. list of monastic leiger-books in Bodl., Ashmole 826,
fo. 124.

MAXSTOKE co. Warw.
Aug. Priory *f.* 1337
No cartulary recorded.
¶ *Other registers etc.*
652. **Oxford, Trinity Coll. MS. 84,**
deposited in the Bodleian Libr. Rough
register (fos. 151, paper) of accompts,
rentals, recitals of court-rolls and other
misc. memoranda, incl. a few notes of
deeds, 1432–90. H. O. Coxe, *Cat. MSS.
Oxon.* ii (Oxford, 1852), *ad loc. FO:* W.
Dilke; T. Warton.

MEAUX co. York
Cist. Abbey *f.* 1151
E. A. Bond, *Chronica Monasterii de
Melsa*, 3 vols. (Rolls ser., 1866–8), edits
Nos. 659–60 and notices MSS. of the
chronicle and cartularies, i, pp. xlix–lviii.
653. **BM., Lansdowne 424.** Cartulary
(fos. 2–77), mid-14th cent., of papal, episcopal and royal charters etc. Rubrics, red
and green initials etc. and a few additions
passim. Contemp. Table, fos. 2–4. Followed
(fos. 78–156) by a 14th–15th cent. supplement (rubrics and red initials), opening
with similar material and continuing with
copies of private deeds arranged topographically. A 17th cent. abstract by F.
Smales in BM., Add. 26736, fos. 3–44 (*FO:*
R. Thornton; J. Smyth), is apparently the
source of extracts, 1747, by T. Wilson in
Leeds, Yorks. Arch. Soc. MS. 415, and of
others by Bp. White Kennett in BM.,
Lansdowne 973, fos. 67v–78.
Fos. 157 (incomplete at the end; fos. 5–
156 numbered, i–cliiii, in the hand of the
supplement). 12¼ × 7¾ in. *FO:* Sir C.
Hildyard, 1553; Bp. J. Gardiner, 1699 (see
the extracts in BM., Harley 6975, fos. 59–
64; Lansdowne 968, ff. 20–9); James West,
1763.
654. **BM., Cotton Vit. C. vi.** Cartulary made, early 15th cent., by T. Burton,
abbot 1396–9 (see Bond, *op. cit.*). Rubrics,
red underlining of titles etc. Contains
abstracts of charters grouped in sections by
subject matter etc. (private grants arranged
topographically, fos. 2–46; grants for
special uses, e.g. *Pro sustentacione monachorum*, fos. 47–51; churches, fos. 52–7;
papal charters, fos. 58–102; a discourse rel.
exemptions from tithes, fos. 103–20; royal
charters, fos. 121–33); followed (fos. 134
ff.) by a feodary, rental, extent and in-

ventories of *Mobilia*, incl. books, all dated
1396. *Mon. Angl.* v, 389 (*a*), lists the headings.
Fos. ii+248. 11¼ × 7½ in. (margins etc.
shrunk by fire, 1731, and the leaves now
mounted).
655. **Untraced.** Cartulary, apparently
arranged topographically in sections, from
which extracts, 1639 etc., down to fo. 196
and mainly of 13th–14th cent. material, are
in Bodl., Dodsworth 53 (*SC.* 4196), fos.
1–9; 95 (*SC.* 5036), fos. 106–10; 127 (*SC.*
5068), f. 46. *FO:* Sir W. Alford; St. Mary's
Tower, York, 1639; perhaps destroyed in
the siege, 1644.
656. **Untraced.** Register *penes* the
Dean & Chapter of York, 17th cent. (*D*).
657. **Untraced.** 'Cartularium penes
dom. Gul. Ayrmine, 1637' (*T*), i.e. Sir
William Armyne *al.* Ayrmine, 1st bart.
658. **Untraced.** Cartulary or register
penes the Rev. Philip Stubbs, archdeacon
of St. Albans 1715–38. A papal privilege
printed from it in *Mon. Angl.* v, 284, also
appears in No. 653, fos. 7v–8.
¶ *Other registers etc.*
659. **Manchester, Rylands Libr., Lat.
MS. 219.** Chronicle of the abbey, late 14th
cent., by T. Burton, abbot 1396–9, in the
author's autograph. Paper. Ed., with No.
660, Bond, *op. cit. FO:* Sir C. Hildyard,
early 17th cent.; Austin Cooper; Sir T.
Phillipps (MS. 6478).
660. **BM., Egerton 1141.** A revision of
No. 659, 14th–15th cent., also autograph;
followed (fos. 132 ff.) by a feodary,
rental, and other miscellanea rel. the abbey's
lands in the same hand. Vellum. A transcript, 1651, by H. Paget is in BM., Add.
26734 (*FO:* R. Thornton; J. Smyth). Ed.,
with No. 659, Bond, *op. cit. FO:* Sir W.
Alford; used by R. Gascoigne, 1622, 1624;
J. Nichols, by gift of a clergyman in
Lincolnshire, *c.* 1795; J. B. Nichols.

MEREVALE co. Warw.
Cist. Abbey *f.* 1148
661. **Untraced.** Cartulary *penes* Richard Chamberlain of Astley, co. Warw.,
registrar of the court of Wards, early 17th
cent. Cited by Dugdale, *Antiq. Warwickshire* ii (2nd ed., 1730), 1085 ff. and W.
Burton, *Description of Leicestershire* (2nd ed.,
Lynn, 1777), 23, 57.

MERTON co. Surr.
Aug. Priory *f.* 1114
No cartulary recorded.

❡ *Other registers etc.*
The following are described by A.
Heales, *The Records of Merton Priory* (1898),
vii–ix, and cited *passim.*

662. **BM., Cotton Cleop. C. vii,** fos.
60–204. Register of leases and other *acta* of
the priory, *c.* 1150–*c.* 1352; begun in the
early 13th cent., with subsequent continuations, and incl. copies of some misc.
royal, papal, episcopal and other documents etc. with (fo. 178) a list of priors.

663. **Oxford, Bodl., Laud misc. 723,**
fos. 24–73. Misc. late 14th cent. register of
court rolls, rentals and other memoranda,
incl. some copies of deeds, writs etc., 1387–
1400.

664. **London, Coll. of Arms, Arundel 28.** Rental, 1391–2, preceded by an
account of the priory's foundation. *FO:*
Ld. Wm. Howard; presented by Henry
Howard, 6th duke of Norfolk, 1678.

METTINGHAM co. Suff.
Coll. of St. Mary *f.* (at Raveningham)
1343

665. **BM., Stowe 939.** 'Monumenta
tangencia ecclesiam de Ravenyngham.'
Gen. cartulary, 14th–15th cent. (*c.* 1400?),
with spaces sometimes left for coloured
initials. Includes copies of royal, episcopal
and papal charters, grouped at the end (fos.
14 ff.).
Fos. i+25. $14\frac{3}{8} \times 10\frac{1}{4}$ in. *FO:* T. Martin;
J. Ives; T. Astle.

666. **BM., Stowe 934.** A late 15th cent.
register, with some conventional pen-work
decoration of initials and an early 16th
cent. section added (fos. 4–29). Principal
contents: (1) surveys, rentals etc. of manors,
1461–1508, with some copies of charters
interspersed, fos. 5–151; (2) copies of royal
charters, 1343–1489, followed by late 14th
cent. papal and episcopal grants, fos. 153–
72; (3) notes of bequests for the celebration
of obits, fos. 152, 174v–184.
Fos. 193 (incl. 11 fly-leaves etc.). $16\frac{1}{4} \times$
$10\frac{3}{4}$ in. Paper. *FO:* J. Harvey, 1714; P. Le
Neve; T. Martin; J. Ives; T. Astle.

❡ *Other registers etc.*
667. **BM., Add. 33985–33990.** Original
accompts etc., 1402–1516. Six vols. Paper.

7—M.C.

FO: T. Martin; T. Manning; the Rev.
C. R. Manning.

MILTON co. Dors.
Ben. Abbey *f.* 964
668. **Untraced.** Cartulary formerly in
the Exchequer (in the office, 1587, of
Thomas Fanshawe, King's Remembrancer),
from which extracts, 16th–17th cent., are
in Winchester Coll. Muniments (chest 2.
170 and Sydling I. 1); Bodl., James 23 (*SC.*
3860), pp. 46–57; *ib.*, Dodsworth 66 (*SC.*
5008), fos. 121–2; *Mon. Angl.* ii, 348–51.
Opened apparently with a narrative
account of the foundation, incl. material
down to at least the mid-14th cent.

MISSENDEN co. Bucks.
Aug. Abbey *f.* 1133
J. G. Jenkins, *The Cartulary of Missenden
Abbey*, 2 vols. (Bucks. Arch. Soc., Records
Branch ii, 1938; Bucks. Record Soc. x,
1955 for 1946), edits No. 670.

669. **Untraced.** Gen. cartulary, ap-
parently 13th cent. (*temp.* Hen. III with
additions?), arranged topographically and
incl. copies of royal and episcopal charters
passim. Extracts, early 18th cent., are in
Bodl., Willis 5 (*SC.* 16298), fos. 1–84, cf.
Jenkins, *op. cit.* i, pp. x–xi, 238 ff. etc.; *ib.*,
Tanner 342, fos. 205v–7.
Fos. 125. Quarto. *FO:* Sir E. Coke;
borrowed from E. Coke Esq. by P. Le
Neve, 1715–16; not in the cat. of Holkham
MSS., 1773.

670. **BM., Harley 3688.** Gen. cartulary
compiled by R. de Welwes and completed 20 Feb. 1330–1. Rubrics, alternate
plain red or blue initials, and additions
passim and at the end (fos. 192 ff.). Contains
copies of deeds arranged in sections,
mainly topographically (fos. 187–91, royal
and episcopal confirmations), with a contemp. Table, fos. 1–15. Ed. Jenkins, *op. cit.*
Fos. 207 (contemp. foliation of fos. 18–
198, i–ccvii; wants lxxvi–lxxxvi, rel.
Chalfont). 14×9 in. *FO:* T. Anderson,
W.S.

671. **Untraced.** Cartulary (?) *penes*
'Lady Dormer', 17th cent. (*D*). Possibly
one of the preceding, or the following.

❡ *Other registers etc.*
672. **BM., Sloane 747.** Register, 15th–
16th cent., of leases, grants to the abbey
and other misc. evidences etc., mainly

temp. H. Honor, abbot 1462–aft. 1505. Paper. Noticed by Sister Elspeth, *Victoria Hist. Buckinghamshire* i (1905), 373.

MODBURY co. Devon
Ben. Priory *f. c.* 1140

673. **Eton College,** Muniments (Modbury Deeds 32). Cartulary, *c.* 1325 with additions down to *temp.* Ric. II, containing copies of 32 deeds etc. A transcript, 1938, by H. N. Blakiston is *ib.*, in the library. Fos. 23 (paginated 1–46). Small quarto.

MONK BRETTON co. York
Clun. and (1280) Ben. Priory *f.* 1153–5

Nos. 674–5 are described and calendared by J. W. Walker, *Abstracts of the Chartularies of the Priory of Monkbretton* (Yorks. Arch. Soc., Record ser. lxvi, 1924).

674. **BM., Lansdowne 405.** The first leaf and quires *iiii–vii* of a late 13th cent. cartulary (aft. 1280) with rubrics and marginal pressmarks. Arranged topographically with additions (fos. 46–65), mainly 13th cent., down to 1336, incl. copies of some papal bulls. Extracts, 1634, from parts now wanting are in Bodl., Dodsworth 147 (*SC.* 5088), 155 (*SC.* 5096), 159 (*SC.* 5100), cf. Walker, *op. cit.*, 217–224.

Fos. 65 (post-medieval numeration, 1, 39–100, from fo. 3). 11 × 7¾ in. and (fos. 56–65) 10 × 6 in. *FO:* T. Holcroft, 1614; Sir W. Armyne, bart., 1633; Millington, bookseller, of London, 1704; W. Clavell, 1709; James West, 1763.

675. **Comdr. M. E. Wentworth,** deposited at Leeds, Yorks. Arch. Soc. Libr. (DD. 57. A.). Gen. cartulary written between 1529 and 1538 with rubrics and black pen-decorated initials coloured red and yellow. Arranged topographically, with copies of four 12th–13th cent. papal charters at the beginning, and preceded (fos. i–iv^r) by a summary Table and (fos. iv^v–vi) by an added catalogue of the priory's library at Worsborough, 1558. A partial transcript is in Bodl., Dodsworth 155 (*SC.* 5096), fos. 25ff. J. S. Purvis, 'New Light on the Chartularies of Monkbretton Priory', *Yorks. Arch. J.* xxxvii (1948), 67–71, prints contemp. evidence rel. its compilation and history down to 1574.

Fos. vi + 352. 11 × 8 in. *FO:* the Prior and Brethren, Worsborough; F. Wortley, bef. 1574; Sir G. Wentworth, Woolley Hall, bef. 1648.

MONKS HORTON co. Kent
Clun. Priory *f.* 1142

676. **BM., Add. 5516,** fos. 1–8. Fragm. of a late 14th cent. cartulary, rather closely written with spaces for small initials. Contains copies of the foundation, royal, papal, episcopal and one or two other charters (20 entries in all), printed by J. R. Scott, 'Charters of Monks Horton Priory', *Arch. Cantiana* x (1876), 269–81.

Fos. 8. 8 × 6¼ in. *FO:* 'John Frognll' (fo. 4v), 16th cent.; E. Hasted, 1790.

677. **BM., Stowe 935.** Gen. cartulary, *c.* 1440–5, made for Prior J. Holbech. Rubrics, blue initials decorated with red etc., and occasional additions. Contains copies of deeds etc., incl. a few royal and episcopal charters *passim*, arranged apparently by grantors and followed (fos. 60 ff.) by a terrier and other memoranda. Copies of papal charters were apparently among the contents of numerous leaves excised *passim*. An abstract, 1627, for Sir E. Dering in BM., Stowe 924, fos. 2–47, showing many of the latter to have been then still present, is copied in Bodl., Top. Kent c. 6 (*SC.* 35720; *FO:* S. Pegge; E. Hasted, 1790; R. Heber (MS. 491); Sir T. Phillipps (MS. 8132)). Transcripts, 1648, of other material now wanting are in BM., Harley 2044, fos. 78–80. *BM. Cat. Stowe MSS.* i, 618–9 (description).

Fos. 80 (post-medieval foliation, 11–(270); lacks leaves *passim*). 14½ × 10 in. *FO:* W. Mantell, 16th cent.; G. Rooke, 1627; W. Somner (*T*).

MONKTON FARLEIGH co. Wilts
Clun. Priory *f.* 1125

678. **Trowbridge, Wiltshire R.O.** (Acc. No. 192/54). Copies, in three 14th and 15th cent. hands, of 14 charters (one entered twice) *temp.* Hen. I–1409, incl. early royal charters and grants etc. rel. Chippenham, Wraxall etc.

Roll of 2 membrs. 52½ × 13 in. *FO:* the Seymour fam., dukes of Somerset, earls & marquesses of Hertford, barons Beauchamp and Seymour; the Bruce, afterw. Bruce–Brudenell fam., earls & marquesses of Ailesbury, 1671; the Cunliffe-Lister fam., barons Masham and earls Swinton, 1887 (with the Jervaulx estate); the Mayor and Corporation of Bradford.

MONTACUTE co. Som.
Clun. Priory *f. c.* 1102
679. **Oxford, Trinity Coll. MS. 85,**
deposited in the Bodleian Libr. Gen. cartulary written, aft. 1305, for S. Rawlin,
prior 1297–1316. Red initials to the
entries, rubrics with blue initials etc., and
numerous additions *passim.* Arranged topographically by counties, with copies of the
foundation and royal charters at the beginning (fos. 18–38) preceded by a Table (fos.
14–16). Calendared in *Two Cartularies of . . .
Bruton and . . . Montacute,* ed. members of
the Council (Somerset Record Soc. viii,
1894), 119–236 etc.; H. O. Coxe, *Cat.
MSS. Oxon* ii (Oxford, 1852), *ad loc.*
Fos. 102 (the leaves of the original compilation numbered i–lxxx, cvi–cxi; wants
xxxvi–xlvi aft. fo. 58). $9\frac{3}{4} \times 6\frac{5}{8}$ in. Presented
by the Rev. J. R. Roberts, 1822.

MORPETH co. Northumb.
v. NEWMINSTER.

MOTTISFONT co. Southt.
Aug. Priory *f.* 1201
680. **Untraced.** MS. book in the Exchequer (King's Remembrancer's office),
17th cent., from which copies of charters
and memoranda of benefactions, down to
fo. 36, are printed in *Mon. Angl* vi, 481–2.
681A. **Mrs. Gilbert Russell,** Mottisfont Abbey, Romsey. Cartulary, 15th–
16th cent., written in a single main hand
which also appears in No. 681B, of deeds
etc., incl. some royal charters, grouped
under the headings Mottisfont, Burbage,
'Merton', 'Wulton' and Timsbury.
Fos. 74. $14\frac{3}{4} \times 10\frac{1}{2}$ in. Vellum. *FO:* the
Sandys fam., barons Sandys; the Mill fam.,
barts.
681B. **Ditto.** Cartulary, 15th–16th
cent., in several hands, of deeds etc.
grouped under the headings (listed at the
beginning) Broughton, Upper & Lower
Eldon, Bossington, Compton, Somborne,
East Dean, Bentley (in Mottisfont), Winchester, Wallop, Andover, Enham, Eling
and 'Berewyke'. Apparently intended as a
continuation of No. 681A and includes
copies of some royal and episcopal charters
etc. *passim.*
Fos. 185 (wants occasional leaves *passim*).
$12\frac{1}{2} \times 9$ in. Paper. *FO:* as No. 681A.

¶ *Other registers etc.*
682. **Ditto.** Register, *c.* 1340, of rentals,
surveys etc. Elaborately written as a single
compilation and prefaced by Walter of
Henley's treatise on husbandry.
Fos. xxv + 91. $11\frac{3}{4} \times 7\frac{1}{2}$ in. *FO:* as No.
681A.
682A. **Oxford, Bodl., Dodsworth 71**
(*SC.* 5013), ff. 1–8, 33–40. Transcripts, 17th
cent., of 36 original deeds, with drawings
of seals.

MOUNTJOY co. Norf.
Aug. Priory *f.* bef. 1210
683. **Untraced.** 'Partem registri . . . scil.
p. 11. non ita pridem penes Will. Bladwell
de Swan(n)ington gen. Hoc una cum cartis
in scaccario abbreviavit cl. Petrus Le Neve'
(*T*).
684. **Untraced.** 'Registrum . . . penes
Clem. Herne de Haver(ing)land arm.' (*T*).

MUCHELNEY co. Som.
Ben. Abbey *f.* 8th cent.
685. **The Earl of Cardigan** (*vice* the
Marquess of Ailesbury), Sturmy House,
Savernake Forest (1953). Gen. cartulary,
late 13th cent. (*temp.* Edw. I), written in
book-hand with alternate plain red and
blue initials. Arranged with the royal
(Anglo-Saxon), episcopal and other ecclesiastical charters at the beginning and misc.
additions at the end (fos. lx ff.), the whole
being preceded by five leaves from a 12th–
13th cent. breviary and two fly-leaves containing a contemp. Table, down to fo. lx,
in charter-hand. Medieval binding. Ed.
E. H. Bates, *Two Cartularies . . . of Muchelney and Athelney* (Somerset Record Soc.
xiv, 1899), 1–112.
Fos. vii + 74 (contemp. foliation of fos.
i–lix on the verso; later medieval foliation
of fos. i–lxiii on the recto). $9\frac{5}{8} \times 6\frac{1}{2}$ in. *FO:*
the Seymour fam., dukes of Somerset,
earls & marquesses of Hertford, barons
Beauchamp and Seymour.

NEATH co. Glam.
Cist. Abbey *f.* 1130
685A. **Untraced.** Cartulary (?) *penes*
Sir E. Stradling (d. 1609) from which extracts, 16th–17th cent., are in Oxford,
Queen's Coll. MS. 288; Bodl., Dodsworth
20 (*SC.* 4162), fos. 76–7; BM., Harley
2273, fo. 299v, etc. Cf. R. Merrick, *A*

Book of Glamorganshire Antiquities (ed.
A. J. Corbett, 1887), iv–v etc.; F. R. Lewis,
'History of the Lordship of Gower' etc.,
Bull. Board of Celtic Studies ix (1937–8),
149–154.

NEWBURGH co. York
Aug. Priory *f. c.* 1150
No cartulary recorded. Copies, 1636, in
Bodl., Dodsworth 91 (*SC.* 5032), fos. 1–67,
of original charters in St. Mary's Tower,
York, in some cases with drawings or des-
criptions of the seals, are headed apparently
erroneously in a later hand, 'Register of
Newburgh Priory' and (fos. 29–67) 'New-
burgh Priory Coucher'.

NEWENHAM co. Devon
Cist. Abbey *f.* 1247
686. **Oxford, Bodl., Top. Devon d.
5.** Gen. cartulary, *c.* 1347, with rubrics etc.,
blue initials and occasional additions.
Arranged topographically with copies of
papal (incl. privileges of the Cistercian
order) and royal charters at the beginning,
preceded (fos. ii–iv) by a preface and contemp. Table, and with misc. historical and
other material at the end (fos. 104v–122).
A partial transcript, 1607, is in Exeter City
Libr. (49/26/2). J. Davidson, *Hist. Newen-
ham Abbey* (1843), 133–41, 225–9 (description and extracts).
Fos. iv + 134. 10⅜ × 7⅛ in. *FO:* R. Rolle;
W. Wavell, M.D.; the Rev. J. Dene; Sir
T. Phillipps (MS. 25088).
¶ *Other registers etc.*
687. **BM., Arundel 17.** Misc. register
and memorandum book, 14th cent. (aft.
1334) with additions, containing material
rel. Axminster, Pelynt etc. and lists of
kings, bishops, abbots, benefactors etc.
BM. Cat. Arundel MSS., 4–5. *FO:* H. (?)
Rolle (fo. 3); Lord Wm. Howard, 1589;
Thomas Howard, 2nd earl of Arundel;
presented by Henry Howard, 6th duke of
Norfolk, to the Royal Society, 1678.

NEWENT co. Glouc.
Ben. Priory *f. bef.* 1086
688. **BM., Add. 15668.** Gen. cartulary
(fos. 50–68), 13th cent. (aft. 1253), written
in book-hand with rubrics and red initials.
Preceded and followed by contemp. and
later misc. additions on blank and added
leaves etc. in a number of 13th–14th cent.

charter-hands, and incl. copies of a few
royal, papal, episcopal etc. documents
passim. BM. Cat. Add. MSS. 1846–1847,
1–2, lists the principal contents.
Fos. 105. 12 × 8½ in. *FO:* (W. T. ?)
Alchin, 1846.
689. **BM., Add. 18461.** Gen. cartulary,
early 14th cent. (aft. 1313), written in book-
hand with red initials etc., spaces for rubrics and occasional additions. Arranged
topographically and incl. copies of royal,
episcopal etc. and occasional papal charters
passim, and of rentals and custumaries towards the end. *Ex libris*, 15th cent., of St.
Mary's Abbey, Cormeilles, fo. 1.
Fos. vi + 132. 12¼ × 9 in. *FO:* F. Tas-
burgh; the Nevill fam., Holt.

NEWHOUSE (*al.* NEWSHAM)
co. Linc.
Praem. Abbey *f. c.* 1143
690. **The Earl of Yarborough,** Brocklesby Park. 'The Black Book of Newsam'.
Parts of a 13th–14th cent. cartulary (*temp.*
Edw. I), with marginal titles, spaces for
initials and a few additions *passim*. In its
present state comprises a collection of loose
folia, bifolia and occasional quires (up to 6
leaves), many roughly cut round the
edges or otherwise mutilated, and contains copies, without names of witnesses, of
about 750 private etc. deeds. Appears originally to have been arranged topographically. Transcripts, 20th cent., are *ib.*
and in Lincolnshire Archives Office (Foster
Libr.). Extracts, 19th cent., from an
English translation, 1694, by Tyrwhitt
Turpine (formerly also at Brocklesby), are
in Manchester, Rylands Libr. Engl. MSS.
134, 221.
Fos. 70 (modern arrangement and
numeration; lacks an indeterminate number *passim*). 12½ × 9¼ in. (irregular).

NEWMINSTER co. Northumb.
Cist. Abbey *f.* 1138
691. **Major G. A. G. Howard, J.P.,**
Castle Howard. Cartulary, mid-14th cent.,
with spaces for initials. Arranged in six
Gradus (subdivided into *Loci*), of which the
first relates to the foundation, site and early
benefactions, and the remainder are topographical, incl. copies of some episcopal
charters *passim*. Additions on blank leaves
and at the end (fos. 136 ff.) include (fos.

152v–4) a Table, c. 1500. Ed., with a roll now kept with the cartulary, J. T. Fowler, *Chartularium Abbathiae de Novo Monasterio* (Surtees Soc. lxvi, 1878 for 1876).

Fos. 154 (numbered 1–155; lacks 77). 8 × 5¼ in. *FO:* Ld. Wm. Howard; E. Cook; Mr. Burn; George, 7th earl of Carlisle (d. 1864), Castle Howard.

NEWNHAM co. Bedf.
Aug. Priory *f. c.* 1165
692. **BM., Harley 3656.** Gen. cartulary, 15th cent., with rubrics, red initials etc. Contains copies of private etc. deeds arranged topographically, preceded (fos. 8–82) by groups of papal (mainly excised), royal, episcopal and other general charters etc. arranged according to type and subject matter, and (fos. 2–7) part of a contemp. Table. A transcript is in Bedford R.O.

Fos. 223 (wants leaves at the beginning, aft. fo. 13, and at the end). 10¼ × 7 in. *FO:* St. John Bapt. Parish Church libr., Bedford, 1704 (T. Fisher, *Gentleman's Magazine* lxxxvii (2) (1817), 136, 578; cf. fo. 1); H. Wanley, 1715 (*T*).

NEWPORT PAGNELL co. Bucks.
Ben Priory.
v. TICKFORD.

NEWSHAM co. Linc.
v. NEWHOUSE.

NEWSTEAD co. Nott.
Aug. Priory *f. c.* 1163
693. **London, Coll. of Arms, Arundel 60.** Gen. cartulary, 1286, with rubrics, red and blue initials etc. and additions *passim.* Arranged in sections, mainly topographically, with the copies of papal, episcopal and royal charters at the beginning (fos. 35–40) and of grants by the priory at the end (fos. 187–210). The four papal charters have been excised or (fo. 35) defaced. A contemp. Table (fos. 5–30) shows a large section for Walkeringham to be wanting aft. fo. 40. Medieval binding. (W. H. Black), *Cat. Arundel MSS. Coll. of Arms* (1829), 126–9, lists heads of contents.

Fos. 216. 8½ × 5¾ in. *FO:* T. Freeman; presented, 1712, by Michael Burton.
694. **Nottingham, Public Libr.** (M. 400). Cartulary, 1344, of 14th cent. grants to the priory, with red headings, initials

etc. and additions down to 1393 etc. Arranged in sections by grantors, with topographical subdivisions and (fos. 1–13) Tables, and incl. some antecedent title deeds of the properties concerned. A 19th cent. abstract is in Bodl., Top. Nott. c.1 Ed., in translation, V. W. Walker & D. Gray, *Newstead Priory Cartulary, 1344 etc.* (Thoroton Soc., Record ser. viii, 1940). R. White, *Dukery Records* (Worksop, 1904), 235–40 (abstract).

Fos. 122. 8¼ × 5½ in. *FO:* the Shilton fam.; Mrs. Keal Smith.
695. **PRO., Exch., K.R.** (Misc. Bks. i. 23). Cartulary of grants to the priory *temp.* Hen. VI, begun 1424–5 for Prior R. Cutwolf and continued in a succession of hands, the earlier leaves with rubrics, red and blue initials etc. Arranged topographically with a Table (fos. 1–10) and general section at the beginning, and incl. copies of a few pleas and some antecedent title deeds.

Fos. 148. 9½ × 6½ in.
⁋ *Other registers etc.*
696. **BM., Add. 35170.** Register, 15th cent., of pleas, legal proceedings etc., 1329–59 etc. *FO:* the Byron fam., Newstead, 16th–18th cent.; R. Farmer, 1771; R. Byron, 1771.

NEWTON LONGVILLE co. Bucks.
Clun. Priory *f. c.* 1080
697. **Untraced.** For extracts, 16th cent., from a register formerly in the possession of New Coll., Oxford, see No. 746 below.

NORTHAMPTON co. Northt.
Aug. Abbey of St. James *f. c.* 1150
698. **BM., Cotton Tib. E. v.** Gen. cartulary, 1313, with red and blue decorated initials, paragraphs etc. Arranged topographically, with copies of royal and episcopal charters included *passim.* Misc. additions on blank and added leaves etc. include (fo. 234) a list of abbots down to 1445. Extracts, c. 1719–21, are in Bodl., Top. Northants e. 5 (*SC.* 16661), fos. 277–497.

Fos. 247. 11¾ × 6½ in. (shrunk and damaged by fire, 1731). *FO:* Francis Tate, 1591.

NORTHAMPTON co. Northt.
Clun. Priory of St. Andrew *f.* 1093
699. **BM., Royal 11 B. ix.** Gen. cartulary, late 13th cent. (*temp.* Edw. I), with

uncompleted rubrication and red initials. Arranged by properties, with copies of the founder's, royal and episcopal charters at the beginning. An added early 14th cent. summary, by quires, at fos. 131v–132 is followed by charred fragms. of leaves apparently containing misc. additions. Fos. 145. *c.* 8½ × 6½ in. (damaged by fire, 1731). *FO:* J. Theyer.

700.   **BM., Cotton Vesp. E. xvii.** Gen. cartulary, 15th cent. (*temp.* Hen. VI ?), with red initials, uncompleted rubrication, and some misc. additions, mainly at the end. Apparently a revision of No. 669. Arranged topographically, with copies of the founder's, royal and papal etc. charters at the beginning and of episcopal ones at fos. 289–95. Summary, by quires, fos. 3–3v. *Mon. Angl.* v, 188 (*f*), lists the contents.

Fos. 321. 12¼ × 8¾ in. *FO:* Sir J. Lambe, 1641 (Bodl., Dodsworth 79 (*SC.* 5020), fo. 9); Christopher, baron Hatton.

¶ *Other registers etc.*

701.   **PRO., Exch., K.R.** (Eccl. Docs., E. 135/20/3). 'Registrum omnium evidenciarum in tempore Willelmi Reknar prioris.' Copies mainly of leases, titles for ordinands etc., *c.* 1519–37.

NORWICH   co. Norf.
Ben. Cath. Priory   *f.* aft. 1094

For the cartularies at Norwich see H. T. Riley, *HMC. First Report* (1870), App., 87–9, whose account is supplemented by W. Holtzmann, *Papsturkunden in England* ii (Göttingen, 1935), 30–5.

702.   **Norwich, D. & C.,** Muniments, 'Reg. I'. Gen. cartulary, *c.* 1306, with rubrics, red and blue decorated initials etc. Arranged topographically with sections of royal and papal charters and of *Cyrographa* at the beginning and misc. additions on blank and added leaves *passim* and at the end (fos. 223 ff.), incl. a section of 13th cent. episcopal charters (fos. 227–49). Preceded (fos. 15–46) by a history of the priory, incorporating copies of many of its early episcopal and some royal charters. Excludes material rel. lands etc. assigned to obedientiaries. H. W. Saunders, *The First Register of Norwich Cathedral Priory* (Norfolk Record Soc. xi, 1939), edits the history.

Fos. 276 + 4. 14 × 9 in.

703.   **Ditto,** 'Reg. II, pt. ii'. (The first part of a ?) cartulary similar in date, arrangement and scope to No. 702, which it follows as far as fo. 167. Written in bookhand, with rubrics and uncompleted coloured initials, and the quires numbered *v–x* from fo. 10. The history of the priory occupies fos. 10–32. Fos. 1–9, 60–4 contain misc. additions. 'Reg. II' was divided, 1937, into two parts, now bound separately; for pt. i, see No. 711.

Fos. 129 (post-medieval numeration, 1–112, excl. some inserted leaves). 13¾ × 9 in.

704.   **Ditto,** 'Reg. VII'. Cartulary, 13th–14th cent. (*temp.* Edw. I), with rubrics, red and blue decorated initials etc. Contains sections of foundation, royal and episcopal charters, fines, and deeds rel. Sedgeford (the first manor in the order of No. 702), with misc. additions *passim* and at the end.

Fos. 94. 9⅞ × 6½ in.

705.   **Ditto,** 'Reg. IV'. Register, 15th cent., in several consecutive hands, of 11th–14th cent. episcopal charters to the priory, with pressmarks. Preceded (pp. 1–14) by a short history of the priory down to *temp.* Hen. III (cf. *Mon. Angl.* iv, 13–14), and followed (pp. 329–45) by a copy of a plea, *temp.* Hen. VII.

Fos. 176 (excl. blank leaves; paginated, 1–345). 10½ × 7 in.

706.   **Ditto,** 'Reg. III'. Cartulary, 15th–16th cent., with rubrics, red pressmarks etc., containing: (1) fos. 49–217, copies of royal charters to the priory, *temp.* Will. II–Edw. IV, with misc. additions at fos. 105–121, 198–215, and an added postmedieval Table at fos. 240–5; (2) fos. 226–239, copies of royal charters to the see. Preceded (fos. 1–45) by a treatise 'De Libertatibus et Franchesiis Ecclesie . . . Norwici', incorporating further copies of royal charters etc.

Fos. 240 (medieval foliation, 1–248; wants 218–25, without apparent loss of material). 9½ × 6¾ in.

¶ *Inventories*

707.   **Ditto** (in a brown cardboard box labelled 'Miscellaneous Norwich'). Fragm. of an inventory of the muniments, 13th–14th cent. (*temp.* Edw. I), written in a rather crude hand. Apparently similar in arrangement to No. 708, than which it seems on internal evidence to be slightly earlier. Contains parts of lists of royal and

episcopal charters with some added entries rel. charters of Edw. III and Hen. IV (?) at the head and on the verso.

Roll, *c.* 70 × 8¾ in.

708. **Ditto** (Library). Inventory of the muniments, early 14th cent., with red titles and numeration of the entries. Arranged in order of pressmarks (*A–C* royal, *D–F* episcopal, *G* fines, *J–Z* topographical), with leaves and spaces left blank for additions, which have however only occasionally been made.

Fos. 36. 14 × 9 in.

❡ *Camerarius*

709. **Ditto**, 'Reg. VI'. Cartulary of the chamberlain (fos. 3–38), 14th cent. (*temp.* Edw. II), with rubrics and red and blue decorated initials. Contains copies of deeds rel. the chamberlain's lands numbered consecutively *i–lxxi* and arranged apparently topographically, followed (fos. 49–55, in similar format) by copies of royal and episcopal charters to the priory. The remaining leaves contain misc. additions, *temp.* Edw. II–16th cent.

Fos. 86. 10 × 6¾ in.

❡ *Cellerarius*

710. **Ditto**, 'Reg. V'. Cartulary of the cellarer (fos. 2–55), late 13th cent. (*temp.* Edw. I), with rubrics and spaces for initials. Arranged topographically, with sections of royal, episcopal etc. charters at the beginning, and followed by misc. additions, incl. further copies of deeds *temp.* Edw. I–15th cent., on added etc. leaves.

Fos. 157. 10¼ × 6½ in.

❡ *Elemosinarius*

711. **Ditto**, 'Reg. II, pt. i'. Cartulary of the almoner, 13th–14th cent. (*temp.* Edw. I), with rubrics, blue paragraphs etc., and misc. additions at the end (fos. 91v ff.) etc. Arranged topographically with a contemp. Table at fos. 5–12, the entries being numbered by places. For 'Reg. II, pt. ii', see No. 703.

Fos. 107. 13½ × 9 in. (cropped).

❡ *Sacristarius*

712. **Ditto**, 'The Sacrist's Book', *al.* 'Reg. XI'. Cartulary of the sacrist (fos. 16–84), early 14th cent., with rubrics, red paragraphs etc. Arranged in sections by places, with pressmarks. Fos. 2–7 contain a kalendar and copies of misc. documents of roughly contemp. date, and fos. 85 ff.,

misc. additions down to the 16th cent. Other additions have been made *passim.*

Fos. 120. 9⅜ × 6⅞ in.

❡ *Other registers etc.*

For further registers etc. at Norwich, see also Riley, *l.c.*

713. **Ditto**, 'Reg. IX'. Letter-book, early 14th cent. (*temp.* Edw. II).

714. **Ditto**, 'Reg. X'. Part of a misc. 14th cent. register of *Acta*, incl. copies of contemp. royal and episcopal documents.

715. **Ditto**, 'Reg. *x*'. 'Proficuum Maneriorum Prioris et Conventus,' 14th cent. (*temp.* Edw. II–III).

716. **BM., Stowe 936.** 'Terrarium Prioratus.' Rentals, 14th cent. *FO:* T. Martin; J. Ives; T. Astle.

NORWICH co. Norf.
Ben. Priory (Nuns), Carrow *f.* 1146

717. **Untraced.** Cartulary from which extracts, 16th cent., from fos. 18–20, are in Bodl., Tanner 342, fo. 150.

NORWICH co. Norf.
Hosp. of St. Giles *f.* 1246

718. **Norwich, Corporation Muniment Room** (case 24). Composite cartulary, 13th–16th cent., comprising: (1) fos. 1–32 (15th cent., rubricated), copies of deeds arranged by parishes etc.; (2) fos. 33–42, added leaves with additions down to the 16th cent.; (3) fos. 43–71 (13th cent., rubricated), copies of deeds, without obvious arrangement, followed by rentals; with additions on added leaves etc. *passim.*

Fos. 71. 12½ × 8½ in.

❡ *Other registers etc.*

719. **Ditto** (case 24). Copies, late 14th cent., of charters, rentals etc. rel. the parish of St. Stephen, Norwich. Paper roll, 50 × 12 in.

NORWICH co. Norf.
Hosp. of St. Paul *f.* bef. 1119
No cartulary recorded.

❡ *Other registers etc.*

720. **BM., Cotton Roll ii. 19.** *Inspeximus* of charters by John (Salmon), bp. of Norwich, 1301.

NOSTELL co. York
Aug. Priory *f. c.* 1114
v. also TOCKWITH.

721. **BM., Cotton Vesp. E. xix.** Gen.

cartulary (fos. 4–135), 13th cent. (aft. 1263), with rubrics and red and blue decorated initials. Arranged mainly topographically with sections of royal and episcopal charters, fines, and charters rel. churches and the almonry, at the beginning (incomplete) and *passim*. Followed (fos. 136–83) by a supplement, aft. 1294, with rubrics and plain red initials. Further additions, incl. a 15th cent. index of places (fos. iv–2), have been made *passim*. Extracts, 1632, are in Bodl., Dodsworth 138 (*SC*. 5078), fos. 1–158.

Fos. 186 (medieval pagination, 5–447, from fo. 4; earlier foliation of fos. 4–135, iii–clxxi; wants leaves *passim*). 11½ × 7½ in. (cropped). *FO:* Col. Charles Fairfax, 1632; Christopher, baron Hatton.

❡ *Other registers etc.*

722.   **BM., Royal App. 85,** fos. 31–4. Fragm., much mutilated, of a late 15th cent. register. Copies, notes etc. of corrodies, *Tituli* and a few deeds, 1485–1500. *FO:* the Cotton Libr. (?).

723.   **Lord St. Oswald,** Nostell Priory. Misc. 15th–16th cent. register of rentals and other material incl. (pp. 158 ff.) copies of deeds, leases etc. Paper, fos. 119. W. T. Lancaster, 'A Fifteenth Century Rental of Nostell Priory' (Yorks. Arch. Soc., Record ser. lxi, 1920), 108 ff. (description and pp. 24–84 (rental) printed).

NOTLEY   co. Bucks.
Aug. Abbey   *f.* 1162
724.   **Untraced.** Cartulary *penes* Sir John Dormer, 16th–17th cent., and the Earl of Abingdon, at Rycote, 1733. Apparently arranged topographically. Extracts, 1610, by Sir R. Grenville in San Marino, Huntington Libr. (ST. 1) are noticed by J. G. Jenkins, 'The Lost Cartulary of Nutley Abbey', *Huntington Libr. Quart.* xvii (1954), 379–96; others, 16th cent., are in Bodl., Dugdale 39 (*SC*. 6527), fos. 68–73v and, down to fo. 96, in BM., Cotton Titus F. vi, fos. 3–5, 70. Reported to have been destroyed at Rycote, mid-19th cent., with an Abingdon cartulary, see H. E. Salter, *Remarks and Collections of Thomas Hearne* xi (Oxford Hist. Soc. lxxii, 1921), 166; but for the latter's survival, see No. 5 above.

❡ *Other registers etc.*

725.   **Oxford, Christ Church,** Treas-

ury. Exemplification, mid-16th cent., of charters of the abbey, made apparently at or after its dissolution, for official use. Written on 23 leaves of vellum, 27 × 22 in., tied with vellum loops at the foot, and arranged topographically. The places concerned are Hillesden, Caversham, Maiden Bradley, Nether Swell, Lyford, Dorton, Pollicott and Claydon.

NUN COTHAM   co. Linc.
Cist. Priory (Nuns)   *f. c.* 1150
726.   **Oxford, Bodl., Top. Lincs. d. 1** (*SC*. 29005). Gen. cartulary (fos. 1–40), early 13th cent., with rubrics and spaces for initials. Arranged mainly topographically, with the copies of papal and royal charters at the beginning, and followed by additions, mainly 13th and 14th cent., incl. a diagram of a plough (fo. 53) and a drawing of a ship (fo. 36). Medieval binding. Extracts, 17th cent., are in *ib.*, Dodsworth 75 (*SC*. 5017), fos. 21–2, 29–34.

Fos. ii + 78 (ink foliation, 1–71, excl. some insertions). 11¼ × 8½ in. *FO:* the North fam., barons North and earls of Guilford, 17th–19th cent.

NUNEATON   co. Warw.
Ben. Priory (Order of Fontevrault)
                                             f. c. 1155
727.   **Untraced.** Roll of charters *penes* the Dean & Chapter of Lichfield, 1638, from which nine royal, papal, episcopal and baronial charters are copied in Bodl., Dugdale 12 (*SC*. 6502), pp. 259–66.

NUNKEELING   co. York
Ben. Priory   *f.* 1152
728.   **BM., Cotton Otho C. viii,** fos. 65–95. Gen. cartulary, 16th cent., written for Joan Alanson, prioress 1521–36, with titles and initials (sometimes pen-decorated) in black. Arranged topographically and incl. copies of one or two royal and episcopal charters *passim*. Extracts, 17th cent., are in Bodl., Dodsworth 118 (*SC*. 5059), fo. 83.

Fos. 31. 7½ × 5 in. (shrunk and damaged by fire, 1731).

OGBOURNE   co. Wilts
Ben. Priory   *f.* 12th cent.
The extant material rel. the English possessions of the Abbey of Bec (incl.

Ruislip Priory), which from the mid-13th cent. were administered from Ogbourne, is surveyed by Marjorie Morgan, *The English Lands of the Abbey of Bec* (Oxford, 1946), 3–8, 151–2; cf. Marjorie Chibnall, *Select Documents of the English Lands of the Abbey of Bec* (Camden Third ser. lxxiii, 1951).

729.   **Windsor, St. George's Chapel,** Muniments (xi. G. 11). Copies, early 13th cent., with red titles, of 38 episcopal, royal, papal and other charters etc., 1086–1199, rel. the lands, churches etc. of Bec in England. Ed. M. Chibnall, *op. cit.*, ix–x, 1 ff.

Roll, 90 × 6½ in.

ORMSBY, NORTH (*al.* NUN)
co. Linc.
Gilb. Priory   *f.* 1148–54

730.   **Untraced.** Cartulary *penes* Robert Rockley of Rockley, co. York, 1638 (*D*). Extracts, 1632, down to fo. 275 by R. Dodsworth in Bodl., Dodsworth 135 (*SC.* 5076), fos. 139–61, describe it as *penes* '— Rookely de Skires', the material extracted extending down to the late 13th cent. and incl. one or two episcopal charters.

OSNEY   co. Oxon
Aug. Abbey   *f.* (as a priory) 1129
H. E. Salter, *Cartulary of Oseney Abbey*, 6 vols. (Oxford Hist. Soc. lxxxix–xci, xcvii–viii, ci, 1929–36), edits the cartularies and original deeds collectively.

731.   **BM., Cotton Vit. E. xv.** Gen. cartulary, *c.* 1200, written in double columns with rubrics etc. and blue, green or light brown initials. Arranged in sections, apparently topographically, and incl. copies of royal and episcopal charters *passim*. Preceded (fos. 1–3) by Annals. Misc. additions, mainly 13th cent., on blank leaves etc. between the sections *passim* and at the end, include (fos. 175 ff.) copies of a series of leases etc. by the abbey, and (fos. 267–75) a 13th–14th cent. index. A detached leaf, apparently once with fos. 258–66 (additions), is now **BM., Add. 4783,** fo. 16 (10⅝ × 7½ in. *FO:* Sir J. Ware; Henry, 2nd earl of Clarendon (part of MS. 15); James, 1st duke of Chandos; J. Milles, D.D.).

Fos. 275 (wants leaves *passim*). 8½ × 6 in. (shrunk and damaged by fire, 1731, and the leaves now mounted). *FO:* Augustine Steward, 1596; Mr. Geffe, 1599.

732.   **Oxford, Bodl., Bodley 477** (*SC.* 2005), fos. ii, iv. *Capitula*, early 13th cent., for a cartulary not known to have been executed. Written partly in red on two blank leaves at the beginning of a 12th cent. MS. of H. de St. Victor, 'De Sacramentis', with some red and green initials etc.

Fos. 2 (iv + 63 in the MS.). 9¼ × 6¼ in. (cropped). *FO:* the libraries of Osney and St. George's Chapel, Windsor; T. Breson; T. Clarke; J. Price; J. Davies, D.D., 1601.

733.   **Oxford, Christ Church,** Chapter Libr. Cartulary, *c.* 1280–4, of the abbey's possessions outside Oxford, with rubrics, plain red or blue initials etc. and additions *passim*. Arranged topographically by *Tituli* (*v–cxxxvii*), grouped by *Ballive*, and incl. copies of some royal etc. charters rel. the abbey's foundation etc. under the *Balliva de Oseneya* (fos. 9–35), and others, with papal, episcopal etc. charters, *passim*. An incomplete contemp. Table, originally at the beginning, is now bound as the last leaf.

Fos. 352 (post-medieval foliation, 1–362, with some errors; wants a few leaves *passim*). 11¾ × 7¾ in. *FO:* W. Cope, 1586; Sir R. Cotton.

734.   **PRO., Exch., K.R.** (Misc. Bks. i. 26). Cartulary in two parts: (1) fos. 1–61, a 15th cent. (*c.* 1460 ?) English translation of No. 733, with uncompleted rubrication, extending down to fo. 93 of that MS. (Barford) and incl. a few entries now wanting there; ed. A. Clark, *The English Register of Oseney Abbey*, 2 vols. (Early Engl. Text Soc., Orig. ser. cxxxiii, cxliv, 1907, 1913 for 1912); (2) fos. 66–112, copies, 16th cent. (aft. 1513), with some rather crude pen-work decoration, of 48 papal charters etc. to the abbey.

Fos. iv + 114. 12 × 9¼ in. Paper.

735.   **Untraced.** Cartulary (?) from which copies, 16th cent., of 23 deeds etc. (mainly 13th cent.) down to *temp.* Hen. IV, rel. Weston-on-the-Green etc., are among Bodl., d.d. Bertie c. 13 (a loose quire of paper, fos. 18 incl. blank leaves, folio). Not obviously identifiable with any of the preceding. Contained upwards of 140 fos.

OSPRINGE co. Kent
Hosp. of St. Mary *f.* bef. 1234
v. also No. 155 above.

736. **Cambridge, St. John's Coll.,**
MS. Aa. 1. 59. Cartulary, late 13th cent.
(aft. 1285), with titles etc. in the hand of the
text (except fo. 1, rubricated). Contains
copies of private deeds, numbered consecutively, preceded (fos. ii–iv) by a contemp. Table; with one or two added
memoranda at fo. iv. M. R. James, *Cat.*
MSS. St. John's Coll. (Cambridge, 1913),
no. 507.

Fos. vi + 66 (wants one or two leaves at
the end). $10\frac{1}{4} \times 6\frac{1}{2}$ in.

OTTERTON co. Devon
Ben. Priory *f. temp.* Will. II
737. **Lord Coleridge,** Ottery St. Mary.
Register of evidences etc. compiled, 1260,
by Prior G. Legat, with later additions.
Comprises a kalendar, custumary, rentals,
extracts from Domesday etc., followed
(pp. 45–93) by a cartulary of royal, episcopal and lay grants interspersed with
other misc. material and some blank
leaves. G. Oliver, *Mon. Exon.* (1846),
256–9 (abstract).

Fos. 48 (17th cent. pagination, 1–93,
excl. fly-leaves; wants leaves *passim*). $6\frac{3}{8} \times$
9 in. *FO:* J. Anstis (*T*); the Rev. D.
Yonge; F. Coleridge, 1833.

OWSTON co. Leic.
Aug. Abbey *f.* bef. 1161
738. **Cambridge U.L., Dd. 3. 87,** art.
20 (bound separately). Fragms. of a 15th
cent. cartulary with red underlinings of
titles etc. Arranged topographically and
incl. copies of a few royal, papal and episcopal documents *passim. Cambr. U.L. Cat.*
MSS. i, 204–10 (list of contents).

Fos. 25 (wants leaves aft. fos. 16, 20).
$10\frac{1}{2} \times 7$ in.

OXFORD co. Oxon
Priory of St. Frideswide *f.* 1002
S. R. Wigram, *Cartulary of the Monastery*
of St. Frideswide, 2 vols. (Oxford Hist. Soc.
xxviii, xxxi, 1895–6), edits Nos. 739–40.
739. **Oxford, C.C.C. MS. 160,** deposited in the Bodleian Libr. Two distinct
cartularies bound up together: (1) pp. 1–
270, cartulary of lands etc. in Oxford,
13th–14th cent. (*temp.* A. de Sutton?, prior

1294–1316), with rubrics etc. and red or
blue paragraphs; arranged in sections
mainly by parishes (pp. 205–21, obedientiaries; pp. 223–70, leases), with 14th cent.
additions *passim*; (2) pp. 271–330, cartulary,
in a succession of 13th cent. hands and incomplete at the end, containing copies of
royal (down to *temp.* Hen. III), papal, episcopal and private charters, without
obvious arrangement, many of the latter
being duplicated in (1), and a number of
others relating to Elsfield.

Fos. 165 (post-medieval pagination, 1–
330). $11\frac{3}{8} \times 8\frac{1}{8}$ in. (cropped). *FO:* T. Allen;
B. Twyne, 1624.

740. **Oxford, Christ Church,** Chapter
Libr. General cartulary, 15th cent. (*temp.*
Hen. VI), written in double columns with
rubrics and red or blue initials etc., and a
few misc. additions *passim*. Arranged
in sections mainly topographically with
the royal, episcopal, papal and other
general charters grouped mainly at the
beginning (pp. 7–72) and those for Oxford,
by parishes, at the end (pp. 303 ff.).

Fos. 258 (post-medieval pagination, 1–
512, omitting fly-leaves). $15\frac{3}{4} \times 11$ in.

OXFORD co. Oxon
Hosp. of St. Bartholomew *f.* bef. 1129
No cartulary recorded.
¶ *Other registers etc.*
741. **PRO., Chancery** (Miscellanea, C.
47/9/7). Copies, 13th–14th cent., of six
royal and two papal privileges, 12th–13th
cent. (a roll).

OXFORD co. Oxon
Hosp. of St. John Bapt. *f.* bef. 1180
742. **Oxford, Magdalen Coll., MS.**
Lat. 275 (formerly Muniments, Arch. C. ii.
3. 13). Gen. cartulary, 13th cent. (aft.
1274), with some of the initials etc. touched
with red. Arranged in sections topographically, with occasional additions incl.
a 15th cent. index of places on the front fly-
leaf. Written apparently by Richard de
Epwell, a professional writer. The Oxford
material (fos. 1–53), arranged by parishes,
is printed with other evidences by H. E.
Salter, *Cartulary of the Hospital of St. John*
the Baptist, 3 vols. (Oxford Hist. Soc. lxvi,
lxviii, lxix, 1914–16).

Fos. 141 + 6. 11×7 in.

OXFORD co. Oxon
Merton Coll. *f.* 1262–4

743. **Oxford, Merton Coll.,** Muniments, 'Liber Ruber' (1. 1). Inventory of the muniments with short abstracts of the deeds, *c.* 1288. Red and blue page headings, marginal pressmarks etc. Arranged mainly topographically, by counties, with the general charters at the beginning and misc. later additions *passim*. A 17th–18th cent. transcript is *ib.*, Muniments 5. 1; a 19th cent. index and analysis is kept in the college Estates Bursary. P. S. Allen & H. W. Garrod, *Merton Muniments* (Oxford, 1928), 29 and pl. ix.

Fos. ii + 36. 11¼ × 8 in.

744. **Ditto,** 'Liber Collegii de Merton' (2. 7). Composite register comprising about six small 14th and 15th cent. compilations, put together apparently at a post-medieval date. Contains copies of misc. evidences and memoranda rel. the college's lands, churches etc., incl. some royal and episcopal documents and sections of 13th–14th cent. deeds for Gamlingay etc.

Fos. *c.* 110. 15 × 10½ in. etc. (irregular).

OXFORD co. Oxon
New Coll. *f.* 1379

745. **Oxford, New Coll.,** Muniments, 'Registrum Secundum'. Register of deeds, 15th–16th cent., in a number of hands. Includes (fos. 1–56) a section headed 'Copia virium et omnium privilegiorum ecclesie Sancti Walerici in Anglia', apparently transcribed from a register, now lost, of Takeley Priory.

Fos. 238. 14¾ × 9¾ in.

746. **Ditto,** 'Liber Niger'. Uncompleted register of deeds etc., *c.* 1530, ruled in red with alternate red and blue initials (sometimes decorated) etc. Fos. 1–46 are apparently transcribed from a register, now lost, of Newton Longville Priory, cf. H. E. Salter, *Newington Longeville Charters* (Oxfordshire Record Soc. iii, 1921), xi–xii, xxx etc.

Fos. 216. 17½ × 13 in.

⁋ *Other registers etc.*

747. **Ditto,** 'Registrum Primum' *al.* 'The White Book'. Act Book, 15th–16th cent.

748. **Ditto,** 'Evidence Books'. Five large 17th cent. registers of deeds, written by William Ball, yeoman beadle of Oxford University, and completed in 1661.

OXFORD co. Oxon
Oriel Coll. *f.* 1326

v. also OXFORD, Hosp. of St. Bartholomew, above.

No cartulary recorded.

⁋ *Inventory*

749. **BM., Lansdowne 386.** Inventory of deeds made, 1397, by the provost and fellows and arranged 'per villas et per campos, per parochias et per vicos', with later additions *passim*. Preceded (fos. 2–7) by a kalendar incl. some names of benefactors and once followed by a copy of the college statutes, now Bodl., Rawlinson Statutes 45. Ed. C. L. Shadwell & H. E. Salter, *Oriel College Records* (Oxford Hist. Soc. lxxxv, 1926), 438–94.

Fos. 52 + 3. 9½ × 6¾ in. *FO:* Richard Graves, 1727 (having been sent to London by the college for a lawsuit, 1726); James West.

OXFORD co. Oxon
St. Mary Magdalen Coll. *f.* 1448

749A. **Oxford, Magdalen Coll.,** Muniments (Adds. 97). Cartulary, late 15th cent., with additions, of deeds rel. the college's properties in cos. Norf. and Suff. Modern binding (originally a roll).

Fos. 33. 30 × 9 in. Paper.

PENRYN co. Cornw.
Coll. of St. Thomas M., Glasney *f.* 1265

750. **W. S. Rashleigh Esq.** (d. 1957), Stoketon. Register, *c.* 1440, of charters and other material incl. a kalendar, statutes, appropriations and taxations of churches, etc. Some red and blue decoration of initials. Index of contents on the last leaf. J. A. C. Vincent, 'The Glasney Cartulary', *Royal Inst. Cornwall J.* vi (1878–81), 213–58 (abstract). T. C. Peter, *Glasney Collegiate Church* (Camborne, 1903), prints a partial analysis with two pls.

Fos. 97. 8 × 6 in. *FO:* Mr. Parsons, an auditor of the Exchequer, 1706 (*T*); J. Mickleton, 1712; J. Rowe; the Rev. W. G. L. Wasey; J. Rashleigh, Menabilly, 1878.

PENTNEY co. Norf.
Aug. Priory *f.* bef. 1135

751. **Anthony Hamond Esq.,** c/o the

Norfolk Record Soc., Norwich. Fragm. (parts of at least two quires) of a 13th cent. cartulary written (fos. 2–6) in a large, rather square charter hand with rubrics etc. Additions (fos. 1, 6 ff.), down to *temp.* Edw. I, include copies of one or two royal and papal documents and (fo. 1v) a feodary of Witchingham. The material otherwise relates mainly to Thurton and Shottesham. Fos. 10. 11½ × 7 in.

752.   **Untraced.** Register *penes* the Duke of Rutland, Belvoir Castle, 17th cent. (*D*).

PENWORTHAM   co. Lanc.
Ben. Priory   *f. c.* 1140
v. No. 382 above.

PERSHORE   co. Worc.
Ben. Abbey   *f. c.* 972
753.   **PRO., Exch., Augm. Off.** (Misc. Bks. 61). Gen. cartulary written in a number of 13th–14th cent. hands with rubrics etc., uncompleted red initials, and 14th cent. additions. Arranged in sections topographically, with copies of episcopal etc. documents and compositions at the end (fos. 104–119) and of royal documents *passim.* A 19th cent. transcript (*FO:* Sir T. Phillipps, MS. 25087) is in Birmingham Reference Libr. (438133). *Mon. Angl.* ii, 413 ff. (partial list of contents etc. and extracts).

Fos. 122 (incl. fly-leaves; wants a leaf aft. fo. 49). 11½ × 8 in. *FO:* W. Bell, 1598 (from a bookseller in Fleet St.); delivered to the keeper of the records of the Augmentation Court, 1620.

PETERBOROUGH   co. Northt.
Ben. Abbey   *f. c.* 655
W. T. Mellows, *Henry of Pytchley's Book of Fees* (Northants. Record Soc. ii, 1927), edits No. 770 and describes the other registers, pp. xxv–xxxvii, 156–7. His photostat copies of those elsewhere are now in Peterborough Cathedral Libr. and his transcripts are with the Northants. Record Soc. For material at Peterborough, see also J. A. Bennett, *HMC. Twelfth Report*, App. ix (1891), 580–5.

754.   **London, Soc. of Antiquaries, MS. 60.** 'Liber Niger.' A composite misc. register incl. (fos. 6–74) a survey of the abbey's manors, *c.* 1125–8, written in 12th cent. book-hand with rubrics and plain red initials, and incorporating copies of a

number of early royal, papal and other charters to the abbey *passim.* The rest of the volume consists of misc. surveys, pleas, lists of fees and other material rel. the abbey's lands, 12th–14th cent., incl. occasional further copies of charters, Annals and other historical material (for which see T. Stapleton, *Chronicon Petroburgense* (Camden Soc., Old ser. xlvii, 1849)) and (fos. 81–3) an inventory of the abbot's muniments (No. 763 below). An 18th cent. transcript is *ib.*, MS. 131. H. Ellis, *Cat. MSS. Soc. Ant.* (1816), 22–9 and *Mon. Angl.* i, 372 (*a*), list the contents, the latter with extracts, pp. 380 ff.

Fos. 264. 10 × 6½ in. *FO:* Sir R. Wingfield; Brownlow, 9th earl of Exeter.

755.   **BM., Egerton 2733.** 'Liber Cartarum et Privilegiorum Johannis de Trikyngham Prioris.' A small 13th cent. register (aft. 1253) with rubrics etc. and red and blue initials and capitals. Contains copies of sixty royal and papal privileges etc. to the abbey, 7th–13th cent., followed (fo. 125) by a feodary and other misc. material, with a Table at fos. 4–6 and a few misc. additions at fos. 6v–11 etc. *BM. Cat. Add. MSS.* 1888–1893, 464–6.

Fos. 199. 3½ × 2¾ in. *FO:* Sir R. Wingfield, 1636, by gift of Ld. Fitzwilliam of Milton; T. Toon, 19th cent.

756.   **Peterborough, D. & C., MS. 5.** 'Liber Cartarum et Privilegiorum Henrici de Pyghtele (*al.* Pytchley) junioris.' Cartulary, mid-13th cent., with rubrics, red initials decorated with blue and some additions, incl. a late 14th cent. Table on 14 preliminary leaves. Contains copies of grants to and by the abbey, early 13th cent., sometimes with marginal notes of the obedientiaries concerned, preceded by notes and copies of royal charters and other misc. material.

Fos. 19 + 219. 7⅝ × 5⅝ in. *FO:* H. Cromwell; Mr. Coates, attorney; restored to the See by Bp. T. White, 1694, and to the Dean & Chapter by the Rev. T. Neve, 1742.

757.   **Ditto, MS. 1.** 'Liber R. de Swaffham.' Gen. cartulary, mid-13th cent., with rubrics and red and blue decorated initials, preceded by a chronicle down to 1246. Arranged with the royal, papal and episcopal charters mainly at the beginning, followed by grants of the abbot to indi-

vidual obedientiaries and copies of other charters without obvious arrangement. Misc. additions *passim*, mainly rel. the abbey's lands, include towards the end some statutes of the Realm and the 'Gesta Herwardi' (ed. C. T. Martin, *Lestorie des Engles* i (Rolls ser., 1888), 339–404). Table, 13th cent., on 10 preliminary leaves. The MS. is described by Martin, *op. cit.*, xlvii–liii.

Fos. ii + 16 + 374. $12\frac{1}{4} \times 9$ in.

758.   **BM., Add. 39758.** 'Liber Walteri de Wytlese' (*al.* Whittlesey), *c.* 1322–9, elaborately written in book-hand with rubrics, illuminated initials and occasional miniatures. Contains the 'Passio SS. Wulfhadi et Ruffini', a chronicle of the abbey down to 1321 and an extent and rental (1321) of the demesne manors, followed (fos. 161–280) by sections of papal privileges, 1146–1296, and royal charters, 664–1329, with misc. additions of a similar nature written in the margins etc. *passim*. *BM. Cat. Add. MSS.* 1916–1920, 172–6, and references there cited.

Fos. 300 (incl. about 50 blank leaves). $9\frac{3}{4} \times 6\frac{1}{8}$ in. *FO:* the Fitzwilliam fam., Milton Hall.

759.   **London, Soc. of Antiquaries, MS. 38.** 'Maior Liber Fratris Johannis Achirche,' Register, mid-14th cent., of charters and other evidences, incl. copies of some royal documents, all apparently rel. the abbey's rights, privileges etc. Rubrics, red and blue decorated initials, paragraphs etc. and some later additions *passim*. Originally arranged to some extent according to subject-matter but now bound in considerable disorder with a later 14th cent. Table at fos. 3v–6v. Includes, among the misc. contents, copies of general charters of liberties etc., inquisitions, compositions, accounts of legal proceedings, lists of fees etc. An 18th cent. transcript is *ib.*, MS. 126. H. Ellis, *op. cit.*, 8–17 (complete list of contents); *Mon. Angl.* i, 373 (*a*) (partial list). Cf. also No. 762.

Fos. i + 236 (contemp. roman foliation, in disorder). $8 \times 5\frac{5}{8}$ in. *FO:* Brownlow, 9th earl of Exeter.

760.   **Peterborough, D. & C., MS. 6.** 'Achirch Rubrum', i.e. the 'Red' or 'Lesser' book of John of Achurch. Similar in date and execution to No. 759 and contains a section (fos. 9–32) of royal charters,

10th–14th cent., followed by copies of pleas. Later 14th cent. Table, fos. 3–8.

Fos. 197 (contemp. foliation, v–ccxiii, from fo. 2). $8 \times 5\frac{3}{4}$ in. Restored to the Cathedral, 1714, by Francis Peck.

761.   **Ditto, MS. 39.** Register, mid-14th cent., without decoration, containing, in addition to extents and other misc. material, sections entitled: (*a*) fos. 1–87, 'Carte Nativorum de Burgo', i.e. notes of grants to private individuals in various places by bondmen of the demesne manors; (*b*) fos. 98–115, 'Carte Antiquorum Registrorum Precentoris', i.e. copies of 53 grants by the abbey etc., 12th–13th cent. Described by W. T. Mellows, *Northants. Notes & Queries*, New ser. v (1921–3), 82–6.

Fos. 148. $7\frac{3}{4} \times 4\frac{3}{4}$ in. *FO:* the Fitzwilliam fam., Milton Hall; W. T. Mellows.

762.   **BM., Cotton Cleop. C. i,** fos. 35–157; **Cleop. C. ii,** fos. 1–165. Cartulary etc., late 14th cent., with rubrics, red and blue paragraphs, red foliation and touching of letters etc., now bound in two parts but originally a single and continuous compilation. A contemp. Table at the beginning shows the contents to be virtually identical with those of No. 759 apart from a lack of some material at the end.

Fos. 288. $5\frac{1}{4} \times 7\frac{1}{2}$ in.

⁋ *Inventory*

763.   **London, Soc. of Antiquaries, MS. 60,** fos. 81–3. Inventory, mid-13th cent., of the abbot's muniments, written in double columns with rubrics, red touching of letters etc. and arranged topographically by counties etc. Now bound up in the 'Liber Niger' (No. 754 above).

Fos. 3. $10 \times 6\frac{1}{2}$ in. *FO:* as No. 754.

⁋ *Sacristarius*

764.   **The Duke of Buccleuch,** Boughton House, Kettering. 'Registrum Fratris Georgii Fraunceys Sacriste', 1404, with headings (boxed) in the hand of the text and some later additions. Contains copies of deeds, extents, rentals etc., 12th–15th cent., rel. the sacrist's lands etc., arranged by places, which are listed by Mellows, *op. cit.*, xxxvi. Medieval binding.

Fos. 224. $10\frac{3}{8} \times 7\frac{1}{4}$ in. *FO:* the Duke of Montagu, Boughton, 1714.

765.   **BM., Cotton Faust. B. iii,** fos. 1–157. A second register of George Fraunceys, in two parts: (1) fos. 8–92 (similar in date and appearance to No. 764

and perhaps originally a part of it, the quires being lettered *k–x* in a contemp. hand), copies of deeds and rentals rel. Pillsgate, Barnack, Bainton etc., co. Northt.; (2) fos. 93–157, contemp. copies of 14th cent. rentals for the same places, with a few 14th–15th cent. additions and corrections.

Fos. 157. 9¾ × 6¾ in. (cropped).

¶ *Other registers etc.*

766.   **BM., Cotton Vesp. E. xxii.** 'The White Book.' Register of W. de Woodford and G. de Croyland, abbots 1295–1321. *FO:* Sir R. Wingfield, 1636; Christopher, baron Hatton, 1637.

767.   **BM., Cotton Vesp. E. xxi,** fos. 45–106. Register of A. de Boothby, abbot 1321–38. *FO:* as No. 766.

768.   **BM., Add. 25288.** Register of W. Genge and J. Deeping, abbots 1396–1438. *FO:* Ld. Robert Montagu.

769.   **Peterborough, D. & C., MS. 2.** 'The Book of Roger Bird.' Register of R. de Ashton and W. de Ramsay, abbots 1438–96.

770.   **Ditto, MS. 7.** 'Liber Feodorum … Henrici de Pygthysle (*al.* Pytchley).' An account of the abbey's fees and lands, late 14th cent., incl. copies of a few misc. charters *passim*. Ed. W. T. Mellows, *op. cit.* Described by A. Hamilton Thompson, *Engl. Hist. Review* xxxiv (1919), 582–4. *FO:* the Fitzwilliam fam., Milton Hall; the Rev. W. H. Hutton.

771.   **BM., Cotton Nero C. vii,** fos. 85–215. Rentals, 14th–15th cent.

772.   **Destroyed.** The former Cotton MS. Otho A. xvii, fos. 94–136, which was burnt in 1731, is described by T. Smith, *Cat. Bibl. Cotton.* (Oxford, 1696), *ad loc.*, as 'Registrum terrarum & praediorum … cum nominibus Tenentium & consuetudinibus & servitutibus debitis'. It was bound with historical and other misc. material rel. Peterborough.

773.   **BM., Cotton Vesp. A. xxiv.** Accompt and memorandum book of Wm. Morton, almoner, 1448–67. Ed. W. T. Mellows, P. I. King and C. N. L. Brooke, *The Book of William Morton* (Northants. Record Soc. xvi, 1954 for 1952–3).

PIPEWELL   co. Northt.
Cist. Abbey   *f.* 1143
774.   **BM., Add. 37022.** The first part

(quires *i–v*, cf. No. 775) of a mid-13th cent. cartulary ('Rubeus Liber cartarum') containing copies of private and a few episcopal charters, arranged mainly topographically. The whole written in sections in two apparently contemp. mid-13th cent. hands, with rubrics and plain red or red and blue decorated initials, and supplemented in a third rather later hand (plain red or blue initials), with further additions in a number of hands *passim*. *BM. Cat. Add. MSS.* 1900–1905, 290.

Fos. 40. 9¼ × 6 in. *FO:* the Soc. of Antiquaries, London (Rolls & Ch. 33).

775.   **BM., Stowe 937.** Further parts of No. 774, with which they are now bound, viz. quires *vii–x, xvi, xxv–xxx* (with part of *vi* misbound in *xxviii* as fos. 69–72), followed (fos. 91 ff.) by other unnumbered quires. Concludes (fos. 114–31) with sections of 'Carte de Terris pertinentibus ad Hospicium' and fines, followed by misc. additions. *BM. Cat. Stowe MSS.* i, 619–21.

Fos. i + 157 (18th cent. pagination, 1–296). 9¼ × 6 in. *FO:* T. Astle.

776.   **BM., Cotton Calig. A. xii,** fos. 8–159. The first part (quires *i–xix*, cf. No. 777) of a 13th cent. gen. cartulary (aft. 1259), with uncompleted rubrication etc. and red initials. Contains copies of deeds etc., incl. some episcopal and occasional royal etc. documents, arranged topographically in sections, the material for some places being preceded by a short introductory narrative. *Mon. Angl.* v, 434 (*a*), lists the heads of sections.

Fos. 152. 9 × 6 in.

777.   **BM., Cotton Calig. A. xiii,** fos. 18–197. Continuation of No. 776, viz. quires *xx–xxxviii* (with part of *iv* misbound as fos. 170–1), followed (fos. 172–97) by a section of misc. 14th cent. etc. additions. *Mon. Angl., l.c.*

Fos. 180. 9 × 6 in.

778.   **BM., Cotton Otho B. xiv,** fos. 150–204. 'Speculum Fratris Willi(elmi) de Lalleford,' abbot *c.* 1320–2 etc. Notes, 14th cent. (*temp.* Edw. II), in narrative form, of grants and other memoranda rel. the abbey's lands, with some decoration of initials, occasionally in red. The material is arranged topographically and apparently extracted from cartularies. Misc. additions at the end include a slightly later Table (fos.

201–3) and list of abbots (fo. 197). *Mon. Angl.* v, 434 (*a*).

Fos. 55. 11½ × 8 in. *FO:* Sir R. Cotton; J. Payne (MS. 30); Egerton, bookseller, 1787.

¶ *Other registers etc.*

779.   **BM., Cotton Julius A. i,** fos. 65–70. Fragm. of a late 14th cent. etc. register containing copies of grants by the abbots and other misc. memoranda, 13th–14th cent.

PLYMPTON   co. Devon
Aug. Priory   *f.* 1121

780.   **Untraced.** Gen. cartulary written by M. de Mimminglond, prior 1305–32, with additions down to the 15th cent. Extracts from fos. 1–256, incl. notes of royal, papal and episcopal charters and a list of priors, are in Bodl., James 23 (*SC.* 3860), pp. 151–70 (from a copy supplied, 1627, by Sir John Eliot, M.P.) and BM., Harley 6974, fos. 28–30 (from notes by Bp. T. Tanner, 1698, when the MS. was *penes* Bp. J. Moore). The cartulary reported as *penes* —— Strode of Plymouth, 1725 (*Mon. Angl.* vi, 52) was perhaps not of the priory but of the Strode fam., Newnham Park, cf. No. 1324 below.

¶ *Other registers etc.*

781.   **BM., Harley 4766.** Rentals, 1408.

PONTEFRACT   co. York
Clun. Priory   *f. c.* 1090

782.   **Comdr. M. E. Wentworth,** deposited at Leeds, Yorks. Arch. Soc. Libr. (DD. 57. B). Gen. cartulary, mid-13th cent. (aft. 1240), written in double columns with rubrics, red, blue or occasionally green initials and misc. additions *passim*. Arranged in eleven sections, mainly topographically, with the copies of founders', ecclesiastical (incl. papal) and royal (from Stephen) charters at the beginning, and of leases by the priory at the end (fos. 76–82). Six unnumbered preliminary leaves contain an incomplete contemp. Table, with postmedieval continuation, and an index of places. Ed. R. Holmes, *Chartulary of . . . Pontefract*, 2 vols. (Yorks. Arch. Soc., Record ser. xxv, xxx, 1899 for 1898, 1902 for 1901).

Fos. viii + 89. 11½ × 7½ in. *FO:* T. Levet, 17th cent.; R. Dodsworth, 1627; Sir T.

Widdrington, 1652; the Wentworth fam., Woolley Hall, presumably through Thomas, Ld. Fairfax.

PONTEFRACT   co. York
Knolles (*al.* Holy Trinity) Coll. and Almshouse   *f.* 1385

783.   **Oxford, Bodl., Barlow 49** (*SC.* 6414), fos. 115–65. Composite cartulary written in a number of 14th and 15th cent. hands, with a few later additions. Contains copies, without obvious arrangement, of about 283 deeds etc., *temp.* Edw. I–*c.* 1410 etc.

Fos. 51 (wants 2 leaves aft. fo. 159) 14¾ × 10¾ in. *FO:* Francis Bunney, 1619; Sir R. Cotton; borrowed by Dr. J. Prideaux.

PONTEFRACT   co. York
Hosp. of St. Nicholas   *f.* bef. 1066

784.   **Untraced.** Cartulary or coucherbook in the keeping of Alderman Skipton, 1619, and subsequently of Alderman Christopher Favell. Extracts, 17th cent., down to fo. 32, are in Bodl., Dodsworth 116 (*SC.* 5057), fos. 19–27; 118 (*SC.* 5059), fo. 152; Top. Yorks. c. 41, fo. 50.

PORTSWOOD   co. Southt.
v. SOUTHAMPTON.

POULTON   co. Chest.
Cist. Abbey   *f.* 1153
v. DIEULACRES.

PRESTON   co. Lanc.
Hosp. of St. Mary M.   *f.* bef. 1177

785.   **PRO., Duchy of Lanc.** (Cartae Misc. iii, fos. 28–33). Fragm. of a 14th cent. cartulary, without decoration. Begins and ends in the middle of entries and includes copies of two or three royal documents *passim*.

Fos. 12. 7¾ × 5½ in.

PYNHAM   co. Suss.
Aug. Priory   *f.* bef. 1151

786.   **PRO., Exch., T.R.** (Ancient Deeds, AA. 388). Copies, late 13th cent. (*temp.* Edw. I), with marginal titles, of about 15 royal (Queen Adeliza), episcopal, baronial and private charters.

Roll of 2 membrs. (now detached), each 24¼ × 9⅞ in. Written on the recto only.

RAMSEY · co. Hunt.
Ben. Abbey   *f. c.* 969

787.   **BM., Cotton Vesp. E. ii,** fos. 1–
78. 'Carte de Rameseia per Robertum de
Dodeford clericum transcripte.' Cartulary,
13th cent. (aft. 1246), with rubrics, red and
blue decorated initials and additions down
to *temp.* Edw. II *passim* and at the end (fos.
66v ff.). Contains copies of charters etc.
arranged and numbered in three sections:
(1) royal, Edgar–Hen. III; (2) others, incl.
episcopal; (3) fines and compositions. Contemp. Table, fos. 2–4. *Mon. Angl.* ii, 551 (*a*),
lists the main contents.
     Fos. 9⅛ × 6 in.

788.   **PRO., Exch., K.R.** (Misc. Bks. i.
28). Composite 14th cent. register, in part
with rubrics or the headings underlined in
red, blue initials (in some sections decorated), red and blue paragraphs etc., and
with misc. additions *passim.* Includes: (*a*)
two inventories of deeds, fos. 21–2r, 25–
31r; (*b*) a collection of misc. royal charters
and writs, compositions, private deeds etc.,
temp. Will. I–Edw. III, fos. 34–69; (*c*) copies
of inquisitions etc., fos. 74–130; (*d*) 'Liber
Benefactorum', a narrative account of
benefactions down to 1066, in three parts,
incorporating copies of some early royal
and other charters (ed. W. D. Macray,
Chronicon Abbatiae Ramesiensis (Rolls ser.,
1886), after T. Gale, *Historiae Britannicae
Scriptores XV*, iii (Oxford, 1691), 385–462),
fos. 132–64; (*e*) copies of charters of
Inspeximus of Edw. III and other royal and
papal charters, writs etc., fos. 165–88; (*f*)
misc. material of a similar nature, incl.
copies of some pleas. Late 14th cent. Table,
fos. 1–7. Ed. W. H. Hart & P. A. Lyons,
Cartularium Monasterii de Rameseia, 3 vols.
(Rolls ser., 1884–93).
     Fos. 272 (medieval foliation, i–ccxxi,
from fo. 10, used by Hart & Lyons, *op. cit.*).
12¾ × 8¾ in. Delivered into the Exchequer
court by Sir H. Williams *al.* Cromwell,
1583.

¶ *Other registers etc.*

789.   **PRO., Exch., K.R.** (Transcripts
of Deeds & Charters, E/132/1/7). Copies,
late 13th cent., of royal charters to the
abbey, *temp.* Edgar–Hen. III, made apparently for presentation to the Exchequer
(fos. 12).

790.   **Oxford, Bodl., Rawlinson B.
333.** 'Historiae Abbatiae.' An early 14th

cent. version of the 'Liber Benefactorum'
(No. 788 (*d*)), similarly incorporating
copies of early royal and other charters etc.,
with a fourth part (down to 1200) added,
in which these copies are more numerous.
Followed (fos. 56–66) by other misc. material. Ed. Macray, *op. cit. FO:* Sir H. Spelman; W. Clavell.

791.   **BM., Cotton Galba E. x,** fos. 8–
58. Surveys, rentals etc., 13th cent.

792.   **Oxford, Bodl., Ashmole 1524,**
fos. 3–20. Fragm. of a letter-book of J.
Sawtry, abbot 1285–1316. Ed. Macray, *op.
cit.*, 368–411.

793.   **BM., Egerton 3663.** Misc. early
14th cent. register of pleas, statutes, surveys, fees etc., incl. copies of some 13th–
14th cent. royal and other charters and
documents. *FO:* C. Ord; Sir T. Phillipps
(MS. 3791).

794.   **BM., Harley 5071.** Fragm. (fos.
11) of a misc. early 14th cent. register of
bounds, liberties etc. Printed by T. Hearne,
T. Sprotti Chronica (Oxford, 1719), 171 ff.
and *Mon. Angl.* ii, 571–9. *FO:* John Murray.

795.   **BM., Cotton Otho B. xiv,** fos.
259–79. Fragms. of 14th cent. registers,
containing copies of Edw. III's charters of
Inspeximus etc. and misc. pleas. *FO:* Sir R.
Cotton; J. Payne (MS. 30); Egerton, bookseller, 1787.

796.   **BM., Cotton Vesp. A. xviii,** fos.
87–151. Misc. 14th cent. register of pleas,
liberties, inquisitions etc., incl. copies of
some royal and other charters and documents *passim*, and (fos. 147–51) a fragm. of
a letter-book of Abbot S. de Eye, 1317–22
(ed. Macray, *op. cit.*, 412–7).

797.   **PRO., Exch., K.R.** (Eccl. Docs.,
E. 135/20/4). Fragm. (fos. 11, mutilated) of
a late 14th cent. register of pleas and related charters.

798.   **BM., Harley 445.** Register of
fines (*gersumae*), 14th–15th cent. *FO:* P. Le
Neve.

799.   **BM. Add. 33450.** Register of
Abbot J. Titchmarsh, 1431–41 etc. *FO:* the
Cromwell fam.; the Fellowes fam., barons
De Ramsey.

800.   **Mrs. Charles Howard,** deposited
in Norwich Central Libr. (Hare MSS.).
Misc. 15th cent. register. A. J. Horwood,
HMC. Third Report (1872), App., 251–2.
FO: the Hare fam., barts., Stow Hall.

RANTON co. Staff.
v. RONTON.

RAVENINGHAM co. Norf.
v. METTINGHAM.

READING co. Berks
Ben. Abbey *f.* 1121
v. also LEOMINSTER.

801.   **BM., Egerton 3031.** Cartulary, late 12th cent. (*temp.* Ric. I), with rubrics and red and blue initials, sometimes decorated. Contains copies of royal (English and Scottish), papal, episcopal and baronial etc. charters arranged in sections according to the status of grantors, with additions down to *temp.* Hen. III *passim* and at the end (fos. 73 ff.). A contemp. Table of the original compilation at fos. 3–6v is followed by lists of relics, books, vestments etc. (fos. 6v–12v). *BM. Cat. Add. MSS.* 1921–1925, 302–3 (description). For the book-lists etc. see also S. Barfield, *Engl. Hist. Review* iii (1888), 113–25.
   Fos. i+114. 11¼ × 8¼ in. *FO:* the Wollascot fam; the Plunkett fam., earls of Fingall (found, 18th cent., in a bricked-up chamber at Shinfield).

802.   **BM., Harley 1708.** Cartulary, *c.* 1257 (?), with rubrics and red and blue decorated initials. Arranged mainly topographically, by counties, with sections of the founder's and other royal charters at the beginning and additions, mainly 13th–14th cent., *passim.* A contemp. Table of fos. 101v–134, written in a similar hand, is now **BM., Add. Roll 19617** (*FO:* as No. 804). *Mon. Angl.* iv, 35 (*a*) (list of contents). *New Palaeographical Soc.*, First ser., pl. 87.
   Fos. 247. 10⅛ × 6⅞ in. *FO:* H. Worsley (*T*).

803.   **BM., Cotton Vesp. E. xxv.** Cartulary, 14th cent. (*c.* 1320–30?), with rubrics and red initials. Arranged mainly topographically with copies of royal charters at the beginning (fos. 6–18), and of fines and episcopal etc. charters, with some other misc. documents, at the end (fos. 96v–138) followed by added sections in a number of mainly 14th cent. hands.
   Fos. 231. 9¾ × 7 in. *FO:* John Davies; E. Ashmole.
¶ *Inventories*
804.   **BM., Add. Roll 19631.** 'Rotulus Cartarum et Munimentorum Scocie.' In-

ventory, late 13th cent., of muniments rel. the abbey's dependency, May priory. Ed. J. Stuart, *Records of the Priory of the Isle of May* (Soc. Antiquaries of Scotland, 1868), cxii–cxiv.
   Roll of 1 membr. 12 × 5¾ in. Presented by the 3rd marquis, afterw. 1st duke, of Westminster, 1873.
¶ *Elemosinarius*
805.   **BM., Cotton Vesp. E. v.** Cartulary of the almoner (fos. 17–40, 57–60, 77–9), mid-13th cent. (aft. 1239), with rubrics and plain red or blue initials etc. Arranged topographically with copies of the foundation and a few other royal and episcopal charters at the beginning, misc. 13th cent. additions at the end (aft. fo. 34) incl. copies of one or two papal and further royal and episcopal charters, and a contemp. Table at fo. 10. The rest of the volume consists of further additions, mainly 13th–14th cent., incl. a kalendar (fos. 11v–16). *Mon. Angl.* iv, 34 (*k*) (summary list of contents).
   Fos. 81 (the original compilation with contemp. foliation, i–xxxi). 8¾ × 6½ in. *FO:* J. Holand, 1605, by gift of Sir J. Dodderidge.
¶ *Other registers etc.*
806.   **BM., Harley 82,** fos. 1–3. Three leaves from a register of Abbot N. Quappelade, containing entries for 1305–11.
807.   **Cambridge U.L., Dd. 9. 38.** Composite 14th cent. register, mainly of constitutions, statutes etc., with copies of about 12 royal, papal and episcopal charters to the abbey added (fos. 75–9) in a later 14th cent. hand at the end of a text of the Rule of St. Benedict.
808.   **Salisbury, Diocesan Registry.** Misc. register of *Acta* etc. (mainly presentations and manumissions), *temp.* Hen. VI–16th cent. Found, 1688, in the archives of the Bp. of London and restored to the see of Salisbury.

REVESBY co. Linc.
Cist. Abbey *f.* 1142
   No cartulary recorded.
¶ *Inventory*
809.   **BM., Egerton 3058.** Inventory of charters, 12th cent. with additions, written in double columns with rubrics and arranged mainly according to the status of

grantors. Noticed, with discussion of its possible history, by A. J. Collins, 'Documents from Penshurst', *Brit. Mus. Quart.* vii (1932–3), 66–8 & pl. xxvii (b).

Roll of 1 membr. 23½ × 4¼ in. *FO:* the Sidney fam., earls of Leicester, barons De L'Isle and Dudley (?).

RICHMOND   co. York
v. also EASBY.

RICHMOND   co. York
Ben. Priory (Cell of St. Mary's Abbey, York)   *f.* bef. 1146
810.   **Untraced.** (Cartulary and ?) rental made, 1504, by John Ledell, *Custos* of the cell, for whom see also No. 356 above. Owned, 1627, by Christopher Pepper of Richmond. Extracts from the rental, prefaced by notes of 13 charters, in Bodl., Dodsworth 159 (*SC.* 5100), fos. 220–7, are printed in *Mon. Angl.* iii, 602–6, nos. iv, v, vii, x.

RIEVAULX   co. York
Cist. Abbey   *f.* 1132
811.   **BM., Cotton Julius D. i.** Gen. cartulary, late 12th cent. (aft. 1179), written in sections with rubrics, red initials etc. Contains copies of charters etc. numbered consecutively, with gaps, *i–ccxxxv*, the royal, episcopal etc. and papal material being grouped mainly at the end (fos. 133 ff.). A contemp. Table at fos. 21–6, printed in *Mon. Angl.* v, 277 (*h*), is preceded (fos. 7–18) by canons of the third Lateran Council, 1179, and (fos. 19–20) a list of lands. Additions, *temp.* Ric. I etc., have been made at the ends of the sections *passim* etc. (fos. 5–6, 114–23, 148–53, 170v–3, 188 ff.). Ed. J. C. Atkinson, *Cartularium . . . de Rievalle* (Surtees Soc. lxxxiii, 1889 for 1887).

Fos. 193. 6¼ × 5 in.
812.   **Untraced.** Register *penes* Wm. Lite of Wilbraham, 17th cent. (*D*).
¶ *Inventory*
813.   **Untraced.** 'Cartarum Rywallensium intitulationes secundum quas iacent in armariolo' etc. Inventory of charters in book form, on vellum, in the possession, 1640, of the 7th earl of Rutland, Belvoir Castle. Not recorded by J. H. Round, *HMC. Rutland* iv (1905). Atkinson, *op. cit.*, 265–77, prints extracts from fos.

1–7 in Bodl., Dodsworth 85 (*SC.* 5026), fos. 53–7, 71v–2, which show it to have been arranged topographically with the royal charters (down to Edw. I, of Edw. III added) at the beginning, and pressmarks.

RIPON   co. York
Minster (Coll. Church)   *f.* bef. 1066
    No cartulary recorded.
¶ *Other registers etc.*
814.   **Ripon, D. & C.** Parts of Act books, 1452–1506, and other registers, bound as a single volume. Ed. J. T. Fowler, *Acts of Chapter of . . . Ripon* (Surtees Soc. lxiv, 1875). *FO:* H. Todd, D.D.

ROBERTSBRIDGE   co. Suss.
Cist. Abbey   *f.* 1176
815.   **Untraced.** Cartulary 'penes heredem Philippi Sidney equitis' (d. 1586, of Penshurst), 1587, from which extracts are in London, Coll. of Arms, Glover's Collections B, fos. 35v–43; Bodl., Dugdale 18 (*SC.* 6508), fo. 66; BM., Harley 4757, fos. 59v–70 (*FO:* P. Le Neve). Reported, 1670, in the hands of his descendant Robert Sidney, 2nd earl of Leicester (*D*). Not recorded by C. L. Kingsford, *HMC. De L'Isle* i (1925).
¶ *Other registers etc.*
816.   **The Marquess of Bath,** Longleat (MS. 37). Formulary, 14th–15th cent. A. J. Horwood, *HMC. Third Report* (1872), App., 181–2 (descriptive note).

ROCHESTER, See of   *f.* 604
v. No. 820 below.

ROCHESTER   co. Kent
Ben. Cath. Priory   *f.* 604 (refounded 1080)
    Much material from the cartularies and other sources is printed by J. Thorpe, *Registrum Roffense* (1769), pt. i.
817.   **Rochester, D. & C.,** Muniments, 'Textus Roffensis' (A. 3. 5), fos. 119–234. Cartulary, early 12th cent. (aft. 1122), finely written in similar format to the 'Textus Roffensis', with which it is bound. Rubrics and red and green initials (the first, fo. 119, elaborately decorated in colour). Contains copies of royal (Anglo-Saxon – Hen. I), papal, episcopal and some other charters and privileges, followed (fos. 217–34) by lists of fees, churches, books etc. An 18th cent. transcript is in BM., Stowe 940. A

facsimile page by Elizabeth Elstob (d. 1756) in BM., Harley 1866, is a remarkable curiosity. Ed. T. Hearne, *Textus Roffensis* (Oxford, 1720), 62–242. F. Liebermann, 'Notes on the Textus Roffensis', *Arch. Cantiana* xxiii (1898), 101–12, and references there cited. N. R. Ker, *Cat. MSS. containing Anglo-Saxon* (Oxford, 1957), no. 373.

Fos. 116 (234 in the MS.). 9 × 6½ in.

818. **BM., Cotton Domit. A. x,** fos. 90–208. Cartulary, early 13th cent., written in book-hand with rubrics and red, blue or occasionally green initials and some contemp. or rather later 13th cent. additions, partly in charter-hand, towards the end. Contains copies of royal (1088–Ric. I), episcopal and other charters, numbered consecutively throughout, the royal ones being grouped mainly at the beginning. Contemp. Table, fos. 92v–96. Misc. additions on the fly-leaves include (fo. 90) a 13th–14th cent. title, 'Liber iii de consu(etu)d(inibus) et copia cart(arum) per H. mo(na)ch(um) eccl(es)ie Roff(e)n(sis)'. An 18th cent. transcript is in Rochester, D. & C. Muniments (A 3. 6).

Fos. 119. 8 × 6 in.

819. **BM., Royal 5 A. iv,** fos. 197–211. A late 13th cent. quire containing copies of eight episcopal and other charters etc. rel. titles, 1177 – c. 1227–38. Spaces for initials; fos. 202v–3, blank. Bound with literary works from the priory library.

Fos. 15. 8¾ × 6 in.

820. **Rochester, Diocesan Registry,** 'Liber Temporalium'. Register, 14th cent. (*temp.* Edw. II–III), of the temporalities of the priory and see, ostensibly compiled to demonstrate the antiquity of the former. Rubrics and some red initials etc. Fos. 3–48 contain copies of Anglo-Saxon and other royal privileges, followed (fo. 15) by deeds arranged topographically and (fo. 45v) fines etc. The rest of the MS. comprises copies of other misc. documents, evidences etc., incl. some historical material. Additions, mainly 14th cent., on blank etc. leaves *passim* and at the end, include a Table (fos. 168–70).

Fos. iii + 176. 14 × 9½ in.

❡ *Other registers etc.*

821. **BM., Cotton Vesp. A. xxii,** fos. 60–129. Register, 13th cent. etc., of custumaries, rentals etc., preceded by copies

of four 12th cent. papal bulls and bound with Annals and other misc. material. Added title, 'Liber ii de consuetud. ecc(lesi)e Roff(e)n(sis) per benedictum mo(na)chum', and annotations by W. Lambarde, 1588, at fo. 2.

822. **BM., Cotton Faust. C. v** (formerly Vit. C. xv). Register of *Acta* etc., 1379–1417.

ROMSEY co. Southt.
Ben. Abbey (Nuns) *f.* 967
v. also *sub* EDINGTON.

RONTON (*al.* **RANTON**) co. Staff.
Aug. Priory *f.* 1135–66
823. **BM., Cotton Vesp. C. xv.** Gen. cartulary, 14th cent. (*temp.* Edw. II–III ?), with rubrics, red initials etc. and some additions. Arranged topographically with copies of the foundation etc. charters at the beginning and of occasional royal, papal and episcopal etc. charters included *passim*. G. Wrottesley, 'The Ronton Chartulary', Wm. Salt Arch. Soc., *Coll. Hist. Staffordshire* iv (1883), 264–95 (abstract).

Fos. 1 + 61. 13 × 9 in. *FO:* T. Povey.

ROWNEY co. Hertf.
Ben. Priory (Nuns) *f. c.* 1164
No cartulary recorded.
❡ *Other registers etc.*
v. also Nos. 1241–5 below.
823A. **Oxford, Magdalen Coll.,** Muniments (Adds. 65). Early 14th cent. roll of deeds (25) rel. Alswick in Layston with Buntingford etc.

824. **PRO., Exch., K.R.** (Ancient Deeds, DD: E. 211, box 11, items with superseded numeration TG. 14344, 14345, 14348). Three 15th cent. rolls dating perhaps from the nunnery's dissolution in 1457, when its possessions were made over to Sir John Fray, or later, containing copies, abstracts etc. of misc. royal and other charters rel. its possessions in various places. Other material in the box relates to the manors of Munden, Wenden etc.

825. **PRO., Exch., K.R.** (Transcripts of Deeds and Charters, E. 132/19.) Another 15th cent. roll, similar to No. 824.

ROYSTON co. Hertf.
Aug. Priory *f.* aft. 1163
826. **BM., Add. 46362** (T). Leaf from a

14th cent. cartulary with rubrics, letters touched with red etc. and spaces for initials, apparently used as a paste-down in the binding of some other book. Contains copies of five charters, incl. two of bps. of Lincoln, with parts of two others. Fos. 1. 10 × 6½ in. (cropped). Presented, 1946, by E. S. M. Perowne Esq.

ROYSTON co. Hertf.
Hosp. of SS. John & James　　f. bef. 1227
827.　**Untraced.** Cartulary *penes* John Wildbore *al.* Welbore of Foxton, co. Cambr., 27 June 1635, from which extracts (private deeds) down to fo. 26 are in Bodl., Dodsworth 153 (*SC.* 5094), fos. 61–3.

RUDHAM co. Norf.
Aug. Priory　　　　　　　　　f. c. 1140
v. COXFORD.

RUFFORD co. Nott.
Cist. Abbey　　　　　　　　　f. 1146
828.　**Lord Savile,** deposited in the British Museum (MSS. Loans No. 41). Cartulary (fos. 17–103), 14th–15th cent. (aft. 1388), arranged topographically in sections. Preceded (fos. 1–16) by two added late 15th cent. quires headed (fo. 1) 'Hic incipit registrum compilatum de Domino Johanne Lyle Abbate . . . MCCCCLXXI', which contain copies of royal (*temp.* Stephen etc.), baronial and other charters followed by deeds rel. the grange of Cratela in Wellow, Eakring etc. Medieval binding, with some rearrangement of the original order of the material. Annotations by R. Thoroton. A transcript, 17th cent., is in BM., Harley 1063 (*FO:* J. Anstis). Fos. xvi + 103. 12¾ × 9 in. *FO:* the Talbot fam., earls of Shrewsbury (?).
829.　**Untraced.** Cartulary *penes* —— Strelley, knt., 1633, from which extracts are printed in *Mon. Angl.* v, 518.
829A.　**Untraced.** Register *penes* Samuel Roper (d. 1658) of Monks Kirby (*D*). Perhaps identical with No. 828 or No. 829.

RUISLIP co. Middx
Ben. Priory　　　　　　　　　f. c. 1090
v. OGBOURNE.

RUMBURGH co. Suff.
Ben. Priory　　　　　　　　　f. 1047–64
v. also ELMHAM.
830.　**BM., Campbell Ch. ix. 9.** Copies, mid-13th cent., in a series of hands, of three episcopal and seven other 12th–13th cent. charters etc. (one duplicated) rel. its possessions in various places, listed by H. J. Ellis, *Index to the Charters & Rolls in the . . . BM.* ii (1912), 641. Roll of 2 membrs. 33½ × 5½ in.

ST. ALBANS co. Hertf.
Ben. Abbey　　　　　　　　　f. c. 793
Early 17th cent. copies of numerous early royal, papal and other privileges to the abbey, from an unspecified source, in Brussels, Bibl. Royale MS. 3723, fos. 151–216, are noticed by W. Holtzmann, *Papsturkunden in England* iii (Göttingen, 1952), 120–3.
831.　**BM., Cotton Nero D. i,** fos. 149–161. Two 13th cent. quires headed (fo. 149) 'Antiqua et Primitiva Munimenta Ecclesie Sancti Albani' etc., containing copies of Anglo-Saxon and royal charters, Offa-Hen. I, followed by 11th–12th cent. papal privileges. Written in double columns with rubrics and red, blue or black initials decorated with red or blue, and now form part of the 'Liber Additamentorum' of Matthew Paris, with annotations in the hand thought to be his, but were apparently once part of another compilation. H. R. Luard, *Matthaei Parisiensis Chronica Maiora* vi (Rolls ser., 1882), 513–6 etc. Fos. 13. 14 × 9½ in.
832.　**Chatsworth Libr.,** co. Derby (Trustees of the Chatsworth Settlement). Vol. i (cf. Nos. 833–4) of a late 14th cent. gen. cartulary, written in double columns with rubrics, alternate red and blue initials decorated with mauve or red (fos. 160–9), black pen-decorated initials filled with yellow), and other letters often touched with yellow. Contains copies of royal (fos. 1–27) and papal (fos. 31–60) charters followed by deeds, down to 1393, rel. St. Albans (fos. 64–159), London (fos. 160–94), Munden in Watford (fos. 194v–206), Oxhey (fos. 207–40) and Snelleshall in Rickmansworth (fos. 241–3). Added (aft. 1411) are: (*a*) a section of deeds for Westwick, on 8 unnumbered leaves aft. fo. 244; (*b*) a Table, on 20 unnumbered leaves at the beginning, showing a further added section for Totternhoe to be wanting; (*c*) a similar Table of Vol. ii, on 16 unnumbered leaves at the end. A few other additions have also been made *passim.* V. H.

Galbraith, *The St. Albans Chronicle* 1406–1420 (Oxford, 1937), xxxix.

Fos. 288 (lacks a few apparently blank leaves *passim*). 15½ × 10½ in. (written space 10½ × 7 in.). *FO:* Sir W. Cavendish, 1540 (?); the Dukes of Devonshire.

833.   BM., Cotton Otho D. iii. Parts of vol. ii of the same (cf. Nos. 832, 834), similarly written with black pen-decorated initials filled with yellow etc. Severely damaged by fire, 1731, and the leaves now mounted and largely fragmentary. Shown by the Table in No. 832 originally to have contained copies of deeds, arranged topographically, rel. a number of places in cos. Hertf., Middx., Bedf. and Bucks. Includes remains of Tables of vols. i & ii at fos. 195–201.

Fos. 201 (originally upwards of 260). 10½ × 7½ in. (shrunk).

834.   BM., Add. 40734, fos. 18–30. A detached section from No. 833 (the original fos. 171–83), containing copies of deeds rel. Codicote, co. Hertf., now bound with a 14th cent. extent of the same. B. Schofield, *Brit. Mus. Quart.* vii (1932), 15. *BM. Cat. Add. MSS.* 1921–1925, 155–6.

Fos. 13. 13¼ × 8⅞ in. (cropped). Acquired of R. L. Hine, 1923.

835.   BM., Arundel 34. Register, 16th cent., of lands acquired by Abbots Wheathampstead (1420–40, 1451–65) and Ramridge (1492–1521). Contains copies of deeds, rentals, extents and other documents etc. arranged according to subject matter, in part topographically, with headings and pen-decorated initials in black. *Mon. Angl.* ii, 210 (*c*).

Fos. 90. 11⅛ × 8 in. *FO:* Ld. Wm. Howard; presented by Henry Howard, 6th duke of Norfolk, to the Royal Society, 1678.

¶ *Elemosinarius*

836.   BM., Lansdowne 375. 'Liber Memorand(orum) Offic(ii) Elemos(inarii)', 14th–15th cent. (aft. 1392). Cartulary (fos. 79–195), with occasional rubrication, arranged topographically and preceded (fos. 51–75) by Tables which refer also to a 'Primum Registrum' and 'Secundum Registrum' of the almoner. Added at the beginning are extracts (fos. 3–5) from a 'Liber Albus' rel. the almonry and (fos. 6–50) an account of a process, 1428, against the rector of Harpole; with some other

misc. memoranda *passim*. *Mon. Angl.* ii, 210 (*b*).

Fos. 199. 8⅛ × 6 in. *FO:* Bp. T. Dove; Henry Dove; Bp. White Kennett; James West.

¶ *Sacristarius*

837.   BM., Cotton Julius D. iii, fos. 1–124. Cartulary of the sacrist, 14th–15th cent. (aft. 1393), with rubrics, some initials touched with red and occasional additions *passim*. Contains copies of deeds, leases and other documents, arranged topographically. Fos. 1–63 should follow 66–124, the first fifteen leaves of the compilation in this form and some others *passim* being now lost. *Mon. Angl.* ii, 208 (*f*).

Fos. 124 (medieval foliation, xvi–xxxii). 7½ × 5¼ in.

¶ *Other registers etc.*

838.   BM., Cotton Tib. E. vi. Misc. 14th–15th cent. register of rentals, custumals, records of legal proceedings and other memoranda rel. the abbey's churches, lands etc., incl. copies (fos. 115v–143v etc.) of a series of early royal, papal, episcopal and other charters rel. its dependencies, and of some further charters *passim*. Severely damaged by fire, 1731. H. H. E. Craster, *Parish of Tynemouth* (*Hist. Northumberland* viii, 1907), 47–68 *passim*, prints the charters for Tynemouth with the aid of 17th cent. transcripts. H. T. Riley, *Reg. Johannis Whethamstede* ii (Rolls ser., 1873), 319–64 (misc. extracts).

839.   BM., Harley 602. 'Liber Memorandorum Domini Johannis Moot.' A misc. 14th cent. register of rentals, leases, acquittances etc., continued in 15th cent. hands. *FO:* R. Starkey, 1615; Sir S. D'Ewes (?).

840.   BM., Cotton Claud. D. i, fos. 3–34. Letter-book of Abbot J. Wheathampstead. Ed. Riley, *op. cit.* ii, 375–476.

841.   London, Coll. of Arms, Arundel 3. History, 15th cent., of the second abbacy (1451–65) of Abbot Wheathampstead, incorporating copies of some charters and other documents. Ed. Riley, *op. cit.* i (1872). *FO:* Ld. Wm. Howard, 1589; presented by Henry Howard, 6th duke of Norfolk, 1678.

842.   Oxford, Bodl., Rawlinson B. 332. Register of the abbots, 1458–88. Paper. Ed. Riley, *op. cit.* ii, pp. lxv–lxxviii, 3–299.

842A.   The   Archdeaconry   of   St.

Albans, deposited at Hertford, Hertfordshire R.O. (ASA. 4). Two leaves ($12 \times 8\frac{1}{2}$ in., cropped) from a register of Abbot Ramridge for 1392; used to bind a courtbook of the archdeaconry for 1565–7. Noticed by C. I. A. Ritchie, 'Abbot Thomas Ramryge's Lost Register', *Engl. Hist. Review* lxxi (1956), 434–5.

843. **Oxford, Bodl., Rawlinson B. 331.** Fragm. (fos. 19) of a misc. 16th cent. register of pleas etc. Paper.

844. **BM., Cotton Nero D. vii.** 'Catalogus Benefactorum', with notes of their benefactions, *c.* 1380 with additions. *Mon. Angl.* ii, 209 (*b*). *FO:* Francis Bacon, 1st viscount St. Alban.

845. **Cambridge, C.C.C., MS. 7,** pp. 203–22. 'Liber de Benefactoribus', 15th cent. An epitome of No. 844. Ed. H. T. Riley, *Trokelowe* (Rolls ser., 1866), 427–64. *FO:* Archbp. M. Parker.

846. **BM., Egerton 3317.** Copies, 14th cent., of court rolls of Aston Abbots, 1288–1344. *FO:* Sir L. Harmsworth.

847. **Cambridge U.L., Ee. 4. 20.** Formulary, 14th–15th cent. Craster, *op. cit.,* 71.

848. **Untraced.** Two leiger-books in the custody of Thomas Fortescue of the royal Wardrobe, 1599 (cf. BM., Harley 4712, fo. 309; Egerton 2714, fo. 31). Extracts, 17th cent., are in Cambridge U.L., Ee. 3. 44. *Cambr. U.L. Cat. MSS.* ii, 84–6.

ST. ASAPH, See of   *f.* 6th cent.
No cartulary recorded.

848A. **Untraced.** 'Llyfr Coch' ('The Red Book'). A misc. early 14th cent register of episcopal *acta* and other material, 12th–14th cent., of which partial 16th–18th cent. transcripts are in Aberystwyth, NLW., Peniarth 231, Add. 7011 and among the records (deposited) of the Church in Wales. Sent to London for a law-suit, 1612. D. L. Evans, 'Llyfr Coch Asaph', *Nat. Libr. of Wales J.* iv. (1945–6), 177–83. J. Conway Davies, *Episcopal Acts . . . rel . . . Welsh Dioceses* i (Hist. Soc. Church in Wales i, 1946), 26–7.

ST. BEES   co. Cumb.
Ben. Priory   *f.* 1120

849. **BM., Harley 434.** Gen. cartulary, 15th cent., with rubrics etc., pen-decorated initials and a few additions. Arranged topographically in 13 books, with a contemp. Table at fos. 3–9, and incl. copies of some royal and one or two episcopal charters etc. *passim.* Ed. J. Wilson, *The Register of . . . St. Bees* (Surtees Soc. cxxvi, 1915).

Fos. 197. $12 \times 8\frac{1}{2}$ in. *FO:* Sir J. Lowther, bart. (*T*); J. Strype (*T*).

ST. BENET OF HULME   co. Norf.
v. HULME.

ST. BURYAN   co. Cornw.
Coll. Church   *f. c.* 930
No cartulary recorded.
⁋ *Other registers etc.*

850. **Cambridge U.L., Ee. 5. 34.** Fragm. of a late 15th cent. register. *Cambr. U.L. Cat. MSS.* ii, 251. *FO:* Bp. J. Moore.

ST. DAVID'S   co. Pembr.
Cath. Church   *f.* 6th cent.
No cartulary recorded.
⁋ *Other registers etc.*

851. **BM., Harley 6280.** 'Liber Statutorum', early 16th cent., incl. copies of numerous episcopal and some royal, papal and other related documents and grants. Transcripts, 17th–19th cent., are in BM., Harley 1249 (calendared in *BM. Cat. Harleian MSS.* i, 630–4); Aberystwyth, NLW., MS. 1404 (Phillipps MS. 21058), and among the records (deposited) of the Church in Wales (SDCh./B. 21–5, five copies); Cambridge, St. John's Coll. MS. 279. *FO:* T. Baker.

ST. JOHN OF JERUSALEM, Order of, in England and Wales.
v. also BADDESLEY, BUCKLAND, MAPLESTEAD, SAMPFORD, TEMPLARS, TEMPLE COMBE.

852. **BM., Cotton Nero E. vi.** Cartulary (cf. No. 853) of the Order's lands in England, begun in 1442. Rubrics etc., blue initials decorated with red at the beginning of sections, red decoration of other capitals and a few additions *passim.* Arranged by *Camere* in two parts, divided into topographical sections (*Tituli*) by preceptories: (1) *Prima Camera* (*Tituli i–lviii,* of which *i–iii,* for London, include copies of a few royal, papal and episcopal privileges), fos. 3–288; (2) *Secunda Camera* (*Tituli i–ii, viii–x*), fos. 289–465. A list of *Tituli* at fo. 2, fragmentary for pt. 2, is printed in *Mon.*

Angl. vi, 800 (*a*). C. Cotton, 'A Kentish Cartulary of the Order of St. John of Jerusalem', *Kent Arch. Soc.*, *Records Branch* xi (1930), 81 ff., calendars fos. 222–86.

Fos. 467 (16th (?) cent. foliation, ii–ccccclxxviii). 15¾ × 11 in. *FO:* Sir T. Penruddock.

853.   **BM., Cotton Nero C. ix,** fos. 23–148. A detached section from No. 852, pt. 2 (*Secunda Camera*) containing *Tituli iii–vi*(*i*?) for Wilbraham, Carlton, Chippenham, Ashley and Silverley, co. Cambr. Separated before the 16th (?) cent. foliation of No. 852 was made.

Fos. 126. 12¾ × 9 in. (closely cropped).

¶ *Other registers etc.*
854.   **BM., Lansdowne 200.** Leasebook, 1492–1500. Wants a few leaves at the end.

855.   **BM., Cotton Claud. E. vi.** Leasebook, 1503–1526.

856.   **PRO., Exch., L.R.** (Misc. Bks. 62). Lease-book, 1528–39.

857.   **PRO., Exch., L.R.** (Misc. Bks. 63). Enrolments of grants of the dissolved priory's lands 'in domo capitulari de Clerkenwell confirmat.', 29–38 Hen. VIII.

ST. MICHAEL'S MOUNT co. Cornw.
Ben. Priory   *f. c.* 1087–91
858.   **The Marquess of Salisbury,** Hatfield (MS. 315). Gen. cartulary, late 14th cent. (aft. 1372); somewhat roughly written with the titles underlined in red etc. and some 'restoration' of faded passages. Includes copies of one or two 12th cent. papal and royal charters. Apparently misbound in places and possibly incomplete. *Mon. Angl.* vi, 990–1, prints four of the more important documents.

Fos. 57. 8 × 5½ in. (cropped).

ST. NEOT'S   co. Hunt.
Ben Priory   *f.* 972–5
G. C. Gorham, *Hist. Eynesbury & St. Neots* ii (1824), 288–317 & Supplement, pp. v–lxvi, prints abstracts of Nos. 859–60 with extracts; cf. *Mon. Angl.* iii, 465 (*l*), 468 (*a*) etc.
859.   **BM., Cotton Faust. A. iv.** Gen. cartulary (fos. 37–114), 13th cent. (aft. 1234), with red page-headings, quire-numbers, numeration of the entries etc. and misc. additions (fos. 1–28, 114–51 and *passim*). Arranged mainly topographically

with sections of papal (almost entirely wanting), episcopal etc. and royal charters, and fines, at the beginning and of 'Carte de tempore Hug. de Sagernum', 1226–34 & undated, at the end (fos. 94 ff.). A contemp. Table (fos. 29–34) shows material to be wanting aft. fos. 80 (for Turvey) and 91 (for various places).

Fos. 151. 9¼ × 6¼ in.
¶ *Sacristarius*
860.   **BM., Stowe 941.** 'Registrum Cartarum Sacristarie', 1286, elaborately written with rubrics and red and green decorated initials etc. Contains copies of 99 charters arranged topographically, with a list of places (fo. 3v) and rental for the town of St. Neots (fos. 55 6).

Fos. 59 (excl. blank leaves). 8¼ × 5¾ in. *FO:* T. Astle.

ST. RADEGUND'S (BRADSOLE)
                                           co. Kent
Praem. Abbey   *f.* 1193
861.   **Oxford, Bodl., Rawlinson B. 336.** Quires *iii–xiii*, with one or two supplementary leaves at the end, of a late 13th cent. cartulary apparently concerned with rents, tithes etc. Rubrics and small red initials. Arranged mainly topographically (*Redditus denar*(*ii*), pp. 139–58; *Redditus bladi*, pp. 159–62; *Redditus feni*, pp. 163–4; churches collated to the abbey, incl. copies of a few royal, papal, episcopal etc. charters, pp. 165 ff.), with some additions *passim*. Followed (pp. 187–298) by a rental and other misc. material, incl. a library list. W. D. Macray, *Cat. MSS. Bibl. Bodl.* v (i) (Oxford, 1862), 604–5.

Fos. 148 (post-medieval pagination, 1–298). 10⅞ × 7 in.
862.   **Untraced.** Cartulary, 'amplus sane et antiquus', containing copies of upwards of 1,235 charters etc. arranged topographically. Extracts by Sir E. Dering, 1631, when it belonged to Henry Heyman of Sellinge (bart. 1641) but was produced by Robert Ladd, 'Iuris-consultus', are copied by E. Hasted in Bodl., Gough Kent 18 (*SC.* 17964). Other extracts, 17th–18th cent., are in BM., Add. 29437, fos. 173–83; Bodl., Rawlinson B. 461, fos. 3–29 *passim.* The cartulary described in *Mon. Angl.* vi, 941–2, as *penes* William Pierpont Esq. is apparently the same.
863.   **Untraced.** Leiger book 'which . . .

remaineth and is to be seen with me Thomas Honywood', 16th cent.; see the extract, of a composition rel. tithes of Hawkinge church, in Cambridge, C.C.C. MS. 101, pp. 135–6. M. R. James, *Cat. MSS. C.C.C.* i (Cambridge, 1912), 191. Possibly one of the preceding.

SALISBURY, See of *f.* 1078

For the records of the Bishop at Salisbury see R. L. Poole, *HMC. Various Collections* iv (1907), 1–12. Much material is printed by W. H. Rich Jones and W. D. Macray, *Charters and Documents illustrating the History of the Cathedral, See, and Diocese of Salisbury* (Rolls ser., 1891).

864. **Salisbury, Diocesan Registry,** 'Liber Evidentiarum B'. Composite misc. register written in a succession of 14th–16th cent. hands, with partial rubrication and spaces for initials. Contains copies of episcopal *Acta*, royal writs, compositions and other documents, incl. some private deeds, with a 14th cent. Table on 8 preliminary leaves.

Fos. *c.* 287 (mainly unnumbered). 11¼ × 7½ in.

865. **Ditto,** 'Liber Ruber'. Similar to No. 864, from which fos. 1–104 are apparently copied, 14th–16th cent. Fos. 113–40 contain copies of a series of papal bulls, 1125–*temp.* Calixtus III (1455–8). Table, on six preliminary leaves.

Fos. 12 + 197. 11½ × 7½ in. Vellum (fos. 1–155) and paper. *FO:* Sir J. Danvers; restored to the bishop, 1674.

866. **Ditto,** 'Liber Niger Episcopi'. Register compiled by Bp. R. Beauchamp, *c.* 1451 with additions, of evidences kept in his palace at Salisbury and in the episcopal manors, for fear of their destruction. Contains copies in a number of hands of deeds, rentals, feodaries, pleas, inquisitions and some papal and royal documents etc.

Fos. 256. 15¼ × 11 in. Paper.

❡ *Other registers etc.*

For other registers etc. at Salisbury, see Poole, *l.c.*

SALISBURY co. Wilts
Cath. Church *f.* (at Old Sarum) 1075–8

For the muniments of the Dean & Chapter at Salisbury, see R. L. Poole, *HMC. Various Collections* i (1901), 338–88;

and for other material, the references cited above for the See.

867. **Salisbury, Diocesan Registry,** 'Vetus Registrum Ecclesie Sarum' *al.* 'Registrum S. Osmundi'. Composite misc. register written mainly in the first half of the 13th cent. (*c.* 1220–40) and incl. a custumary (pp. 1–37), visitations of the prebendal churches 1220–6 (pp. 73–88) and accounts of the removal of the church from Old to New Sarum (pp. 119–24, 133–66). Two of the quires (pp. 41–72), in consecutive main hands with additions marginally and on preliminary leaves (pp. 38–40), contain copies of royal, papal, episcopal, monastic and some other charters and privileges to the cathedral, 12th–13th cent. A further quire (pp. 95–110) contains copies of charters, 1125–1222, rel. the prebendal church of Heytesbury, followed (p. 103) by others, 1190–1225, rel. Mere, Wokingham, Teynton etc. and extracts rel. the privileges of Abingdon Abbey, 1224. Other misc. charters are copied elsewhere *passim.* Ed. W. H. Rich Jones, *The Register of St. Osmund,* 2 vols. (Rolls ser., 1883–4). A collation of the MS. by C. Wordsworth is in W. H. Frere, *The Use of Sarum* i (Cambridge, 1898), xliv–xlix.

Fos. 91 (post-medieval pagination, 1–182). 10⅝ × 7 in.

868. **London, Inner Temple, MS. 511. 18.** Cartulary (pp. 1–158), late 13th cent., with uncompleted red initials and underlining of headings. Contains copies of the charter of St. Osmund followed by royal (down to Hen. III), episcopal and other charters rel. the cathedral and its churches etc., with a few additions down to *temp.* Edw. I at the end. Pp. 159–238 are added 15th–16th cent. quires containing similar 13th–15th cent. material. Pp. 239–46 contain a late 14th cent. Table. A list of contents was printed by Sir T. Phillipps (Middlehill, 1822: two folio sheets).

Fos. 124 (later pagination, 1–247). 8¼ × 5¾ in. *FO:* W. Petyt.

869. **Salisbury, D. & C.,** Muniments, 'Liber Evidentiarum C' (ii. 3). Cartulary (pp. 37–366), late 13th cent., similar in arrangement to No. 868, with uncompleted rubrication and spaces for initials. Added leaves and quires at the beginning and end contain misc. additions incl. copies of constitutions, Chapter acts 1320–6 etc.

Fos. 282 (post-medieval pagination, 1–391, continued as foliation down to 477). $10\frac{1}{8} \times 6\frac{3}{4}$ in.

❡ *Other registers etc.*

For other material at Salisbury see Poole, *ll. cc.*

870. **Oxford, Univ. Coll. MS. 166,** deposited in the Bodleian Libr. Rental and custumary, 14th cent.

SALISBURY co. Wilts
Hosp. of St. Nicholas *f.* bef. 1214

871. **Salisbury, Diocesan Registry** (by deposit of the steward of the hospital). Composite 15th cent. cartulary comprising: (1) pp. 1–24 (rubricated, with plain red or blue initials, paragraphs etc.), copies of deeds rel. various places, arranged topographically; (2) pp. 27–91 (with uncompleted red initials), copies of deeds and (pp. 51 ff.) rentals rel. E. and W. Harnham; (3) pp. 103 ff. (and on blank and added leaves elsewhere *passim*), additions in a succession of 15th–16th cent. hands. Ed. C. Wordsworth, *St. Nicholas' Hospital, Salisbury* (Wilts. Record Soc., 1903).

Fos. 80 (paginated, 1–154, omitting 3 leaves; wants 4 others *passim*). 11×8 in.

SALISBURY co. Wilts
Coll. of St. Nicholas de Vaux *f.* 1260

872. **BM., Add. 28870.** Cartulary, *c.* 1447, made for Simon Hutchins, 'Socius collegii'. Arranged topographically by estates in cos. Berks, Dors. and Wilts, with a few later additions. Described by C. Wordsworth, *St. Nicholas' Hospital, Salisbury* (Wilts. Record Soc., 1903), pp. 283–91. For the binding see W. H. J. Weale, *Early Stamped Bookbindings in the BM.* (1922), no. 41.

Fos. 213 + iii (wants 8 leaves at the beginning and a few others *passim*). $12\frac{1}{4} \times 8\frac{1}{4}$ in. *FO:* W. Boucher; H. Penruddocke Wyndham.

SAMPFORD, LITTLE co. Essex
Knts. of St. John
v. also ST. JOHN OF JERUSALEM, MAPLESTEAD.

873. **Oxford, Bodl., Rawlinson Essex 11** (*SC.* 15998), fos. 1–8. Fragm. of a late 13th cent. cartulary (*temp.* Edw. I), rel. lands of the Knights Hospitallers in Little Sampford (dependent on the pre-ceptory at Little Maplestead ?). Contains copies of about 80 deeds etc., 12th–13th cent. At fo. 8v, a 16th cent. note states, 'Totus iste liber registratur a principio usque in finem'.

Fos. 8. $10\frac{1}{4} \times 6\frac{3}{8}$ in. *FO:* the Rev. W. Holman.

SANDFORD co. Oxon
Preceptory of Knts. Templar *f.* 1239–40
v. also TEMPLARS.

874. **Oxford, Bodl., Wood empt. 10** (*SC.* 8598). Gen. cartulary, late 13th cent. (*temp.* Edw. I), with rubrics, spaces for initials and one or two additions. Contains copies of deeds etc., incl. royal and episcopal charters, rel. cos. Oxon, Bucks., Berks, Wilts, Southt. and the Isle of Wight etc., arranged topographically. Ed. Agnes M. Leys, *The Sandford Cartulary*, 2 vols. (Oxfordshire Record Soc. xix, xxii, 1938, 1941 for 1940).

Fos. iv + 115. $10\frac{1}{2} \times 6\frac{3}{4}$ in. *FO:* J. Powell.

❡ *Other registers etc.*

875. **Oxford, C.C.C. MS. 320,** deposited in the Bodleian Libr. Rental, 1513, of lands at Sandford and Littlemore, made for T. Docwra, prior of the hospital of St. John of Jerusalem. *FO:* W. Hillary, 1617; the Rev. R. Davis, 1697 (*T*).

SANDTOFT co. Linc.
Ben. Cell of St. Mary's Abbey, York *f.* 1147–86

v. No. 1099 below.

SAWLEY co. York
Cist. Abbey *f.* 1148

876. **BM., Harley 112.** Cartulary, 14th cent. (aft. 1333), with rubrics and spaces for small initials, containing copies of baronial, private and occasional episcopal charters and deeds arranged topographically in twelve sections by presses (*Casae*) with a few misc. additions *passim* and at the end (fos. 188 ff.). Ed. J. McNulty, *Chartulary . . . of Sallay in Craven*, 2 vols. (Yorks. Arch. Soc., Record ser. lxxxvii, xc, 1933–4).

Fos. iii + 198. $9\frac{7}{8} \times 6$ in. *FO:* Sir A. Darcy; Sir S. D'Ewes.

SCOKIRK co. York
v. TOCKWITH.

SELBORNE co. Southt.
Aug. Priory *f.* 1233
For the material preserved in the muniments of Magdalen Coll., Oxford, which does not include a cartulary, see W. D. Macray, *Cal. Charters & Documents rel. Selborne and its Priory* (Hampshire Record Soc., 1891), vii–xiv, and references there cited.

SELBY co. York
Ben. Abbey *f. c.* 1070
877. **BM., Add. 37771.** Gen. cartulary, 13th–14th cent., with uncompleted rubrication, red and blue initials, and additions *passim*. Arranged topographically, with a section of royal charters at the beginning, preceded by a contemp. Table (fos. 2–7) and a 15th cent. index of places (fo. 1v), and incl. copies of a few episcopal and papal charters. Ed. J. T. Fowler, *The Coucher Book of Selby*, 2 vols. (Yorks. Arch. Soc., Record ser. x, xiii, 1891–3). *BM. Cat. Add. MSS.* 1906–1910, 131–2.

Fos. 222. 13½ × 8¾ in. *FO:* Sir T. Walmesley (*D*); the Barons Petre; Sir T. Brooke, bart., 1868.

❡ *Other registers etc.*
878. **PRO., Duchy of Lanc.** (Misc. Bks. 8). 'Registrum de tempore Galfridi de Gaddesby', abbot 1341–67. Cf. No. 879.
879. **Oxford, Bodl., Top. Yorks d. 2** (*SC.* 35210). Two leaves from No. 878 or a similar register, for 1341–2. *FO:* J. Haslewood; Sir T. Phillipps (MS. 6574).
880. **Untraced.** Lease-book, of which a 17th cent. transcript is in Leeds Public Libr. The material copied is 12th–13th cent. and for 1355–62.
881. **BM., Cotton Vit. E. xvi**, fos. 97–162. Part (mutilated) of a register *temp.* J. Shirburn, abbot 1368–1407, incl. some copies of deeds. Cf. No. 882.
882. **BM., Cotton Cleop. D. iii**, fos. 184–202. Another part of No. 881 or a similar register, late 14th cent. *Mon. Angl.* iii, 497 (*f*).

SELE co. Suss.
Ben. Priory *f.* bef. 1096
883. **Oxford, Magdalen Coll., MS. Lat. 274** (formerly Muniments, Arch. C. ii. 3. 12). Composite gen. cartulary, begun in the 13th cent. (*temp.* Hen. III) and continued down to the 15th cent. in a series of mainly

13th–14th cent. hands, with occasional rubrication. Contains copies of grants to and leases by the priory, with some other misc. material, preceded by copies of the foundation, episcopal and other (incl. one or two papal) charters and documents rel. churches, tithes etc. Incomplete 14th–15th cent. Table, on four preliminary leaves. A 19th cent. transcript is *ib.*, Muniments, Arch. D. 7. 27. Ed. (in translation) L. F. Salzman, *The Chartulary of . . . Sele* (Cambridge, 1923). Described by P. Marchegay, 'Cartulaires français en Angleterre', *Bibl. École des Chartes*, Fourth ser. i (1855), 131–5.

Fos. 71. 9⅞ × 7¼ in.

SEMPRINGHAM co. Linc.
Gilb. Priory *f. c.* 1131
884. **Destroyed.** Cartulary formerly *penes* the earls of Lincoln (*D*). Stated to have been burnt in a fire at Staple Inn (*P*).

SHAFTESBURY co. Dors.
Ben. Abbey (Nuns) *f. c.* 888
885. **BM., Harley 61.** Cartulary, early 15th cent., of royal and some other charters etc., incl. grants by the abbesses, 9th–15th cent., and (fos. 37–89) terriers, custumaries etc. of manors. Rubrics, red numeration of the quires and folios etc. Intended apparently as a register of rights, privileges etc. given and conceded rather than of title-deeds. *Mon. Angl.* ii, 474 (*u*) (list of contents). Hutchins, *Hist. Dorset* iii (1868), 22–4 (extracts).

Fos. 124. 11½ × 7¾ in. *FO:* 'W.P.'; Sir S. D'Ewes.
886. **BM., Egerton 3135.** Cartulary, early 15th cent., contemp. with No. 885 and in similar though rather smaller format. Contains copies of deeds arranged topographically rel. lands in Fovant, Donhead St. Mary and Shaftesbury given by Robert Osegod *al.* Fovent and Edith his wife for the endowment of a chantry of St. Catherine. The deeds of gift etc., 1396–1407, are copied at fos. 109–18 and the form of ordination of the chantry, 1415, by their daughter Abbess Cecilia Fovent is added in a contemp. hand at fos. 100v–103v. A. J. Collins, *Brit. Mus. Quart.* x (1935–6), 66–8 (discussion).

Fos. 123 (wants about 15 leaves *passim*, incl. 11 aft. fo. 65). 10¼ × 7 in. *FO:* J. Wild,

1784; Sir T. Phillipps (MS. 11732; from Payne, bookseller, 1845).

❡ *Inventory*

887.   **BM., Egerton 3098.** 'Kalendare Munimentorum.' Inventory of deeds begun, 1500, by Alexander Katour, sacristan, for Abbess Margery Twynyho at the advice of her brother Christopher, steward of the abbey, and completed after her death in 1505, see the preface (fos. 1–2). Red paragraphs, half-lines and touching of initials. Arranged mainly topographically by manors, with some general sections (*Cantarie, pro Abbatissa* etc.) at the end. Hutchins, *op. cit.* iii, 86–8 (abstract). H. I. Bell, *Brit. Mus. Quart.* viii (1933–4), 18–22 (discussion, with translation of the explanatory preface).

Fos. iv + 34. 9½ × 6¼ in. *FO:* the Rev. C. Twinyhoe, 18th cent.; Twinyhoc W. Erle (d. 1908).

❡ *Other registers etc.*

888.   **Untraced.** Leiger-book in the evidence room, early 17th cent., of Lord Arundell at Wardour Castle, see the brief extracts from fo. 482 in BM., Add. 29976, fo. 13. The castle was destroyed in 1643.

SHAP   co. Westm.
Praem. Abbey   *f.* (at Preston Patrick)
                                                            c. 1190

889.   **Untraced.** Cartulary *penes* Lord Wm. Howard at Naworth, 29 Jan. 1638–9. Extracts from fos. 6–59 are in Bodl., Dodsworth 45 (*SC.* 4187), fos. 17v–20, and others from an early 17th cent. transcript (untraced) are in *ib.*, Dodsworth 159 (*SC.* 5100), fos. 181–7, 189. These are copied in BM., Harley 294, fos. 207v–9v. H. M. Colvin, *The White Canons in England* (Oxford, 1951), 382 (a note).

890.   **Untraced.** 'Registra . . . penes . . . ducem Wharton' (*T*), i.e. Philip, duke of Wharton (1698–1731).

SHEEN   co. Surr.
Carthus. Priory   *f.* 1414
    No cartulary recorded.

❡ *Inventory*

891.   **BM., Cotton Otho B. xiv,** fos. 5–149. Inventory of the muniments, late 15th cent. (aft. 1483), of which the organisation is described in a Prologue (fo. 7). Bold red and blue initials, headings etc. Arranged in sections by sources of

endowment (incl. lands of the suppressed alien priories of Wareham, Carisbrooke, Hayling, Lewisham and Ware), with further subdivision by places and in some cases for papal and royal charters. Each section is prefaced by a separate Table. *Carte non sigillate* are grouped together at the end (fos. 136–49).

Fos. 145 (11–149 with contemp. foliation, i–clv; wants leaves towards and at the end). 11½ × 8 in. (cropped). *FO:* Sir R. Cotton; J. Payne (MS. 30); purchased of Egerton, bookseller, 1787.

SHERBORNE   co. Dors.
Ben. Abbey   *f.* 7th cent. (?)

892.   **BM., Add. 46487.** Cartulary (fos. 3–32, 69–74 (misbound)), 12th cent. (*c.* 1146), of royal, papal and episcopal charters, 9th–12th cent., in Latin and Anglo-Saxon; followed by Passion narratives, collects, Gospel lessons, prayers and (fos. 67–8, originally at the end of the book) a list of vestments. Written in a good book-hand with rubrics and red, green and blue initials, often decorated and in the non-cartulary parts of the MS., which include two miniatures of evangelists, sometimes illuminated. Copies of pleas, *temp.* Edw. I, have been added at fo. 2. Medieval binding, oak boards with enamels. T. Hearne, *Leland's Itinerary* ix (Oxford, 1712), 156–65 (2nd ed. ii (Oxford, 1744), 50–9); cf. *Id., Remarks & Collections* iii (ed. C. E. Doble, Oxford Hist. Soc. xiii, 1889), 419 ff. etc. Described, with a full list of contents, by F. Wormald, 'The Sherborne "Chartulary"', *Fritz Saxl Memorial Essays*, ed. D. J. Gordon (1957), 101–19.

Fos. lvi (19th cent. interleaving) + 88. 11¾ × 7¼ in. *FO:* William, 5th baron Digby of Gleashill, 1712 (?); T. Lloyd, 19th cent.; Sir T. Phillipps (MS. 3626).

❡ *Other registers etc.*

893.   **Untraced.** Roll of charters preserved 'in Curia Augmentacion(um) penes Christoferum Masters custodem ibi 3 April 1648', from which extracts are in Bodl., Dodsworth 63 (*SC.* 5005), fos. 90–2. Apparently a confirmation of charters by the bp. of St. David's, 1301 (?).

SHOTTESBROOK   co. Berks
Coll. of St. John Baptist   *f.* 1337

894.   **BM., Egerton 3029.** Gen. cartu-

lary (fos. 15–21, 34–9, 59 ff.), late 14th cent. (aft. 1386), with small blue and red initials etc. Arranged topographically, with extensive additions *passim* and some duplication of material. *BM. Cat. Add. MSS.* 1916–1920, 344–5 (description). T. Hearne, *Leland's Itinerary* v (2nd ed., Oxford, 1744), 119 ff.

Fos. i + 124. 14¼ × 10 in. *FO:* the Weldon fam.; Stephen Edwards, 1694; F. Cherry, 1711; Sir T. Mostyn, bart., 1744; the Lloyd-Mostyn fam., barons Mostyn.

SHREWSBURY co. Salop
Ben. Abbey *f. c.* 1083–90
895. **Aberystwyth, NLW., MS. 7851.** Gen. cartulary, late 13th cent. (*temp.* Edw. I), with red and blue initials, occasionally decorated, and consecutive red numeration of the entries. Arranged apparently according to subject matter, in part topographically, with copies of royal, episcopal etc. charters at the beginning, after charters rel. the foundation, and *passim*. Additions include incomplete late 14th cent. Tables and an index by grantors at the end. Transcripts, 18th–19th cent., are in BM., Add. 30311 (*FO:* W. Mytton); Shrewsbury Public Libr., MS. 1A; Bodl., Top. Salop d. 2, fos. 1–57 (*FO:* Sir T. Phillipps, MS. 18316). E. D. Jones, 'The Cartulary of . . . Shrewsbury', *Nat. Libr. of Wales J.* v (1947–8), 175–8 (description). Cited extensively from a transcript by R. W. Eyton, *Antiq. Shropshire* (1854–60).

Fos. 225 (paginated, 1–433, from fo. 9). 12 × 8¾ in. *FO:* Sir H. Spelman ('ut putatur', Bodl., Dodsworth 135 (*SC.* 5076), fos. 91v–3); Sir R. Lee, bart., 1636 (*N*); stated by Eyton (Bodl., Top. Salop d. 2) to have been exchanged, 1638, with Sir R. Leveson for the Lilleshall cartulary (No. 577 above); E. Lloyd, 1824 (from a scrap heap); Sir T. Phillipps (MS. 3516).

SIBTHORPE co. Nott.
Parish Church
896. **BM., Add. 27372.** Register, mid-14th cent., of deeds, records of legal proceedings etc., mainly rel. the foundation, *temp.* Edw. II, by T. de Sibthorpe of chapels and chantries of St. Mary at Sibthorpe and in the church at Beckingham, co. Linc. Arranged in sections according to subject matter and incl. copies of some

royal and episcopal charters etc. *passim*. Cited in *Thoroton's Hist. Nottinghamshire*, ed. J. Throsby, i (1797), 326 ff.

Fos. 83 (incomplete at the beginning). 13½ × 10 in. *FO:* R. Thoroton, 1677; the Rev. L. A. Sharpe, 1866.

SIBTON co. Suff.
Cist. Abbey *f.* 1150
897. **BM., Arundel 221.** Cartulary (fos. 32–143), 13th cent., with spaces for rubrics and initials, containing copies of private deeds arranged topographically and omitting the names of witnesses. Breaks off in the middle of an entry at the end and is perhaps also incomplete at the beginning since it lacks material for Sibton and Peasenhall. Preceded and followed by misc. 14th cent. additions incl. (fos. 144–51) copies of 12th–13th cent. etc. papal bulls, listed with some of the other misc. contents in *BM. Cat. Arundel MSS.*, 63–4.

Fos. i + 153. 10¼ × 7¼ in. *FO:* Ld. Wm. Howard; Thomas Howard, 2nd earl of Arundel; presented by Henry Howard, 6th duke of Norfolk, to the Royal Society, 1678.

898. **A. P. Levett-Scrivener Esq.,** Sibton Abbey. Part (quires *i–v*, cf. No. 899) of a cartulary made, 1414, by J. de Gislingham, with a few misc. additions, and arranged topographically incl. names of witnesses. Contains sections for Sibton, Sibton Hall, and Jurdis and Falesham manors in Peasenhall and Bruisyard, the first of which includes copies of confirmations of Stephen, Eugenius III and Thomas Becket, and of one or two later royal writs. Transcripts, 19th cent., are in BM., Add. 8172 (Jermyn MSS.), fos. 233–344; 19082 (Davy MSS.), fos. 37–79. See also *Mon. Angl.* v, 560–1, nos. iv–viii.

Fos. 48 (paginated, 1–96). 11½ × 8 in. Paper. *FO:* the Howard and Scrivener fams., Sibton (cited, 19th cent., as of John Fisher, bishop of Salisbury, who married Dorothea Scrivener).

899. **Oxford, Bodl., Rawlinson B. 421.** A further part of No. 898 (quires *xiii–xviiii*), containing sections for Heveningham with Thorpe, Walpole, Dernford and Wenhaston. W. D. Macray, *Cat. MSS. Bibl. Bodl.* v (i) (Oxford, 1862), 672.

Fos. 50. 11½ × 8 in. Paper. *FO:* W. Clavell.

¶ *Other registers etc.*

900. **A. P. Levett-Scrivener Esq.**, deposited at Ipswich, E. Suffolk R.O. (50/9/15.1). Copies (a roll), late 13th cent., of a royal confirmation of charters, 52 Hen. III, and three 12th cent. papal bulls. *FO:* as No. 898.

901. **Ditto** (50/9/15(1)–(5)). Four loose quires from a register of rentals etc., *c.* 1320–30 with additions, incl. contemp. copies of some royal licences to alienate, episcopal confirmations etc. *FO:* as No. 898.

902. **The Earl of Iveagh,** Elveden Hall (Iveagh Collections, 345 (i)). Copies (a roll), late 14th cent., of five deeds rel. Mundham etc. *FO:* T. Astle; C. Ord; Sir T. Phillipps (part of MS. 3848).

SKEWKIRK (*al.* **SCOKIRK**) co. York
v. TOCKWITH.

SLAPTON co. Devon
Collegiate Chantry *f.* 1373

903. **Oxford, Bodl., Wood empt. 3** (*SC.* 8591). Register, late 14th cent., containing copies of the foundation charter of Sir Guy de Brien and confirmations by the bishop and dean & chapter of Exeter. Some illuminated borders, initials etc. displaying the arms of the grantors.
Fos. iii + 13. 14¾ × 11 in. *FO:* R. Sheldon.

SNELSHALL co. Bucks.
Ben. Priory *f.* 1203–19
J. G. Jenkins, *Cartulary of Snelshall Priory* (Bucks. Record Soc. ix, 1952 for 1945), prints abstracts of both cartularies.

904. **BM., Add. 37068,** fos. 51–78. Three quires of a cartulary written in the second half of the 13th cent., containing copies of 55 private deeds arranged topographically. Formerly stitched to the inside of the cover of No. 905.
Fos. 30 (incl. blank leaves; 17th–18th cent. foliation, 1–30). 7⅛ × 5⅛ in. *FO:* E. Arnold, 17th cent.; J. Selby, 1715 (*T*); the Lowndes *al.* Selby-Lowndes fam.

905. **BM., Add. 37068,** fos. 1–50. Cartulary, 13th–14th cent. (aft. *c.* 1280), written in book-hand with spaces for rubrics and initials, and with a few additions. Contains copies of in all 161 private deeds, arranged topographically and repeating much of the material in No. 904.

Fos. 50 (17th–18th cent. foliation, 1–49, duplicating 15). 10½ × 7½ in. *FO:* as No. 904.

SOUTHAMPTON co. Southt.
Aug. Priory of St. Denys, Portswood *f.* 1127

906. **BM., Add. 15314.** Cartulary, 14th cent. (aft. 1342), with rubrics etc. Contains copies of private deeds, arranged topographically, with additions on blank etc. leaves *passim* which include copies of a few royal charters etc.
Fos. 126 (incl. 9 preliminary leaves; lacks at least two leaves at the beginning and three at the end). 13 × 9¼ in. *FO:* the Rev. E. Ferrers ('Feb. 1816 . . . bought at Harfield's sale', fo. 5); the Rev. C. W. Knyvett.

SOUTHAMPTON co. Southt.
Hosp. of St. Julian *al.* 'Domus Dei' *f. c.* 1197

907. **Oxford, Queen's Coll.,** Muniments (4. G. 4). Cartulary, late 14th cent., with occasional pen-work decoration of letters elongated into the upper margin. Arranged mainly topographically, with misc. additions at the beginning, end and at fos. 50–2. Fos. 53–64, which contain copies of royal charters (Ric. I–Edw. I) and other 13th cent. material, appear originally to have been the opening leaves of an earlier 14th cent. compilation. H. T. Riley, *HMC. Second Report* (1871), App., 138–9 (descriptive note).
Fos. 102. 13¾ × 8¾ in.

SOUTHWARK co. Surr.
Aug. Priory of St. Mary Overy *f.* 1106

908. **BM., Add. 6040.** Fragm. of a 13th cent. cartulary, with rubrics. Fos. 1–2 contain copies of parts of 25 deeds rel. Mitcham etc. and fos. 3–4 (fly-leaves?) contain misc. additions.
Fos. 4. 10 × 8 in. (cropped and mutilated). *FO:* T. Martin, who took them from some children's drum-heads made in Exeter; W. Bray.

¶ *Other registers etc.*

909. **BM., Cotton Faust. A. viii,** fos. 151–78. Part of a misc. 14th cent. etc. register of pleas, inquisitions, rentals etc. Bound up at the end of Annals and other material. *FO:* Magdalen Coll., Oxford, cf. Bodl., James 2 (*SC.* 3839), p. 207.

SOUTHWARK co. Surr.
Hosp. of St. Thomas M. *f.* bef. 1170 (?)
910. **Oxford, Bodl., Rawlinson D. 763,** fos. 1–31. Four (non-consecutive ?) quires from an early 15th cent. cartulary containing copies, with marginal titles, of deeds and a few royal documents rel. London and co. Surr., arranged roughly topographically. W. D. Macray, *Cat. MSS. Bibl. Bodl.* v (iii) (Oxford, 1893), 500–1 (list of places).

Fos. 31 (wants leaves or possibly quires at the beginning and aft. fos. 8, 16). 12 × 8 in.
911. **BM., Stowe 942.** Gen. cartulary, 16th cent. (aft. 1525), with marginal titles and occasional pen-work decoration of initials. Arranged mainly topographically with copies of charters rel. the foundation and papal bulls (scored through with a pen) at the beginning (fos. 1–7r). Calendared by L. Drucker, *Chartulary of the Hospital of St. Thomas the Martyr, Southwark* (1932, privately). *BM. Cat. Stowe MSS.* i, 622–3, lists the parishes etc.

Fos. 321. 14 × 9½ in. Paper. *FO:* G. Brander; T. Astle.

SOUTHWELL co. Nott.
Minster (Coll. Church) *f.* bef. 956
912. **Southwell Minster, MS. 1.** 'Liber Albus.' Composite cartulary begun (pp. 1–61) *c.* 1335 and continued in 15th cent. (pp. 62–441) and 16th cent. (pp. 442–50) hands. The early leaves rubricated, with red and blue decorated initials. Opens with copies of papal bulls from 1160 and royal charters from Hen. I, and includes statutes, extracts from court rolls and other miscellanea as well as copies of episcopal, private and further papal and royal charters etc. Medieval binding. An 18th cent. abstract is in BM., Add. 24817. A. F. Leach, *Visitations and Memorials of Southwell* (Camden Soc., New ser. xlviii, 1891), ci–cviii (summarised list of contents). W. D. Macray, *HMC. Twelfth Report,* App. ix (1891), 539–40 (description).

Fos. iv + 238 (paginated, 1–476; 451 ff. mainly blank). 12⅞ × 8½ in.

SOUTHWICK co. Southt.
Aug. Priory *f.* (at Portchester) 1133
913. **Mrs. E. S. Borthwick-Norton,** deposited at Winchester, Hampshire R.O. ('Priory Register No. 1'). Gen. cartulary, 12th–13th cent., with rubrics and red and green initials. Arranged in sections, apparently according to subject matter, with extensive additions, mainly 13th cent., made without regard to the original arrangement, and copies of royal, papal and episcopal charters included *passim.* Fos. 34–53 contain added 13th cent. rentals, lists of tenants etc., followed (fo. 53v) by further misc. additions, mainly 14th cent. A number of leaves are mutilated by damp.

Fos. 58 (wants a few leaves *passim*). 12¾ × 8¼ in. (fos. 34–58, 11½ × 8¼ in.). *FO:* the White, Norton, Whitehead and Thistlethwayte fams., Southwick Park.
914. **Ditto** ('Priory Register No. 2'). Composite register, 13th–15th cent., comprising: (1) fos. 1–19, a 14th cent. quire containing: (*a*) copies of episcopal etc. documents, 1357–9, rel. Swindon church, fos. 1–4; (*b*) a rubricated section of royal charters (Hen. I–Edw. III), writs, inquisitions, pleas etc., fos. 5–16; (*c*) misc. later additions, fos. 17–19; (2) fos. 20–49, two rubricated quires in a similar hand to (1), containing: (*a*) an inventory of deeds, 1366 with additions, arranged by places with subdivisions by *Cophini* (*i–xiii*), fos. 20–35, 44r; (*b*) part of a similar inventory, 13th cent., on loose inserted leaves, also arranged by *Cophini* (*iii–xvi*), fos. 36–43; (*c*) misc. additions incl. (fos. 45v–49) a perambulation, 1300, of the forests of Hampshire, fos. 44v–49; (3) fos. 50–106, seven quires, written in several 14th–15th cent. hands, containing: (*a*) copies of further writs, inquisitions, pleas etc., down to *temp.* Hen. IV, fos. 50–62r; (*b*) a cartulary, with red page-headings (incl. the pressmark '*xvi*'), of the manors of Boarhunt Herbelyn, Boarhunt Herberd etc., acquired *c.* 1362–9, fos. 62v–96; (*c*) misc. additions, incl. material rel. Hinton Burrant down to *temp.* Hen. VI and an undated taxation, fos. 97–106.

Fos. 106. 13 × 8½ in. *FO:* as No. 913.
915. **Ditto** ('Priory Register No. 3'). Gen. cartulary, 1396, with rubrics and spaces for initials. Arranged by *Cophini* (*i–xv*), with a contemp. Table at fos. 255v–70. Fos. 1–12 are added quires containing copies of papal bulls etc., without pressmarks. Fos. 120–35 are interpolated, apparently from a slightly earlier compilation. Extracts, 1831, by Sir F. Madden are in BM., Add. 33280, fos. 31–273 etc.

Fos. 271 + 1. 12 × 9¾ in. *FO:* as No. 913.

916. **BM., Harley 317.** Quire from a late 14th cent. cartulary, with rubrics and blue initials. Headed *Cophinus septimus* and contains copies of deeds, 1380–6, rel. the gift by Bernard Brocas of the manors of East Hoe, Hannington Lancelevy etc., with some misc. additions at the end. A transcript by Sir F. Madden is in BM. Add. 33280, fos. 275–85.

Fos. 6. 12¾ × 8 in. *FO:* Sir S. D'Ewes.

917. **Winchester College,** Muniments (Portsmouth I. 10). Part of a 14th–15th cent. cartulary, written without decoration in a number of hands. Contains material down to *temp.* Edw. III rel. Portsmouth and Stubbington, with contemp. marginal annotations and occasional pressmarks (*xii*).

Fos. 34. 12⅝ × 9 in.

❡ *Inventories*

v. also No. 914.

918. **Mrs. D. Daly,** deposited at Winchester, Hampshire R.O. (5. M. 50). Inventory of charters begun in a 12th–13th cent. hand resembling that of No. 913 and continued in a succession of 13th–14th cent. hands. Arranged by *Cophini (i–xi)* with some marginal headings in red.

Roll of 5 membrs. 126 × 6¾ in. *FO:* as No. 913 (?).

❡ *Other registers etc.*

919. **Mrs. E. S. Borthwick-Norton,** deposited *ib.* 'Rememoratorium terre de Porcestre', 1405. Register of extents, custumaries and rentals rel. Portchester. *FO:* as No. 913.

SPALDING   co. Linc.
Ben. Priory   *f.* 1074

Maurice Johnson, 'Introduction to the Minute Books of the Spalding Society', *Bibl. Top. Britannica* iii (1790), no. xx, 13–8, gives some account of the cartularies etc.

920. **BM., Add. 35296.** Vol. i (cf. No. 921) of a gen. register of charters and other misc. evidences, *c.* 1331, written with rubrics, red initials etc. and arranged in five parts. Contains the first three parts: (1) foundation, site etc., fos. 8–86; (2) royal and other temporal liberties, fos. 87–279; (3) papal and other spiritual liberties, incl. appropriations of churches etc., fos. 280–430; with a summary contemp. Table of pts. 1–5 at fos. 3–7 and

additions *passim* and in the form of a 14th–15th cent. supplement at the end (fos. 430v–445). Medieval binding. A transcript, 1772, by W. Cole in BM., Add. 5844, fos. 73–232, is partially calendared in *Mon. Angl.* iii, 211 (*c*). *BM. Cat. Add. MSS.* 1894–1899, 242–4 (description).

Fos. 449. 13⅛ × 9 in. *FO:* Sir R. Ogle; J. Oldfeild, 1659; Maurice Johnson; lent, bef. 1772, by Mrs. Elizabeth Wingfield to W. Greaves *al.* Beaupré-Bell; Bertram, 1st earl of Ashburnham (MS. App. 237).

921. **BM., Harley 742.** Vol. ii (cf. No. 920), containing the two final parts: (4) topographical, fos. 2–320; (5) miscellaneous, incl. (fos. 323–36) charters of the almonry, fos. 321–46; with misc. additions *passim* and at the end. A summary contemp. Table of pts. 4–5 at fo. 1, repeated from vol. i, is printed with some additional notes in *Mon. Angl.* iii, 213 (*b*). P. Marchegay, 'Cartulaires français en Angleterre', *Bibl. École des Chartes*, Fourth ser. i (1855), 135–7 (description).

Fos. 352. 13¼ × 9¼ in. *FO:* Sir R. Ogle; Bp. E. Stillingfleet.

❡ *Other registers etc.*

922. **Cambridge, Gonville & Caius Coll., MS. 376.** Misc. register, early 15th cent. M. R. James, *Cat. MSS. Gonv. and Caius Coll.* i (Cambridge, 1907), no. 314 (list of contents). *FO:* J. Oldfeild, 16th cent.; Martin Johnson; W. Moore (MS. D. 117).

923. **Spalding, Gentlemen's Society.** 'Mintling Register', 15th cent. Lists etc. of villein holdings etc., arranged topographically with copies of other misc. documents and memoranda entered on blank leaves *passim.* Johnson, *l.c.,* 16–7. *FO:* R. Ogle 1546; Maurice Johnson; Alexander, 1st baron Peckover.

SPINNEY   co. Cambr.
Aug. and (1449) Ben. Priory   *f.* bef.
                               1227–8

924. **Untraced.** 'Registrum Burgony.' Cartulary (?) *penes* Isaac Barrow of Spinney, 1638, from which genealogical extracts down to fo. 54 by Sir S. D'Ewes, to whom the title cited is probably to be ascribed, are in BM., Harley 294, fo. 174v. Presumably identical or a confusion with the register of which ownership is ascribed to D'Ewes himself (*D*).

STAFFORD co. Staff.
Aug. Priory *f. c.* 1174
925. **Untraced.** Cartulary of unstated
ownership (perhaps that ascribed, 17th
cent., to (Walter) Fowler, owner of the
priory's site (*D*) and to Thomas Fowler of
Pendeford, 1796 (*P*)), from which extracts
down to *temp.* Hen. IV by Sampson
Erdeswick (d. 1603) are in BM., Harley
506, fos. 32v–43 *passim*. The latter are used
by the Rev. F. Parker, '"Chartulary" of
the Priory of St. Thomas . . . Stafford',
Wm. Salt Arch. Soc., *Coll. Hist. Staffordshire* viii (1887), 123–201, with original
charters then in the Phillipps collection
(MSS. 7891–8069; provenance unstated).
¶ *Other registers etc.*
926. **Oxford, Bodl., Auct. F. 3. 10**
(*SC.* 2582), fos. ii, iii. Two mutilated pieces
of a 14th–15th cent. roll, containing copies
of deeds *c.* 1280–14th cent. Used as end-
papers in the binding of a 13th–14th cent.
MS. from the priory.

STAMFORD co. Linc.
Ben. Priory of St. Michael at (Nuns) *f. c.*
1155
v. also No. 1326 below.
927. **Untraced.** Cartulary *penes* Geoffrey Minshull, 1657, from which extracts
are printed in *Mon. Angl.* iv, 260–3 *passim*.
¶ *Inventory*
928. **PRO., Special Collections** (Rentals & Surveys, SC. 11/426). Inventory,
13th cent., of 85 charters, arranged and
numbered topographically in five sections
with spaces for additions, of which few
have in fact been made. The verso contains a rental in the same hand.
Roll of 3 membrs. *c.* 60 × 7 in.
¶ *Other registers etc.*
928A. **Untraced.** The source of the
notes, 17th cent., in Bodl., Dodsworth 59
(*SC.* 5001), pp. 165–8, of ten charters (incl.
four of bps. of Lincoln) 'ex quibusdam
Antiquis Rotulis in pergameno penes me
Rogerum Dodsworth'.

STANLEY co. Wilts
Cist. Abbey *f.* (at Loxwell) 1151
No cartulary recorded.
¶ *Inventory*
929. **BM., Harley 6716.** Repertorium
of the muniments, 13th cent. (aft. 1245),
written in columns across the length of the

page with small red and green initials etc.
and pressmarks. The order of the entries,
which differs from that of the pressmarks,
is: (1) papal charters; (2) fines; (3) royal
charters; (4) in alphabetical order of places;
with additions throughout in the right-
hand column, left vacant apparently for
this purpose. Fos. iv–2 contain one or two
later memoranda. Ed. W. de G. Birch,
'Collections towards the History . . . of
Stanley', *Wilts. Arch. & Nat. Hist. Mag.*
xv (1875), 239–79.
Fos. 17. 12 × 6 in.

STANLOW co. Chest.
Cist. Abbey *f.* 1172
v. WHALLEY.

STAUGHTON, GREAT co. Hunt.
Parish Church
930. **Westminster Abbey,** Muniments
(No. 5807). 'Registrum Munimentorum
Ecclesie de Stokton. Magna.' Copies, late
14th cent., with pen-decorated initials, of
15 charters, 1334–69, incl. one confirmation
of J. Hotham, bp. of Ely.
Roll of 2 membrs. 44 × 13½ in.

STIXWOULD co. Linc.
Cist. Priory (Nuns) *f. c.* 1135
931. **BM., Add. 46701.** Gen. cartulary,
late 13th cent., with rubrics etc. Arranged
topographically with misc. additions at the
end (fos. 110 ff.), and incl. copies of charters of bishops and the earls of Chester in the
first section, for Stixwold.
Fos. x + 125. 8¼ × 6 in. *FO:* the Coventry
fam., barons & earls of Coventry.

STOGURSEY co. Som.
Ben. Priory *f.* 1100–7
932. **Eton College,** Muniments (Stogursey Deeds 48). 'Hec sunt munimenta
facta prioratui de Stokes Curci de diversis
dominis ut subsequuntur.' Copies, early
14th cent., of 26 charters, incl. a few episcopal and capitular ones, *c.* 1100–1300. Ed.
T. D. Tremlett & N. Blakiston, *Stogursey
Charters* (Somerset Record Soc. lxi, 1949
for 1946), 42–53.
Roll of 3 membrs.

STOKE BY CLARE co. Suff.
Ben. Priory *f.* (at Clare) 1090
933. **BM., Cotton App. xxi.** Gen. cartulary, 13th cent. (aft. 1250), with rubrics,

red and green initials, and some misc. additions *passim*. Arranged in the order of the muniments, of which there is an inventory at fos. 1–12, with sections of royal (incl. fines), baronial, episcopal etc. and papal charters at the beginning (fos. 13–73), of deeds rel. pittances and the almoner at the end (fos. 179 ff.), and otherwise topographically. A consecutive numeration of the entries, *i–ccccli*, seems to follow the pressmarks of deeds since against some (omitted in the inventory) the number is replaced by the words 'vacat', 'ignoro' or 'nul'. The use of a 'long hundred' (200 = *cll*, 219 = *cllxix*, 220 = *cc* etc.) is apparently an *ad hoc* device, to allow expansion of an earlier series of figures, since the first hundred (*xcix*, *c*, *ci* etc.) is of orthodox length.

Fos. 212. $9\frac{1}{2} \times 7$ in.

STONE
co. Staff.
Aug. Priory
f. c. 1135
v. also KENILWORTH.

934.   **BM., Cotton Roll xiii. 6.** Copies, 12th cent., in at least two hands, of 23 royal, episcopal and founders' charters down to *temp.* Hen. II. H. J. Ellis, *Index to the Charters & Rolls in the . . . BM.* ii (1912), 711, lists the contents, *sub* Stone Priory *passim*.

Roll of 3 membrs. $49\frac{1}{4} \times 8\frac{3}{8}$ in. *FO:* Christopher, baron Hatton (*D*).

935.   **BM., Cotton Vesp. E. xxiv.** Gen. cartulary (fos. 1–12, 17–28), 13th cent. (aft. 1235), with rubrics and (fos. 13–6, 29–43) misc. contemp. and later additions. Arranged mainly topographically with copies of *Privilegia* (royal, papal and episcopal) at fos. 17–18v and occasionally elsewhere *passim*. Transcripts, 18th cent., are in BM., Stowe 943 and Cambridge, Trinity Coll. MS. R. 5. 7. G. Wrottesley, 'The Stone Chartulary', Wm. Salt Arch. Soc., *Coll. Hist. Staffordshire* vi, pt. i (1885), 1–28 (abstract).

Fos. 43. $8\frac{3}{8} \times 5\frac{3}{8}$ in. *FO:* as No. 934.

STONELEIGH
co. Warw.
Cist. Abbey
f. (at Radmore) 1141
936.   **Major A. M. H. Gregory-Hood, M.C.,** deposited at Stratford-upon-Avon, Shakespeare Birthplace Libr. ('The Gregory Leiger-Book', pp. 193–256). Cartulary, 13th cent. (*temp.* Hen. III), with a

9—M.C.

single red opening initial, incl. copies of royal, episcopal and baronial charters at the beginning and *passim*. Much mutilated by damp, and now bound up with a fragm. of a cartulary of Coventry Cathedral Priory (No. 275 above) in a 16th cent. register of the Gregory family (No. 1249 below).

Fos. 32. $7\frac{5}{8} \times 5\frac{3}{4}$ in. *FO:* the Gregory (afterw. Gregory-Hood) fam., Stivichall and Loxley Hall.

937.   **Lord Leigh,** deposited *ib*. Register, *c.* 1392, with uncompleted rubrics and red initials, of charters and other evidences rel. the abbey's possessions in Stoneleigh and its hamlets, made by Thomas Pype. Book *i* of a compilation stated (preface, fo. 2) to comprise four books (*ii* similar evidences rel. other places, *iii* misc. memoranda, *iv* privileges, compositions for tithes, pleas etc.). Opens as a narrative incorporating copies of royal and some other charters, and becomes after fo. lxx an uninterrupted sequence of these, intermixed with custumals, rentals and other misc. evidences and memoranda. Ends with a list etc. of abbots (fo. clxxviii) and misc. additions (fo. clxxxi). A 16th cent. transcript is kept with the volume. A photostat copy is in Birmingham Reference Libr. Extracts are in Bodl., Dugdale 12 (*SC.* 6502), pp. 31 ff. Of Bks. *ii–iv*, nothing further is known. *HMC. Second Report* (1870), App., 49 (anonymous note). An edition for the Dugdale Soc. is in preparation.

Fos. i + 206. $12\frac{1}{8} \times 8\frac{3}{4}$ in.

STRATFORD LANGTHORNE
co. Essex
Cist. Abbey
f. 1135
No cartulary recorded.
¶ *Other registers etc.*
938.   **Untraced.** 'Domesday' *al.* 'The Legier'. Extracts, 17th cent., in Dublin, Trinity Coll. MS. F. 1. 20, fos. 38–9 (transcribed, 1891, in BM., Add. 34078) relate to compositions with Haliwell Priory, London, concerning tithes in Ruckholt manor etc. in Leyton.

STRATFORD-UPON-AVON
co. Warw.
Guild of the Holy Cross, BVM., & St. John Bapt. *f.* (as a single corporation) 1406
No cartulary recorded.

¶ *Other registers etc.*

939. **Stratford-upon-Avon Corporation,** Shakespeare's Birthplace Libr. Guildbook, *c.* 1460, with retrospection to 1406 and continuations down to 1535. Ed. J. Harvey Bloom, *Register of the Gild of the Holy Cross* (1907).

STUDLEY co. Oxon
Ben. Priory (Nuns) *f.* bef. 1176
940. **Untraced.** Cartulary *penes* T. Allen (d. 1632) of Gloucester Hall, Oxford, from which extracts by B. Twyne (1579 ?–1644) are in Bodl., Twyne 24, pp. 642–61 (cited by J. Dunkin, *Hist. Bullingdon & Ploughley* (1823), 130–40). Apparently arranged topographically, incl. copies of royal and episcopal charters.

¶ *Other registers etc.*

941. **Capt. J. K. Henderson,** Warren Farm, Horton-cum-Studley. 'Studley Chartulary.' A 16th–17th cent. book of writings, incl. a copy of a terrier of the priory, made apparently for a member of the Croke fam. and bound up *c.* 1823. *FO:* the Croke fam., Studley.

SWAFFHAM BULBECK co. Cambr.
Ben. Priory (Nuns) *f. c.* 1150–63
941A. **Untraced.** 'Transcript of the Black-book of Swaffham, which concerns the building of their Church etc.' Listed by E. Bernard, *Cat. MSS. Angliae* ii (i) (Oxford, 1697), 373, no. 9631, as MS. 445 in the libr. of Bp. J. Moore, but not now among his MSS. in Cambridge U.L. Like extracts in BM., Harley 5019, fos. 52, 223v ff. and elsewhere, may in fact have been copied from the Peterborough Abbey 'Liber R. de Swaffham' (No. 757 above). No cartulary of the house is otherwise recorded.

SWAVESEY co. Cambr.
Ben. Priory *f.* bef. 1086
942. **Untraced.** 'Liber Prioratus,' from which extracts by St. Loo Kniveton are reproduced in Bodl., Dodsworth 130 (*SC.* 5071), fo. 68 (from fo. 156 of the original) and *Mon. Angl.* vi, 1001–2.

TAKELEY co. Essex
Ben. Priory *f.* 1066–86
943. **Untraced.** Cartulary, from which transcripts, 15th–16th cent., are in Oxford,

New Coll. Muniments, 'Registrum Secundum', fos. 1–56; cf. No. 745 above.

TANDRIDGE co. Surr.
Aug. Priory *f.* (as a hosp.) *temp.* Ric. I
No cartulary recorded.

¶ *Other registers etc.*

944. **BM., Harley 4785.** Copies, 16th-17th cent., of rentals, court-rolls etc., 15th-16th cent. with additions down to *temp.* James I. Paper. *FO:* P. Le Neve.

945. **BM., Harley 4786.** Copies, 16th-17th cent., of royal letters patent, *temp.* Hen. VIII–Eliz. I, rel. its former lands. Paper. *FO:* as No. 944.

TATTERSHALL co. Linc.
Coll. Church *f.* 1439–40
946. **PRO., Exch., T.R.** (Ancient Deeds, AA. 313). A loose 15th cent. quire containing copies of seven charters etc., 1439–53, rel. the college's foundation, endowment etc.
Fos. 14 (paginated, 1–28; 19 ff. blank). 12 × 8¼ in. Paper.

TAVISTOCK co. Devon
Ben. Abbey *f. c.* 974
H. P. R. Finberg, 'Some early Tavistock Charters', *Engl. Hist. Review* lxii (1947), 352–77, edits No. 947, and describes Nos. 948 & 950; see also *Id.*, 'Church and State in Twelfth-century Devon', *Trans. Devon. Assoc.* lxxv (1943), 245–57.

947. **The Duke of Bedford,** Woburn Abbey (Muniments, table 3, drawer A. 3). Cartulary, 13th cent., with rubrics and spaces for initials, the verso of the last leaf being written in another hand of similar date. Contains copies of 59 papal, royal, episcopal and lay charters, *c.* 1103–early 13th cent., with one duplicate.
Fos. 18. 7½ × 5 in.

948. **Untraced.** Gen. cartulary stated by White Kennett in his copy of the *Mon. Angl.*, now in the Bodleian Libr., to have been written *c. temp.* Hen. IV, opening with a history of the foundation. Copies, early 17th cent., for Ralph Brooke, of notes by Sir W. Pole (1561–1635), by whom it was used for his *Description of Devonshire* (printed 1791), are in Oxford, Queen's Coll. MS. 152, fos. 219v–223. Other 17th cent. extracts are printed in *Mon. Angl.* ii, 494 ff. Subsequently used,

early 18th cent., by W. Wotton for the compilation of a list of abbots, see Bodl., Willis 73 (*SC*. 16367), fos. 34v, 42v–43.

Fos. (upwards of 220). *FO*: J. Maynard, lessee of Woburn, 17th cent. (*D*); not in the catalogue of the Duke of Bedford's archives, 1753–5.

¶ *Other registers etc.*

949. **BM., Egerton 3671,** fos. 1–47. Parts, much decayed, of a misc. register or memorandum book rel. the abbey's temporalities, *temp.* J. May, abbot 1402–21, etc. Includes copies of a number of misc. 13th–15th cent. deeds, apparently rel. its tenants. The name 'J. Cowne' written twice, 18th–19th cent., in the margin of fo. 2. Acquired, 1950.

950. **The Duke of Bedford,** *ib.* (table 3, drawer A. 3). 'Liber Albus.' Extents, 1411–23, of lands of the sacrist and other obedientiaries etc. Paper. The name 'Ro. Farrer' written on fos. 1, 38.

TEMPLARS, Order of, in England & Wales *f. c.* 1128
v. also ST. JOHN OF JERUSALEM, SANDFORD. No cartulary recorded.

¶ *Other registers etc.*

951. **PRO., Exch., K.R.** (Miscellanea, E. 163/1/1A). Fragm. of a 12th–13th cent. roll, containing abstracts of five 12th cent. royal charters to the Order. Three are printed by Beatrice A. Lees, *Records of the Templars in England* (1935), 138, 166, 174.

TEMPLE COMBE co. Som. Preceptory of Knts. of St. John *f.* (for Knts. Templar) *c.* 1185
v. also ST. JOHN OF JERUSALEM. No cartulary recorded.

¶ *Inventory*

952. **Winchester College,** Muniments (Longload 2). 'Kalendar Omnium Cartarum et Munimentorum.' Inventory 'renewed' 1396–7 by W. Hulles, preceptor (cf. No. 17), of 106 deeds rel. the preceptory and its manors. Arranged mainly topographically.
Roll of 1 membr. $23\frac{1}{2} \times 8\frac{3}{4}$ in.

TEWKESBURY co. Glouc. Ben. Abbey *f. c.* 715
953. **BM., Cotton Cleop. A. vii,** fos. 70–106. Abstract or calendar of charters

etc., 13th cent. (aft. 1238), incl. notes of royal, episcopal and baronial charters, mainly towards the beginning, and a few complete transcripts towards the end. Rubrics, red initials and (fos. 97v ff.) misc. additions down to *temp.* Edw. I. Bound (fos. 1–69) with Annals etc. (ed. H. R. Luard, *Annales Monastici* i (Rolls ser., 1864), 43 ff.) and printed almost completely in *Mon. Angl.* ii, 67–83.

Fos. 37 (earlier post-medieval foliations, 66–101, 68–103). 7 × 5 in. (cropped).

¶ *Other registers etc.*

954. **BM., Add. 36985.** 'Registrum Theokusburiae secundum originale examinatum.' A 16th cent. transcript of an account of the abbey's founders and benefactors, calligraphically written with heraldic illustrations. *BM. Cat. Add. MSS.* 1900–1905, 271. *FO*: Sir Justinian Isham, 5th bart., 1733, and his descendants at Lamport Hall.

955. **Untraced.** 'Registrum Tewksburiense, secundum Originale vere et perfecte Examinatum; with the Pedigrees of the Founders.' E. Bernard, *Cat. MSS. Angliae* ii (Oxford, 1697), 112, no. 4225. *FO*: Sir H. St. George (MS. A. 21).

956. **Destroyed.** 'Series Fundatorum Monasterii de Theoksbury,' included among misc. historical material in the former Cotton MS. Otho D. i, which was burnt in 1731; cf. T. Smith, *Cat. Bibl. Cotton.* (Oxford, 1696), 74.

956A. **Untraced.** Registers cited, without further means of identification, as in the hands, 16th–17th cent., of: (1) Baron Spencer (of Wormleighton), cf. Bodl., Dugdale 48 (*SC*. 6536), fo. 56v; (2) John Selden (*T*); (3) St. Loo Kniveton (*T*); (4) Henry Ferrers of Baddesley Clinton (*T*).

THAME co. Oxon Cist. Abbey *f.* 1137
957. **The Marquess of Bath,** Longleat (MS. 44). Gen. cartulary, *c.* 1203, with red initials (sometimes with ornamental penwork), headings and marginal titles. Arranged in sections mainly topographically (royal charters, fos. 43v, 45–7; papal etc., fos. 56–61) with additions, mainly bef. 1250, on added leaves (fos. 4–19, 62–83) and *passim*. A partial 17th cent. abstract of fos. 1–58 is in BM., Cotton Julius C. vii, fos. 287–304. Ed. H. E. Salter, *The Thame*

Cartulary, 2 vols. (Oxfordshire Record Soc. xxv, xxvi, 1947–8 for 1943–4).
Fos. 87. 10¾ × 6½ in. *FO:* Sir T. Thynne, 1st viscount Weymouth, 1712 (*T*).

THANINGTON   co. Kent
Hosp. of St. James 'extra muros civitatis Cantuariae'   *f.* bef. 1164
958.   **BM., Add. 32098.** (The first part of a ?) cartulary compiled, 1474, by W. Hadlegh, subprior of Christ Church, Canterbury, and *Custos* of the hospital. Arranged topographically in two sections: (1) fos. 1–19, Bredgar, incl. copies of some royal, papal and episcopal charters; (2) fos. 20–1 (titles underlined and initials touched in red), Elham and Blodbene in Elham.
Fos. 21+2 unnumbered. 13¾ × 9¾ in. *FO:* the Towneley fam.

THELSFORD   co. Warw.
Trinitarian Priory   *f.* early 13th cent.
959.   **Destroyed.** Part of a gen. cartulary, 15th–16th cent. (*temp.* Hen. VII ?), destroyed by fire at St. Mary's Church, Warwick, 1694. A list of contents is printed by E. Bernard, *Cat. MSS. Angliae* ii (Oxford, 1697), 205–6, no. 6711, who states that the remainder of the book was reputedly with the Lucy fam., Charlecote.
960.   **Destroyed** (?). Fragm. of the same or another cartulary *penes* W. Staunton, 1838, and thought to have been destroyed by fire at Birmingham Reference Libr., 1879. An abstract by Sir T. Phillipps (MS. 11505) remained in his collection at Thirlestaine House in 1939.

THETFORD   co. Norf.
Clun. Priory   *f.* 1114
961.   **Thetford Corporation,** Muniments. Register, 15th cent., of deeds etc. rel. grants to the priory *temp.* Hen. IV–V, with additions down to *temp.* Edw. IV at the end. Titles etc. underlined in red and some conventional pen-work decoration of initials. Contains, in all, 55 entries, incl. copies of some 14th cent. title-deeds of the properties concerned. W. D. Macray, *HMC. Various Collections* vii (1914), 122–7 (calendar).
Fos. i+23 (post-medieval pagination, 1–46; 38 ff. blank, except for post-medieval notes). 10½ × 7½ in. *FO:* P. Le Neve, 1705; T. Martin; J. Ives; Augustus Henry, 3rd

duke of Grafton, who presented it to the borough in 1809.
¶ *Other registers etc.*
962.   **Oxford, Bodl., Gough Norf. 18** (*SC.* 18074). Misc. 14th–15th cent. register of charters, extents, fees and other memoranda (fos. 49, paper). *FO:* P. Le Neve; T. Martin.
963.   **Cambridge U.L., Add. 6969.** Register of accompts, 1483–1540. J. H. Harvey, 'The Last Years of Thetford Cluniac Priory', *Norfolk Archaeology* xxvii (1939–41), 1–27. *FO:* C. Ord (from Booth, bookseller); the dukes of Newcastle, Clumber.

THORNEY   co. Cambr.
Ben. Abbey   *f. c.* 972
964.   **Cambridge U.L., Add. 3020, 3021.** Gen. cartulary, 14th cent. (*temp.* Edw. II), with rubrics, red, blue or green initials, and additions *passim* (many in the hand of a single late 14th cent. supplementor). Arranged mainly topographically by counties in nine parts (*i* royal, *viii* fines and compositions, *ix* papal, episcopal and *De gestis Abbatum*), and now bound in two volumes.
Fos. 472 (contemp. foliation by parts). 13¼ × 8¼ in. *FO:* the Fane fam., earls of Westmorland.
965.   **Destroyed.** The former Cotton MS. Vit. D. v, fos. 175–201, which was burnt in 1731, is described by T. Smith, *Cat. Bibl. Cotton.* (Oxford, 1696), *ad loc.*, as 'Registrum chartarum Monasterii de Thorney in insula Eliensi'. Quarto.
966.   **Untraced.** Cartulary and rental *penes* Maurice Johnson of Spalding, 1725; see his letter to Bp. T. Tanner (8 Nov.) in Bodl., Tanner 342, fo. 19v.
¶ *Inventory*
967.   **BM., Cotton App. xlv,** art. 12. Repertorium of the muniments, 15th cent., with additions (fos. 17v–20 etc.). Arranged partly by places and partly by subject matter (advowsons, compositions, tithes etc.), with pressmarks which appear to refer to two series of receptacles with red and green lettering respectively. Severely damaged by fire, 1731, the writing faded, and the leaves now mounted and apparently in some disorder, with loss of material.
Fos. 25. 11¾ × 4 in. etc. Paper.

THROWLEY co. Kent
Ben. Priory *f. c.* 1150 (and granted,
1424, to Syon Abbey)
968. **St. Omer, Bibl. publ. MS. 746,**
pt. ii, fos. 185–262. Part of a 15th cent. cartulary of the lands of the abbey of St.
Bertin, at St. Omer, in England. Contains
copies of documents, 1151–1367, incl. one
papal, three royal and a number of episcopal charters etc., rel. Throwley and
Chilham. *Cat. gén. MSS. des Departements*
iii (1861), 334.
Fos. 78. 11½ × 8¾ in. Paper.

THURGARTON co. Kent
Ben. Priory *f. c.* 1150
969. **Southwell Minster, MS. 3.** Gen.
cartulary, *c.* 1340, with rubrics, red and
blue decorated initials, and misc. additions
at the end (fos. 155 ff.). Arranged mainly
topographically, with separate sections for
royal and episcopal charters etc. and fines,
and with a list of places prefixed on a loose
leaf at the front. Extracts, 17th cent., for G.
Holles are in BM., Lansdowne 207, fos.
22–68. A modern transcript of fos. 87–162
is in Lincolnshire Archives Office (Foster
Libr.). W. D. Macray, *HMC. Twelfth
Report*, App. ix (1891), 543–4 (descriptive
note).
Fos. 196. 12¼ × 8¼ in. *FO:* the Cooper
fam., Thurgarton, 16th–17th cent. The
cartulary cited as *penes* Lady Stanhope,
1615 (Bodl., Dodsworth 126 (*SC.* 5067),
fos. 123–40) and the earl of Chesterfield
(*Mon. Angl.* vi, 191–2) is apparently the
same, or a transcript.

TICKFORD
(*al.* **NEWPORT PAGNELL**) co. Bucks
Ben. Priory *f.* 1100
970. **Untraced.** 'Registrum Evidentiarum', from which brief late 16th cent.
extracts, from fos. 1–7 (foundation, royal
and episcopal charters), are in BM., Harley
2188, fo. 125. Other extracts are reported
by A. J. Horwood, *HMC. Second Report*
(1871), App., 5 (no. 15) and E. Bernard,
Cat. MSS. Angliae ii (Oxford, 1697), 392,
no. 31, to exist in an untraced volume of
MS. collections formerly at Wrest Park
(Grey & De Grey fams.).

TILTY co. Essex
Cist. Abbey *f.* 1153
971. **Destroyed** (?). 'Two slender but

closely written volumes' containing abstracts, begun 1 Jan. 1444, of charters,
rentals and court rolls, made by John
Feryng, collector of the abbey's rents, and
arranged topographically. Thought to have
been destroyed by fire at Easton Lodge,
1918. An English translation, *c.* 1900, by
W. C. Waller is deposited at Chelmsford,
Essex R.O. (T/B3). For some account of
the MSS., cf. *id.*, 'Records of Tiltey Abbey'
etc., pt. i, *Trans. Essex Arch. Soc.*, New ser.
viii (1903), 353–62.
Fos. 63 + 50. *FO:* the Maynard fam.,
barons & viscounts Maynard; Frances,
countess of Warwick, 1903.

TINTERN co. Monm.
Cist. Abbey *f.* 1131
No cartulary recorded.
¶ *Other registers etc.*
972. **BM., Arundel 19.** Copies, 16th
cent., in several hands, of 5 confirmations
of Edw. I and a few other misc. 13th cent.
papal and episcopal etc. charters, mainly
rel. Woolaston church. Paper. *BM. Cat.
Arundel MSS.*, 5–6. *FO:* Ld. Wm. Howard;
presented by Henry Howard, 6th duke of
Norfolk, to the Royal Society, 1678.

TITCHFIELD co. Southt.
Praem. Abbey *f.* 1232–3
No cartulary recorded. H. M. Colvin,
The White Canons in England (Oxford,
1951), 384–5, notices Nos. 973 & 976.
¶ *Other registers etc.*
973. **The Duke of Portland** (Welbeck
MS. I. A. 2), deposited in the British
Museum (MSS. Loans No. 29/55). 'Rememoratorium de Tychefeld.' A misc. late
14th cent. register of legal proceedings,
extents, rentals, custumaries, fees, perambulations etc.
974. **Ditto** (MSS. Loans No. 29/59).
Register of court rolls, *temp.* Edw. I–III.
975. **Ditto** (MSS. Loans No. 29/58).
Register of rentals etc., late 14th cent.
976. **Ditto** (Welbeck MS. I. A. 1, MSS.
Loans No. 29/56). Library list, 1400, and
other miscellanea.

TOCKWITH
(*al.* **SKEWKIRK**) co. York
Aug. Cell of Nostell Priory *f. temp.* Hen. I
v. also NOSTELL.
977. **Manchester, Rylands Libr., Lat.**

MS. 225. Cartulary, early 16th cent., carelessly or hastily written with many revisions and corrections. Contains copies of 69 charters etc. of the cell, arranged partly by grantors and partly according to type. Formerly bound with *ib.*, Lat. MS. 251 (cartulary of the Wilstrop fam., No. 1342 below). Ed. G. C. Ransome, 'The Chartulary of Tockwith alias Scokirk', *Miscellanea* iii (Yorks. Arch. Soc., Record ser. lxxx, 1931), 151–206.

Fos. 32. $12\frac{1}{4} \times 8\frac{1}{4}$ in. Paper. *FO:* P. E. Towneley (?), 1831 (*P*).

TORRE   co. Devon
Praem. Abbey   *f.* 1196
978.   **Dublin, Trinity Coll., MS. E. 5. 15.** Cartulary, 13th cent. (aft. 1251), with rubrics. Shown by a Table at fos. 23v–6 originally to have comprised a section of papal charters (fos. 17–23) followed by entries arranged topographically and numbered consecutively 1–220 (omitting 190–199); but this arrangement is disrupted by subsequent misc. additions, 1258–1409, to an equivalent volume *passim*, and 200–20 are lost. G. Oliver, *Mon. Exon.* (1846), 184–91 (abstract).

Fos. 170. $8\frac{1}{2} \times 6$ in. *FO:* R. Connell, 1668; the Rev. W. Barry, 18th cent.
979.   **PRO., Exch., K.R.** (Misc. Bks. i. 19). Cartulary, 15th cent., with rubrics, red and blue initials etc. and a few additions of *temp.* Edw. IV etc. Arranged topographically in sections, with an imperfect section of papal charters at the beginning. Some preceding material may also be lost since in its present state the MS. includes no copies of royal charters except licences to alienate in mortmain *passim*. Oliver, *op. cit.*, 178–84 (list of contents).

Fos. 114. $13\frac{1}{4} \times 8\frac{1}{4}$ in. *FO:* the heirs of John Gaverock, 16th cent.; delivered into the Exchequer by Richard *al.* William Melford, by order of the Court, 1579.
980.   **Untraced.** Register among the deeds of the Rev. R. Lane of Coffleet in Brixton, co. Devon. Cited, early 19th cent., by *Mon. Angl.* vi, 924.

TUTBURY   co. Staff.
Ben. Priory   *f.* aft. 1080
981.   **London, Coll. of Arms, Arundel 59.** Gen. cartulary, 15th cent. (aft. 1451), made for Prior T. Gedney. Rubrics,

red and blue decorated initials, borders etc. Arranged with the copies of papal, episcopal, founders' (Ferrers) etc. charters at the beginning (fos. 17 ff.) and of extents, rentals etc., followed by a few misc. additions (which also occur on the front flyleaves), at the end (fos. 139v ff.). Includes copies of a few royal documents *passim*. Contemp. Table, fos. 10–5. Medieval binding. Transcripts, extracts etc., 18th-19th cent., are in BM., Add. 6714, fos. 1–160 (*FO:* T. Astle; the Marquess of Townshend; Adam Wolley); Cambridge, Trinity Coll. MS. R. 5. 3 (given by T. Astle); Cambridge U.L., Add. 3874, pp. 1–248; Stafford, Wm. Salt Libr., MS. 459 (1). (W. H. Black), *Cat. Arundel MSS. Coll. of Arms* (1829), 110–26 (list of contents). An edition by A. Saltman for the Wm. Salt Arch. Soc. is in preparation.

Fos. 171. $7\frac{1}{2} \times 5\frac{1}{4}$ in. *FO:* John Hawuth (?), *temp.* Eliz. I; the Earls of Devonshire (*Mon. Angl.* iii, 393–5); Sir H. Agard, 17th cent.; presented to the college by M. Burton, 1710.

TWYNHAM   co. Southt.
v. CHRISTCHURCH.

TYNEMOUTH   co. Northumb.
Ben. Priory   *f.* bef. 1089
No cartulary recorded.
¶ *Other registers etc.*
982.   **The Duke of Northumberland,** Syon House, Brentford (Muniments, D. xi. 1). Composite misc. 14th cent. register (fos. 218), mainly of terriers, rentals, fees, notes of legal proceedings and other memoranda rel. the priory's lands. Includes: (*a*) fos. 77–104, a rubricated section of deeds, leases etc. *temp.* R. Tewing, prior 1315–40, etc. with later 14th cent. continuations down to fo. 122; (*b*) fos. 159–76, part of a register of the same prior, 1328–40. H. H. E. Craster, *The Parish of Tynemouth* (*Hist. Northumberland* viii, 1907), 86, note 2 (description); used by W. S. Gibson, *Hist. Monastery at Tynemouth*, 2 vols. (1846–7), and J. Brand, *Hist. Newcastle upon Tyne* ii (1789). *FO:* Sir Roger Portington, 16th-17th cent.

VALE ROYAL   co. Chest.
Cist. Abbey   *f.* (at Darnhall) 1274
No cartulary recorded.

❡ *Other registers etc.*

983. **Untraced.** The 'Ledger-Book' *al.* 'Green Book'. Register (fos. 116) of misc. material, *temp.* Edw. I–Hen. VI. A transcript, 1662, is in BM., Harley 2064, fos. 4–64 (Randle Holme MSS.). Extracts, 1624, are in BM., Harley 2060, fos. 91–110 etc. Ed., in translation (from the transcript), J. Brownbill, *The Ledger-Book of Vale Royal Abbey* (Lancs. & Cheshire Record Soc. Publns. lxviii, 1914). *FO:* T. Marbury, 1624; Sir T. Mainwaring, bart., 1662.

WALDEN co. Essex
Ben. Abbey *f.* (as a priory) 1136
984. **BM., Harley 3697.** Gen. cartulary, 1387, made for Abbot J. Pentlow. Rubrics, red and blue decorated initials and a few misc. additions *passim.* Arranged mainly topographically, with sections of foundation, royal and episcopal charters at fos. 18–42, of papal privileges at fos. 69v–75, and of some other general types of charter *passim.* Contemp. Table, fos. 5–16. *Mon. Angl.* iv, 135 (*x*) (list of contents).

Fos. 267. 16¾ × 10⅜ in. The names of William, John and Edmund Hayward, and of Nathaniel Cole of Langston, co. Southt., scribbled, 16th–17th cent., on fly-leaves. *FO:* the Earl of Suffolk, 1640 (*D*).

❡ *Other registers etc.*

985. **Untraced.** 'Liber de Fundatione': a history of the house down to 1200. Transcripts, late 16th cent., are in BM., Arundel 29; Cotton Vesp. E. vi, fos. 25–71. Ed., in transl., H. Collar, 'The Book of the Foundation of Walden Abbey', *Essex Rev.* xlv (1936), 73–236 *passim;* xlvi (1937), 12–234 *passim;* xlvii (1938), 36–220 *passim. Mon. Angl.* iv, 141, no. ii. *FO:* R. Glover.

WALLINGFORD co. Berks
Coll. of St. Nicholas *f.* bef. 1107
986. **Oxford, St. John's Coll.,** Muniments (III. 1). Register, early 16th cent., containing copies of the principal charters of endowment of the earls of Cornwall and kings of England etc., with an added Table at the end. The folios are indented at the top, like a chirograph, suggesting that there was a second copy. Contemp. binding.

Fos. 46. 10½ × 7½ in. *FO:* W. Boxe.

WALSALL co. Staff.
Parish Church.
987. **BM., Cotton Nero C. xii,** fos.

121–56. Cartulary, 14th–15th cent., in several hands, containing copies of royal, episcopal and private charters etc., 12th–15th cent., rel. the foundation and endowment of chantries.

Fos. 36 (17th cent. foliation, 1–37; lacks 10). 12 × 8½ in. Vellum and paper. Titlepage and headings throughout in the hand of Sir Wm. Dugdale.

WALSINGHAM co. Norf.
Aug. Priory *f. c.* 1153
988. **BM., Cotton Nero E. vii.** Gen. cartulary, late 13th cent. (aft. 1293), elaborately written with rubrics, red and blue decorated initials etc. and misc. additions (fos. 1–7, 135 ff., and *passim*). Arranged topographically in sections, by deaneries, and incl. copies of a few royal, papal and episcopal charters in those for Walsingham. A 15th cent. index at fos. 139–46 also covers the contents of some 30 missing leaves, of which two (fos. 77, 78 in the medieval foliation) are now **Oxford, Bodl., Top. Norf. b. 1** (*SC.* 31413; *FO:* W. H. Crawford). *Mon. Angl.* vi, 72 (*b*) (list of places).

Fos. 180 (medieval foliation, 1–(203)). 16¾ × 10¼ in. *FO:* Samuel Roper.

WALTHAM co. Essex
Aug. Abbey *f.* (as a priory) bef. 1060
989. **BM., Harley 391.** Gen. cartulary, *c.* 1220, with rubrics and extensive misc. additions on added etc. leaves *passim.* Arranged in sections by grantors (royal, fos. 33–54; lay, fos. 77–92, 139–44 (misbound); ecclesiastical etc., incl. episcopal, fos. 97–112; papal, fos. 121–38, 145–51). *Mon. Angl.* vi, 58 (*t*) lists the major contents. W. Winters, 'Historical notes on . . . MSS . . . of Waltham Holy Cross', *Trans. Royal Hist. Soc.* vi (1877), 231–51.

Fos. iv + 182 (wants a few leaves *passim*). 9 × 6½ in. *FO:* Sir W. Hayward; P. Le Neve.

990. **BM., Cotton Tib. C. ix,** fos. 48–260. Gen. cartulary, 13th cent. (*temp.* Hen. III), with rubrics etc., red paragraphs and some red initials. Contains sections of royal and papal charters, each with its own Table, followed (fos. 84–165) by copies of private etc. deeds arranged and numbered by places and (fos. 197–231) terriers; with misc. additions *passim,* mainly at the end.

Fos. 213. $11\frac{1}{4} \times 7\frac{3}{4}$ in. (shrunk by fire, 1731, and the leaves now mounted).

991.   **BM., Harley 4809.** Sections *vii–xxi* of a 14th cent. cartulary (aft. 1353), with rubrics etc. Contains copies of private deeds etc. arranged and numbered in sections by places, with occasional additions *passim*. Section *xix* for Stansted wants 30 entries at the beginning (bef. fo. 138). The places are listed in *Mon. Angl.* vi, 58 (*k*). Winters, *l.c.*, 230–1.

Fos. 193. $12\frac{1}{2} \times 8\frac{3}{4}$ in. *FO:* Sir W. Hayward; P. Le Neve.

992.   **BM., Harley 3739.** Cartulary, 16th cent. (cf. No. 993), of documents rel. the abbey's rights, privileges etc. in churches, manors, forests etc., made *temp.* R. Fuller, abbot 1526–40. Elaborate pen-decorated initials with grotesques. Includes copies of numerous royal and episcopal charters etc. (from the 11th cent.), but no papal ones. An added 16th cent. Table (fos. 215–9) is printed with abbreviation in *Mon. Angl.* vi, 59 (*a*). Winters, *l.c.*, 256–63.

Fos. 219 (16th cent. pagination, 1–436). 13×9 in. Paper. *FO:* W. Hamby; James Hay, 2nd earl of Carlisle, 1655 (*T*); Browne Willis, 1719 (*T*).

993.   **BM., Add. 37665.** Cartulary similar in date, scope and execution to No. 992, the material being substantially but not completely identical, with some differences of arrangement. *BM. Cat. Add. MSS.* 1906–1910, 96–7.

Fos. 284. $13\frac{3}{8} \times 9\frac{3}{8}$ in. Paper. *FO:* Sir T. Phillipps (MS. 13892).

994.   **Untraced.** Cartulary *penes* R. Dodsworth, 1639, and afterw. of Sir T. Widdrington (*D*), from which extracts are in Bodl., Dodsworth 159 (*SC.* 5100), fos. 212–7.

⁋ *Other registers etc.*

995–996.   **BM., Harley 3776, 3766.** 'Codex Ruber.' A 14th cent. collection of misc. religious and historical tracts etc. E. G. Millar, 'A MS. from Waltham Abbey in the Harleian Collection', *Brit. Mus. Quart.* vii (1932–3), 112–8. *FO:* W. Bowyer, 1565 (?); Ld. Wm. Howard; J. Warburton.

WANGFORD   co. Suff.
Clun. Priory   *f.* bef. 1159
No cartulary recorded.

⁋ *Other registers etc.*

997.   **The Earl of Stradbroke,** deposited at Ipswich, E. Suffolk R.O. (Henham collection). Register of court-rolls etc., late 15th cent. with additions, incl. some copies of deeds rel. Henham etc.

WARDEN   co. Bedf.
Cist. Abbey   *f.* 1136

998.   **Manchester, Rylands Libr., Lat. MS. 223.** The latter part (?) of an early 13th cent. cartulary (fos. 5–8, an incomplete section of papal charters, late 12th cent.), with some headings and initials in red and misc. additions *passim*. Comprises copies mainly of private deeds etc. arranged topographically, the royal charters having been apparently among material now lacking at the beginning. A 19th cent. abstract is in BM., Add. 24465, fos. 24–39v. Ed. G. H. Fowler, *Cartulary of . . . Old Wardon* (Bedfordshire Hist. Record Soc. xiii, 1930). *Mon. Angl.* v, 370 (*g*).

Fos. iv + 110 (13th (?) cent. foliation, 139–245, in disorder; lacks about 30 leaves *passim*). $8\frac{3}{4} \times 6\frac{5}{8}$ in. *FO:* B. H. Bright, 1824; Sir T. Phillipps (MS. 21708).

⁋ *Other registers etc.*

999.   **BM., Harley 4765.** Fragm. (fos. 6) of a 14th–15th cent. register containing material rel. tithe disputes, 1368–78 etc. Fowler, *op. cit.*, 6–7. *FO:* P. Le Neve.

WARE   co. Hertf.
Ben. Priory   *f.* bef. 1081
v. No. 891 above.

WAREHAM   co. Dors.
Ben. Priory   *f. temp.* Hen. I
v. No. 891 above.

WARTER   co. York
Aug. Priory   *f. c.* 1132

1000.   **Oxford, Bodl., Fairfax 9** (*SC.* 3889). Gen. cartulary, early 14th cent., with rubrics etc. and red and blue initials. Arranged topographically in sections with a contemp. list of places at fo. 6 and additions at the beginning, end and between the sections *passim*. The first section, for Warter incl. copies of some royal charters, is followed (fos. 20–2) by a section of papal charters. A 20th cent. transcript is in Manchester Reference Libr. (Farrer MSS.).

Fos. 107 (lacks 2 leaves aft. fo. 22 containing material for Askham and Barton). $12\frac{1}{2} \times 8\frac{1}{2}$ in. *FO*: R. Dodsworth; Sir T. Widdrington.

WARWICK co. Warw.
Coll. of St. Mary *f.* 1123
1001. PRO., Exch., K.R. (Misc. Bks. i. 22). Gen. cartulary, 15th cent. (*temp.* Hen. VI?), with some rubrication and additions *passim*. Arranged in sections topographically with the copies of general, incl. papal and episcopal charters, at the beginning and an inventory of vestments, relics, books etc. at fos. 197v–201. Noticed by J. Harvey Bloom, 'An Introduction to the Cartulary of St. Mary's, Warwick', *Trans. Bristol & Glouc. Arch. Soc.* xxxvii (1914), 79–91.

Fos. 227. $11\frac{1}{8} \times 7\frac{1}{8}$ in. *FO*: Henry Ferrers.

WELBECK co. Nott.
Praem. Abbey *f.* 1153–4
1002. BM., Harley 3640. Gen. cartulary, 14th cent. (*temp.* Edw. II–III?), with marginal rubrics, small red initials etc. Arranged topographically with sections of royal, papal and other general charters at the end (fos. 116 ff.), followed by misc. contemp. and later additions. Other additions have been made *passim*. Bound up with: (*a*) fos. 1–15, an 18th cent. synopsis by H. Wanley, printed by R. White, *Dukery Records* (Worksop, 1904), 241–55; (*b*) fos. 16–37, leaves from other 13th–14th cent. registers incl. (fos. 26 ff.) a 'Liber Memorandorum scriptus a fratre Johanne de Whyten', 1305–6; (*c*) fos. 160–74, an *Abbreviatio Cartarum* or recital of grants to the abbey, written in a 14th cent. hand which has made additions elsewhere and arranged topographically. A. Hamilton Thompson, *The Praemonstratensian Abbey of Welbeck* (1938), 5–6 etc. (description etc.).

Fos. 175 (xv + 160). $13\frac{1}{4} \times 9\frac{1}{2}$ in. *FO*: R. Whalley, 1613 (BM., Stowe 529, fo. 242); Robert Pierrepont, 1st earl of Kingston-upon-Hull, 1631 (Dodsworth).

WELLESBOURNE co. Warw.
v. THELSFORD.

WELLS co. Som.
Cath. Church *f. c.* 704
The cartularies at Wells are described briefly by H. T. Riley, *HMC. First Report* (1870), App., 92–4. A fuller account by J. A. Bennett, *HMC. Tenth Report*, App. iii (1885), is superseded by that of W. H. B. Bird, *HMC. Wells* i (1907).

1003. Wells, D. & C., Muniments, 'Liber Albus I' (R. I), fos. 2–64. Gen. cartulary, *c.* 1240, with rubrics, red numeration of the entries, and a few additions *passim*. The material is 11th–13th cent., and includes copies of royal, papal and episcopal documents, with a Table at fos. 6–7. The rest of the volume, which was apparently kept by the chancellor, consists of copies of misc. 14th cent. documents, mainly *acta* of the dean & chapter. Bird, *op. cit.*, ix, 1–304 (calendar).

Fos. 57 (292 in the MS., numbered 2–299; wants a few leaves *passim*). $12\frac{3}{4} \times 8\frac{1}{2}$ in.

1004. Ditto, 'Liber Ruber' (R. II), pt. i. Composite 13th–14th cent. register of *acta* and other documents rel. the cathedral's affairs, calendared by Bird, *op. cit.*, xi, 529–37. Includes (fos. 3v–7v) a rubricated late 13th cent. Table, apparently of No. 1003, printed by H. E. Reynolds, *Wells Cathedral* (1880?), 115–121. Pt. ii is a chapter act-book, 1487–1513.

Fos. 77. $11\frac{3}{4} \times 7\frac{1}{8}$ in.

1005. Ditto, 'Liber Fuscus' (R. IV). Cartulary (fos. 1–28), 14th cent. (*temp.* Edw. II–III?), with pen-decorated initials and marginal headings in the hand of the text. Followed by: (*a*) fos. 28v–42, misc. 14th cent. additions of charters etc.; (*b*) fos. 43–64v, custumals, extents etc., partly in the hand of (*a*) and partly later 14th cent.; (*c*) fos. 68–81, further copies of charters, perambulations of forests etc. in a number of 14th–16th cent. hands. Perhaps the cartulary whose compilation was ordered, 1331, by J. de Godelee, see 'Liber Ruber' (No. 1004), fo. 25. Riley, *l.c.*, 93 ('a small folio volume etc.'). J. Armitage Robinson, *Somerset & Dorset Notes & Queries* xvi (1919), 208. See also No. 1006 and Bird, *op. cit.*, 305–55.

Fos. 81. $13 \times 8\frac{3}{4}$ in. Restored from the bishop's muniments, *c.* 1919.

1006. Ditto, 'Liber Albus II' (R. III). Gen. cartulary, *c.* 1500, containing copies of deeds and other material, 8th–15th cent., incl. numerous royal, papal and episcopal charters etc. Fos. 1–87v are a direct copy of No. 1005, fos. 1–77. A Table on ten unnumbered preliminary leaves is followed by an added 17th cent. index. Bird, *op. cit.*, ix, 305–528 (calendar).

Fos. 24+451 (numbered, 1–457; wants 105–8, 254). 14¾ × 9½ in.

❡ *Other registers etc.*

For other registers at Wells, see also Riley, *l.c.* etc.

1007. **Ditto**, 'Book of Charters'. A 16th cent. register containing copies of letters patent of Elizabeth I and Henry VIII, with T. Bekynton's statutes (1460) for the choristers.

WENLOCK co. Salop
Clun. Priory *f.* 1080–1
No cartulary recorded.

❡ *Other registers etc.*

1008. **The Duke of Sutherland,** and his Trentham Trustees, deposited in the British Museum (MSS. Loans No. 39). Quire (fos. 12, 11¼ × 8 in.) from a rubricated mid-14th cent. register, now inserted at the beginning of a cartulary of Lilleshall Abbey (No. 577). Contains copies of episcopal and other documents, 1342–4, rel. Stoke St. Milborough, Madeley and Clun churches. Catchword, 'capellis predictis'. *FO:* cf. No. 577.

1009. **Lord Forester,** Willey Park, Broseley. Memorandum book (of Prior R. Bruge?), early 16th cent. Extracts, 1853, from fos. 1–52 by R. W. Eyton are in Bodl., Top. Salop d. 2, fos. 119–47. Not found by Lord Forester, 1953.

WESTMINSTER co. Middx.
Ben. Abbey *f.* 958

For a description of the cartularies see, most fully, J. Armitage Robinson and M. R. James, *MSS. of Westminster Abbey* (Cambridge, 1909), 93–102 etc.

1010. **Westminster Abbey,** Muniments (No. 4254). Two non-consecutive bifolia from a late 13th cent. cartulary (aft. 1269), with rubrics etc. and spaces for initials. Copies of grants to the abbey in Amwell, *temp.* Abbot R. de Ware.

Fos. 4. 10¼ × 7 in.

1011. **BM., Cotton Faust. A. iii.** Cartulary of privileges etc., 13th–14th cent. (*temp.* Edw. I) etc., with rubrics and red or blue initials. Comprises sections of: (1) royal charters down to Edw. I, fos. 4–143; (2) papal privileges, fos. 149–217; (3) com-

positions etc. and charters of bishops and abbots, fos. 218–355. Each section is prefaced by a Table and followed, after occasional intermediate additions, by a supplement, *c.* 1400, and a few later 15th cent. additions. A late 13th cent. copy of Sulcard's historical prologue is inserted as fos. 11–16.

Fos. 356. 9 × 5¾ in. (cropped).

1012. **BM., Cotton Titus A. viii,** fos. 2–64. Cartulary of privileges, 14th cent. (*temp.* Edw. II?), with rubrics and red and blue decorated initials. Similar in scope to, but less systematically arranged than No. 1011, and contains considerably less material, opening with Sulcard's historical prologue. Copies of documents rel. St. James's Hospital, *temp.* Edw. III, are inserted as fos. 32–3.

Fos. 63. 8⅛ × 6 in. (cropped). Bound with unconnected material. *FO:* Archbp. M. Parker.

1013. **Westminster Abbey** (Muniment Bk. 11). 'Domesday.' Gen. cartulary, 14th cent. (aft. 1308), with rubrics, red and blue decorated initials etc. and additions down to 1445 *passim*. Contains sections of papal and royal charters with extracts from Domesday Book (fos. 1–78), followed by copies of evidences arranged (*a*) topographically by counties (fos. 79–348) and (*b*) by obedientiaries etc. (fos. 349–656), with copies of compositions and similar general documents, arranged according to type, at the end.

Fos. 685. 14⅝ × 9½ in.

1014. **Ditto** (Mun. Bk. 12). Composite misc. 14th–15th cent. register, incl.: (*a*) fos. 1–25 (rubricated, with red and blue decorated initials etc. and an illuminated border, fo. 1), indexes of papal bulls etc. 'in prima cista', down to 1389; (*b*) fos. 117–200, sections, in some cases written uniformly with (*a*), of charters and other evidences, mainly 14th cent., rel. various places, incl. copies of some royal documents. The names of the places and the contents of the rest of the volume are noticed by Robinson & James, *op. cit.*, 94–5.

Fos. 214. 15⅛ × 10 in.

1015. **Ditto** (Mun. Bk. 1). 'Liber Niger Quaternus.' A renewal, *c.* 1474–85, by Thomas, Ld. Clifford, monk, of an older (early 15th cent.?) register of the same name. Rubrics etc. and spaces for initials.

Comprises three books, which in the original were apparently distinct compilations but here follow each other without break: (1) fos. 1–76, copies of charters etc., mainly 14th cent. (down to 1408), arranged topographically and the earlier ones taken from No. 1013, to which this may have been intended as a supplement; (2) fos. 76v–93, copies of misc. charters, documents and other memoranda rel. the abbey's affairs, 1332–1417; (3) fos. 93v–151, similar copies, for the most part of misc 14th cent. charters etc. dealing with the abbey's rights, privileges and jurisdiction, but incl. some inventories. Table of the whole, on 8 preliminary leaves. An edition by the late Sir Charles Strachey, C.M.G., awaits publication.

Fos. viii + 151 (contemp. roman foliation). 13½ × 10 in.

1016. **London, Coll. of Arms, Young 72.** Another late 15th cent. version of No. 1015, in similar format, with some slight rearrangement of the material (Bk. 1, fos. 1–79v; 2, fos. 80–97v; 3, fos. 98–160). Contemp. index, of Bks. 2 & 3 only, on six unnumbered leaves at the end. No Table. Stamped leather binding, c. 1500. (S. Bentley), *Abstract of . . . a Cartulary of . . . St. Peter, Westminster* (1836, privately).

Fos. x + 160 (contemp. roman foliation). 12½ × 8¼ in. *FO:* B. R. Spiller; S. Bentley, 1836.

1017. **Westminster Abbey,** Muniments (No. 9580). Table, 16th cent. (*temp.* Hen. VIII), of fos. 1–95 of an unidentified cartulary. Lists 247 deeds, mainly rel. Westminster and adjacent parts of London and concerned with rents.

Fos. 2 (conjoint). 23¼ × 8¼ in. Paper.

¶ *Other registers etc.*

1018. **BM., Add. Roll 15895.** Extracts, 15th cent. (*temp.* Hen. VI), from royal and papal privileges to the abbey.

1019. **PRO., Exchequer K.R.** (Transcripts of Deeds and Charters, E. 132/35). Similar to No. 1018.

1020. **BM., Cotton Claud. A. viii,** fos. 22–39. Extracts from Flete etc., 1450, by R. Sporley, incl. copies of a few early papal and royal charters etc.

1021. **Westminster Abbey** (Mun. Bk. 3). Appropriations of churches, *temp.* J. Islip, abbot 1500–32.

1022. **Cambridge U.L., Kk. 5. 29.** Extents of manors etc., *temp.* Edw. II etc. *FO:* Bp. J. Moore (but is not the register listed by E. Bernard, *Cat. MSS. Angliae* ii (Oxford, 1697), 366, no. 9400, as no. 214 in his library, which remains unidentified).

WESTMINSTER co. Middx.
Coll. Chapel of St. Stephen *f.* 1347

1023. **BM., Cotton Faust. B. viii,** fos. 2–53. Register, mid-15th cent. (aft. 1443), with spaces for initials and additions (fos. 33 ff.) down to 1509, containing copies of indentures and other documents rel. the endowment of obits. Preceded (fos. 2–7) by a kalendar. A table of obits, with notes of the sums distributable amongst members of the college for their celebration, is inserted as fo. 52.

Fos. 51. 10¼ × 7¼ in. (cropped).

WESTWOOD co. Kent
v. LESNES.

WESTWOOD co. Worc.
Ben. Priory (Order of Fontevrault)
f. temp. Hen. II

1024. **BM., Cotton Vesp. E. ix,** fos. 2–9. Cartulary, 13th cent. (aft. 1226), with marginal titles. Contains copies and abstracts of 64 private etc. deeds, arranged topographically with occasional later 13th cent. additions *passim*. The recto of the first leaf and the lower half of the verso of the last are blank. An 18th cent. transcript is in BM., Lansdowne 227, fos. 3–40. *Mon. Angl.* vi, 1004–10, prints 44 of the entries.

Fos. 8. 8¼ × 6 in.

WETHERAL co. Cumb.
Ben. Priory *f.* 1106–12

1025. **Carlisle, D. & C.,** Muniments. Gen. cartulary (fos. 23–151), early 14th cent., with rubrics etc. and extensive misc. additions (before, after and *passim*). Arranged mainly topographically with copies of the founder's (R. Meschin), royal, papal, episcopal etc. charters at the beginning, and a section of pleas at the end (fos. 140–51). Table, in another hand, fos. 19–22. An early 18th cent. transcript is in BM., Harley 1881, fos. 3–142 (*FO:* H. Todd, D.D.). Ed. J. E. Prescott, *The Register of . . . Wetheral* (Cumberland & Westm. Antiq. & Arch. Soc., 1897), in whose numeration no. 232 is the last entry of the original compilation, and who leaves the misc. material largely untouched; cf. *id.*, 'Notes on the MS. Register of Wetheral etc.', *Trans. Cumberland & Westm. Antiq. & Arch. Soc.* xv (1899), 285–7.

Fos. vii+217. 8 × 5½ in. *FO*: Ld. Wm. Howard; Carlisle Dean & Chapter, 17th–18th cent.; lost aft. 1812 and found, 1897, in the library at Castletown, co. Cumb., from which it was restored by G. Mounsey-Heysham.

WHALLEY co. Lanc.
Cist. Abbey *f.* (at Stanlow) 1172
1026. **PRO., Exch., K.R.** (Transcripts of Deeds & Charters, E. 132/7). Copies, 13th cent., of about 70 charters (private, and of the earls and constables of Chester), rel. grants to the abbey in various places. Rubrics, red paragraphs, and a few 15th cent. additions, of deeds *temp.* Edw. I, on the verso.
Roll of 4 membrs., in two pieces, joined at the top. *c.* 42 × 9 in., *c.* 54 × 9 in.

1027. **BM., Egerton 2600.** Three late 13th cent. quires, with some additions, perhaps from a larger register. Contents: (*a*) fos. 1–12, 30–5 (32–3 blank), copies of grants by the abbots and other misc. deeds, memoranda etc., *temp.* Hen. III–Edw. I; (*b*) fos. 13–26, an inventory of deeds, arranged topographically in 18 *Tituli*, and followed (fos. 27–30) by a list of rents. Wants a leaf aft. fo. 24 (*Tituli* 16–17) which is copied in a 17th cent. transcript by Randle Holme in BM., Harley 2064, fos. 87–96.
Fos. 35. 7 × 5 in. *FO*: the Rev. J. C. Jackson, 1881.

1028. **BM., Egerton 3126.** Gen. cartulary made, *c.* 1342 (?), for Abbot J. de Lindley, with some additions. Red initials, paragraphs, underlining of titles etc. Arranged topographically in 20 *Tituli*, with a Table at fos. 7–26v, 30v. A section of papal charters rel. the abbey's churches follows *Titulus iv* (fos. 88–95). Copies of royal and episcopal documents are included *passim*. Extracts, 17th cent., apparently from this MS., are in Dublin, Trinity Coll. MS. F. 1. 20, fos. 76–97. Ed. W. A. Hulton, *The Coucher Book of Whalley Abbey*, 4 vols. (Chetham Soc. x,

xi, xvi, xx, 1847–9). *Mon. Angl.* v, 640 (*c*) (list of *Tituli*).
Fos. iii+420. 9 × 6 in. *FO*: Sir R. Ashton, bart., 1627 (*D*); the Curzon fam., viscounts Curzon & earls Howe.

¶ *Other registers etc.*

1029. **BM., Add. 10374.** 'Liber loci Benedicti de Whalley' *al.* 'The Lesser Coucher Book'. Misc. register of pleas, writs, inquisitions and other memoranda, incl. a formulary, 14th cent. (*temp.* Edw. I–II etc.). T. D. Whitaker, *Hist. Whalley* i (4th ed., 1872), 149–83 etc. (extracts). *FO*: R. Ashton, 1658 (see the extracts in BM., Harley 2064, fo. 81v etc.); R. Heber, 19th cent.

1030. **Manchester, Rylands Libr., Lat. MS. 461.** Copies and extracts, 17th cent., for Sir R. Ashton, bart., of about 150 misc. documents rel. the abbey. Taken from various sources. *FO*: Joseph Mayer.

WHERWELL co. Southt.
Ben. Abbey (Nuns) *f. c.* 986
1031. **BM., Egerton 2104.** Gen. cartulary, late 14th cent. (aft. 1364), with some additions at the beginning and end. Contains copies of grants to and by the abbey, 13th–14th cent., and other misc. documents etc., incl. (fos. 43–5) a narrative history down to 1261. The papal charters are grouped at fos. 17v–24, the episcopal at fos. 96–9, and the royal are entered *passim*. Fos. 3–13 contain a 14th–15th cent. Table. Fos. 200–11 are a separate contemp. compilation containing copies of 32 charters rel. tithes of the sacrist. *BM. Cat. Add. MSS.* 1861–1875, ii, 971–2.
Fos. 224. 10 × 6¾ in. *FO*: Charles, 5th baron de la Warr, 1669 (*D*); the Iremonger fam., Wherwell; purchased of W. Cutter, 1869.

WHITBY co. York
Ben. Abbey *f.* (as a priory) bef. 1077
J. C. Atkinson, *Cartularium Abbathiae de Whiteby*, 2 vols. (Surtees Soc. lxix, lxxii, 1879, 1881), edits Nos. 1032–3.
1032. **The Hon. Mrs. Henry Strickland,** Barton Hill House, Whitwell, co. York. Composite gen. cartulary, 12th–16th cent., arranged apparently according to subject matter and incl. copies of royal, papal and episcopal charters, and of some grants by the abbey, *passim*. Consists of

four main parts, mostly with decorated initials etc.: (1) fos. 1-70, eight quires (*i-viii*), preceded by a ninth (fos. 1-7) without signature, *c.* 1240 with 13th-15th cent. additions (Atkinson, *op. cit.*, nos. iv-cclxxviii); (2) fos. 71-137, six quires, *c.* 1400 with some early 15th cent. additions (*id.*, nos. cclxxix-ccclxxxiii); (3) fos. 138-41 (misbound at the beginning of the volume), book catalogue, memorial of the foundation etc., late 12th cent. (*id.*, 341 & nos. i-iii); (4) two unfoliated quires of paper at the end, the first early 16th cent. (*id.*, nos. ccclxxxiv-cccxcix) and the second blank. Fos. 142-3, misbound with two blank leaves betw. (1) and (2), contain a 15th cent. index (*id.*, 342-4).

Fos. iv + 171 (15th cent. foliation, 1-143, as above). 8¾ × 6 in. *FO:* the Cholmley and (18th-20th cent.) Strickland fams.

1033. **BM., Add. 4715.** Composite gen. cartulary, based on a mid-13th cent. compilation (rubricated, with red, blue and green decorated initials), of which fos. 9-15, 25-8, 73-5, 83-6, 107-12, 122-7, 148-67, are the surviving leaves. Extensively supplemented, 14th cent. (*temp.* Edw. III), with some intermediate and subsequent misc. additions. Arranged mainly topographically, with a section of *Conventiones* at fos. 124-48 followed by others of archiepiscopal, royal and papal charters (fos. 148v-166) and a 15th cent. index (fos. 181-3).

Fos. iii + 191. 6¾ × 5⅛ in. *FO:* W. Horncastle, 17th cent.; Charles Mason, D.D., 18th cent.

¶ *Other registers etc.*

1034. **Major E. R. F. Compton,** Newby Hall, Ripon (Muniment Room). Copies, 15th-16th cent., of royal charters of *Inspeximus* (fos. 15-28), notes of rents (fos. 29-33) and other miscellanea (fos. 2-9). Fos. 33. *c.* 8½ × 6 in.

1034A. References to a cartulary bought by the Earl of Kent at the auction, 1687, of the library of William Cecil, Ld. Burghley (*T*), are apparently to extracts, 1584, from No. 1032 or No. 1033 in Bodl. Eng. misc. c. 121, fos. 91-2 (*FO:* the Grey and De Grey fam., Wrest Park).

WIGMORE co. Heref.
Aug. Abbey *f.* (at Shobdon) 1131-41
No cartulary traced. Cartularies etc. of

the Mortimer fam., earls of March, at Wigmore Castle (cf. Nos. 1292-4 below), have sometimes wrongly been attributed to the abbey.

WILTON co. Wilts
Ben. Abbey (Nuns) *f.* 890
1035. **BM., Harley 436.** Cartulary, early 14th cent. (?), with rubrics, red and blue initials etc., containing copies of about 36 royal etc. charters in Anglo-Saxon and Latin down to 1208 (mainly 10th cent.). Ed. R. C. Hoare and others, *Registrum Wiltunense* (1827). *Mon. Angl.* ii, 318 (*d*) etc. (list of contents, with extracts).

Fos. iii + 91. 10¾ × 7¼ in. *FO:* Philip Herbert, 5th earl of Pembroke, 1658 (*D*); G. Hickes.

WIMBORNE co. Dors.
Minster (Coll. Church) *f.* bef. 705 (?)
1036. **PRO., Exch., K.R.** (Eccl. Docs., E. 135/3/21). Register, 16th cent., with elaborate pen-drawn initials, containing copies of about 8 royal, episcopal and other charters, 1497-1526, rel. the chantry founded by Margaret, countess of Richmond.

Fos. 12. 12¼ × 9½ in.

WINCHCOMBE co. Glouc.
Ben. Abbey *f. c.* 787 (?)
Nos. 1037-8 are edited by D. Royce, *Landboc . . . de Winchelcumba,* 2 vols. (Exeter 1892, 1903). Their contents are listed in *Coll. Top. et Genealogica* ii (1835), 16-37, and they are discussed by (James Dutton, 3rd) Lord Sherborne in *Trans. Bristol & Glouc. Arch. Soc.* xii (1887-8), 220-7. Extracts from John Prynne were lithographically reproduced by Sir T. Phillipps (Middlehill, 1854; pp. i + 225).

1037. **Lord Sherborne,** deposited at Gloucester, Gloucestershire R.O. (D. 678). 'Landboc', *al.* 'Vol. i', *al.* 'Liber B'. Cartulary (pp. 33 ff.), 13th cent. (*temp.* Hen. III), with rubrics, small red initials etc., containing copies of deeds, rentals and other material, arranged by obedientiaries etc. (*Ecclesia, Mensa Abbatie, Cantaria, (Succentor), Sacristeria, Altar Beate Marie, Refectorium, Infirmaria, Elemosinaria*). Contemp. Table, pp. 17-22. Extensive additions down to 1332 *passim* (especially at the beginning, pp. 108-115, 120-6, 155 ff.)

include (pp. 1–4) a second Table. Pp. 181–96 are a quire from a late 12th cent. compilation (fines and grants by the abbey).

Fos. 132 (post-medieval pagination, 1–275; pp. 31–237 with later medieval foliation, 3–117). 10 × 7 in. *FO:* Sir John Alleyn.

1038.   Ditto. 'Liber A' *al.* 'Vol. ii'. Gen. cartulary made, 1422, by Abbot J. Cheltenham. Rubrics etc. and black pen-decorated initials, sometimes touched with colour. Arranged mainly topographically with copies of documents rel. the election of Abbot Cheltenham and of papal and royal charters at the beginning, preceded by a later 15th cent. Table on ten unnumbered leaves, and with other later 15th cent. additions at the end (pp. 475 ff.).

Fos. 10 + 255 (post-medieval pagination, 1–510). 11½ × 7¾ in. *FO:* as No. 1037.

1039.   Destroyed. 'Renovatio privilegiorum ac aliorum munimentorum . . . labore . . . Richardi Kedremister . . . Abbatis', begun in 1523 and arranged in at least five books or parts, opening with a historical narrative incorporating copies of early charters. Belonged, 1644, to Sir William Morton (*D*), who had it of a Gloucestershire farmer, and was destroyed at his chambers in the Great Fire of London, 1666, see A à Wood, *Athenae Oxonienses* i (ed. Bliss, 1813), 63. Extracts are in *Mon. Angl.* ii, 302–12; Bodl., Dodsworth 65 (*SC.* 5007), fos. 1–4.

❡ *Other registers etc.*

1040.   Lord Sherborne, deposited *ib.* 'Rentale maneriorum', 1355. *FO:* as Nos. 1037–8.

1041.   London, Lambeth Palace, MS. 854. Copies, 16th cent., of agreements with the abbot of Hailes and Bartholomew de Sudeley 'super communiam habendam in campis de heiles et Sudeleya' etc., 13th–14th cent. M. R. James, *Cat. Lambeth MSS.* (Cambridge, 1932), 811, assigns the MS. to Hailes, but on p. 10 the monks of Winchcombe are described as 'Nos'. *FO:* W. Griffith, 17th cent.

WINCHESTER   co. Southt.
Ben. Cath. Priory (Old Minster) *f. c.* 604

1042.   BM., Add. 15350. Cartulary, *c.* 1130–50, of royal and other charters to the priory, 688–1048. Elaborately written in

book-hand with fine large red, blue, green and brown decorated initials, and supplementary material down to *temp.* Hen. II added, with some 14th cent. notes of later charters, at the beginning and end (fos. 3–8, 116v–120). Index of contents, 13th cent., fo. 2v. Contemp. binding (W. H. J. Weale, *Early Stamped Bookbindings in the BM.* (1922), no. 3). Used extensively by J. M. Kemble, *Codex Diplomaticus* (1839–48), see vol. vi, pp. ix–x. Cf. also No. 1043.

Fos. 121. 15½ × 11 in. *FO:* T. Daccombe, 1550; purchased from the Dean & Chapter of Winchester, 1844.

1043.   BM., Add. 29436, fos. 10–48. Cartulary, mid-13th cent. (aft. 1242), of royal, episcopal and some other charters to the priory, 11th–13th cent. Rubrics, red and blue decorated initials, and some misc. additions at the end (fos. 39 ff.). Bound with a history of the priory down to 977 (fos. 4–9, 15th cent.), copies of charters and agreements between the priory and the bishop 1280–1331 etc. (fos. 49–71, 15th cent.), and custumaries (fos. 72–80, 13th cent.), each with separate 17th cent. foliations. *BM. Cat. Add. MSS.* 1854–1875, ii, 636–7 (list of contents). V. H. Galbraith, 'Royal Charters to Winchester', *Engl. Hist. Review* xxxv (1920), 382–400, prints 49 charters from this and No. 1042.

Fos. 39 (83 in the MS.). 10 × 7⅜ in. *FO:* T. Daccombe, 1550; Sotheby's sale-cat., 10 June 1873, lot 875 (property of a gentleman deceased).

1044.   Winchester, D. & C., Muniments. Composite misc. register written in a number of hands, mainly of the first half of the 14th cent., with some late 13th–late 14th cent. elements and additions. Contains copies of a variety of royal, papal, episcopal and other documents, 11th–14th cent., rel. the priory's affairs and possessions, incl. *acta* and a few private deeds, arranged roughly according to subject-matter, by quires (numbered 1–23). A late 14th cent. Table on twelve preliminary leaves shows the second half of the compilation (quires 24–43) to be wanting. Calendared by A. W. Goodman, *Chartulary of Winchester Cathedral* (Winchester, 1927).

Fos. 275 (bound, 19th cent., in 3 vols., fos. 12 + 125, 64, 74). 12¼ × 8¼ in. Many leaves mutilated.

¶ *Other registers etc.*

1045.   **BM., Harley Roll CC. 21.** Two detached fly-leaves (a bifolium), containing misc. copies of documents and other memoranda, *temp.* Edw. I–III, written in contemp. hands. A note by T. Daccombe (cf. Nos. 1042–3), 1558, orders the delivery of 'thys boke' to Sheen Priory. 12¾ × 9⅝ in.

1046.   **BM., Harley 315,** fos. 46–7. Two further detached fly-leaves, similar to No. 1045, and with similar contents. Fo. 46 has a note of the gift of the book from which they came by N. de Tarrant (prior, d. 1309). 13 × 9⅞ in.

WINCHESTER   co. Southt.
Ben. Abbey, Hyde (New Minster) *f.* 965

1047.   **BM., Cotton Domit. A. xiv,** fos. 22–237. Cartulary, 13th cent. (aft. 1263), with rubrics etc. Contains copies of charters etc., incl. occasional royal and episcopal documents, arranged and numbered in sections topographically (fos. 181–5, fines), with substantial misc. additions down to the 15th cent. *passim* and at the end (fos. 211 ff.). Bound (fos. 2–21) with a chronicle of the abbey 1035–1121, ed. E. Edwards, *Liber Monasterii de Hyda* (Rolls ser., 1856), 283–321. *Mon. Angl.* ii, 434 (*a*) (list of places and major contents).

Fos. 216. 7⅞ × 5½ in.

1048.   **BM., Harley 1761.** Cartulary (fos. 23–195), late 14th cent. (*temp.* Ric. II), with rubrics etc. Similar in arrangement and scope to No. 1047, of which it is apparently a revision, and with similar misc. additions, incl. (fos. 14–22) Annals 874–1478. A contemp. Table at fos. 3v–8 and an alphabetical index at fos. 10–13 show sections for Stoneham, Sanderstead and Lingfield, with part of that for Chiseldon, to be wanting. Possibly to be associated with the MS. is a bifolium used as the wrapper of **Winchester College** Muniments, Woodmancote court-rolls 1541–59, the first leaf containing copies of five deeds rel. Winterbourne, apparently in the hand of the main 15th cent. supplementor. A 16th cent. paper book of extracts is *ib.* (Woodmancote drawer). *Mon. Angl.* ii, 433 (*a*) (list of major contents). Edwards, *op. cit.,* lxxxviii–xc (description).

Fos. 195 (wants leaves *passim*). 13 × 9½ in. *FO:* J. Fisher, 16th cent.; P. Le Neve.

¶ *Other registers etc.*

1049.   **BM., Cotton Vesp. A. viii.** Illuminated charters and laws of King Edgar, 966, with an added charter of Hen. I. *Mon. Angl.* ii, 428 (*b*), 439–42.

1050.   **BM., Stowe 944.** Register and Martyrology, 11th cent., incl. copies of a few 10th–11th cent. charters etc. Ed. W. de G. Birch, *Liber Vitae* (Hampshire Record Soc., 1892). *FO:* W. Clavell; the Rev. G. North; M. Lort, D.D.; T. Astle.

1051.   **The Earl of Macclesfield,** Shirburn Castle. 'Liber Abbatiae.' Chronicle 455–1023, written 14th–15th cent. and incl. copies, with Latin and English translations, of a number of Anglo-Saxon royal and other charters, wills etc. An abridgement, 1572, by John Stow (*FO:* Sir R. and (1697) Sir H. St. George) is in BM., Lansdowne 717. Ed. Edwards, *op. cit.*

1052.   **BM., Stowe 58.** Another, 16th–17th cent., version of No. 1051. *FO:* P. Le Neve; J. Edmondson; A. C. Ducarel; T. Astle.

WINCHESTER   co. Southt.
Hosp. of St. Cross   *f.* 1132

1053.   **BM., Harley 1616.** 'Liber Primus.' Register, late 14th cent., of misc. documents etc. rel. the hospital's affairs. Red and blue paragraphs and, occasionally, initials. Includes copies of papal, royal and episcopal charters, records of legal proceedings, surveys, rentals, inventories etc., mainly *temp.* Edw. III–Ric. II. Contemp. and later additions on the fly-leaves include (fos. 67v–8) a list of Masters. A 19th cent. transcript is at Winchester, Hosp. of St. Cross (Muniments). *Mon. Angl.* vi, 722 (*n*) (list of major contents).

Fos. 68. 7¼ × 4½ in. *FO:* H. Worsley (*T*).

1054.   **Winchester, Hosp. of St. Cross,** Muniments, 'Register of St. Cross'. 'Liber Secundus,' *c.* 1409. Similar to No. 1053, the contents of which it partially duplicates. Large red and blue initials, paragraphs etc. Also incorporates copies of some 14th cent. rentals etc. and a few later additions. *List of Muniments, Deeds and Documents preserved in the Strong Room at the Hospital* (1902, privately), 1, no. 7 (descriptive note).

Fos. 1 + 128. 10½ × 7¼ in.

¶ *Other registers etc.*

1055.   **Ditto.** A late 14th cent. quire

containing exemplifications of the foundation charter, bulls of Innocent II and Lucius II, a charter of Hen. II, and a composition with the bp. of Winchester, 1185. *List of Muniments etc.*, 8, no. 1.

Fos. 4. $12\frac{1}{2} \times 8\frac{3}{4}$ in.

WINCHESTER   co. Southt.
Coll. of the BVM   *f.* 1382
1056. **Winchester College**, Muniments, 'Register H' (chest 1, no. 45). Cartulary, 15th cent., in a number of hands, with a few later additions. The earliest sections rubricated, with red initials. Arranged mainly by estates and incl. copies of some royal and papal charters etc. to alien priories with whose lands the college was endowed (for which cf. T. F. Kirby, *Annals of Winchester College* (1892), 23–5).

Fos. 265. $14 \times 9\frac{7}{8}$ in.
1057. **Ditto**, 'Register X'. A collection of loose 15th cent. quires and sheets, written in hands which are also found in No. 1056. They contain copies of deeds etc., similarly arranged and apparently made as drafts, fair copies etc.

Fos. *c.* 101 (16th cent. numeration, 26–389, with gaps). $14\frac{3}{4} \times 10\frac{3}{8}$ in.
1058. **Ditto**, 'Evidentiae Δ, Θ' (chest 1, nos. 43 (a) & (b)). Cartulary, 16th cent. (*temp.* Eliz. I), with pen-decorated initials and occasional key-words etc. in red. Arranged topographically in two vols.

Fos. 344, 341. 14×10 in.
1059. **Ditto**, 'Registrum Rubrum'. A late 16th cent. cartulary, arranged topographically.

Fos. 219. $20 \times 13\frac{1}{2}$ in.
⁋ *Other registers etc.*
1060. **Ditto**, 'Liber Albus' *al.* 'Vetus Registrum' (chest 1). Register of *Acta*, 15th–16th cent., incl. (fos. 31–45) 15th cent. inventories of books, vestments, furniture etc.

WINDSOR   co. Berks
Royal Coll. Chapel of St. George *f.* 1348
For the material at Windsor see J. N. Dalton, *MSS. of St. George's Chapel* (Windsor, 1957).
1061. **Windsor, St. George's Chapel,** Muniments (iv. B. 1). 'The Arundel White Book' *al.* 'The White Leiger'. Register, 15th cent., of statutes etc., royal (Edw. III) and papal charters and documents, appro-

priations of rectories, documents rel. the spiritualities of the abbey of Bec and other miscellaneous material. Begun by J. Arundel, dean 1417–52, perhaps as a result of the visitation of 1430, with additions down to the 16th cent. Titles and initials in red etc., sometimes illuminated. Arranged according to subject matter, with a Table at fos. 158–62.

Fos. 163. 15×11 in.
1062. **Ditto** (iv. B. 2, iv. B. 3). 'The Denton Black Book.' Register, 16th cent., bound in two vols., of papal bulls rel. the Chapel, St. Anthony's Hospital London, Sandleford Priory and North Marston; chantry foundation documents, 15th–16th cent.; and misc. deeds rel. Windsor properties, 13th–16th cent. Begun, 1517, by Canon James Denton and completed before his death in 1532. Titles and initials with decorative penwork; illuminated border and initial to fo. 1.

Fos. 337 (vol. i, fos. 1–146; ii, fos. 147–337). 13×10 in.
⁋ *Inventory*
1063. **Ditto** (xi. D. 24). 'Catalogue of the College Books and Papers', 16th cent. An incomplete list of the principal registers, accompt books, court rolls, counterparts of leases etc.

Fos. 2. 12×7 in. Paper.
⁋ *Other registers etc.*
1064. **PRO., Exch., T.R.** (Misc. Bks. 113). A 16th cent. collection of statutes and other misc. documents and memoranda rel. the Chapel and order of the Garter, incl. an inventory, 1516–17, of the Chapel's jewels etc.

WOBURN   co. Bedf.
Cist. Abbey   *f.* 1145
1065. **Untraced.** Registers reported, 18th cent. (*T*) and 1833 (*P*), as in the possession of the dukes of Bedford; see Gladys Scott Thomson, 'Woburn Abbey and the Dissolution of the Monasteries', *Trans. Royal Hist. Soc.*, 4th ser. xvi (1933), 129 ff.

WOMBRIDGE   co. Salop
Aug. Priory   *f.* 1130–5
1066. **BM., Egerton 3712.** Gen. cartulary, late 15th cent. (aft. 1481 ?), with initials and more important titles in red, sometimes with black penwork decoration. Arranged in sections by places, with the

copies of royal, papal, episcopal etc. charters at the end (fos. 79–93) and a few additions *passim*. Bound in at the back as fos. 97–9, apparently from an earlier binding, are a copy of a composition, 1294, rel. Wroxeter church and two leaves of a service book. An abstract, 1824, by George Morris is printed as 'Abstracts of . . . the Chartulary of Wombridge' etc., *Trans. Shropshire Arch. & Nat. Hist. Soc.*, First ser. ix, 305 ff.; xi, 325 ff.; Second ser. i, 294 ff.; ix, 96 ff.; x, 180 ff.; xi, 331 ff.; xii, 205 ff. (1886–1900).

Fos. iii + 99 (lacks the opening leaf, aft. fo. 1). 12 × 8¾ in. *FO*: E. Lloyd, 1824 (from a scrap heap); Sir T. Phillipps (MS. 3517); G. P. Mander.

WOODBRIDGE   co. Suff.
Aug. Priory   *f. c.* 1193
1067.   **Untraced.** Register cited by J. Stow, *Annales of England* (1601), preface, among 'authors out of whom these Annales are collected'. Perhaps identical with the register from which a list of bodies buried in the priory church is noticed by J. Weever, *Ancient Funerall Monuments* (1631), 752–3.

WOODHAM FERRERS   co. Essex
v. BICKNACRE.

WORCESTER   co. Worc.
Ben. Cath. Priory *f. c.* 743 (refounded
                                   c. 974–7)
For the registers at Worcester see R. L. Poole, *HMC. Fourteenth Report*, App. viii (1895), 165–84, whose account is at some points supplemented by W. Holtzmann, *Papsturkunden in England* ii (Göttingen, 1935), 60–6.
1068.   **BM., Cotton Tib. A. xiii,.** Two 11th cent. cartularies, with a 15th cent. index of places added at fos. 165–6, as follows: (1) fos. 1–118, copies, early 11th cent. (*temp.* Archbp. Wulstan, 1002–23(?)) with some 11th–12th cent. additions, of deeds arranged in sections by counties, followed without break (fos. 57 ff.) by copies of leases, with a section rel. co. Warw. apparently misplaced at fos. 103–9 and some further misc. additions at fos. 114–8; (2) fos. 119–200 (rubricated, with red initials), copies, 1090–1100, of royal, episcopal and other charters, notes of bounds and

other evidences, compiled and in part written by Hemming, and arranged according to subject matter in four main groups, preceded by a fifth (fos. 119–34) containing a narrative survey of the priory's lost possessions and preface. Ed. T. Hearne, *Hemingi Chartularium Ecclesiae Wigorniensis*, 2 vols. (Oxford, 1723), from an 18th cent. transcript, now Bodl., Rawlinson B. 445, made for Richard Graves of Mickleton. N. R. Ker, 'Hemming's Chartulary', *Studies in Medieval History presented to F. M. Powicke*, ed. R. W. Hunt, W. A. Pantin, R. W. Southern (Oxford, 1948), 49–75 (critical study).

Fos. 200 (15th cent. foliation, i–clxxxxvi, disturbed by the misplacement of two quires in pt. ii). Damaged by fire, 1731, and the leaves now mounted. Written space, (1) 7½ × 4⅛ in., (2) 7½ × 4⅜ in. *FO*: John Alderford, Abbots Salford, late 16th cent.
1069.   **BM., Cotton Nero E. i,** pt. ii, fos. 181–4; **Add. 46204.** 'The Oswald Cartulary.' Five leaves, with fragms. of two others, from a late 11th cent. cartulary, written in double columns with rubrics and red initials. Apparently an abbreviated version of No. 1068 (1) and thought to be from the compilation which was bound, by order of St. Wulstan, with Offa's Bible (of which single leaves may be BM., Add. 37777, 45025). N. R. Ker, *l.c.* I. Atkins & N. R. Ker, *Cat. MSS. Bibl. Wigorn.* 1622–3 (Cambridge, 1944), 77–9. I. Atkins, *Antiquaries J.* xx (1940), 220–3. W. H. Stevenson, *HMC. Middleton MSS.* (1911), 196–9.

Fos. 5 + 2 fragms. Written space, 14 × 10 in., approx. *FO*: (Add. 46204) the Willoughby fam., Middleton Hall, 16th cent.; found at Wollaton Hall, a family seat, 19th cent.; acquired from Lord Middleton, 1946.
1070.   **Worcester, D. & C.,** Muniments, 'Reg. I' (A. 4). Gen. cartulary, 13th cent. (*c.* 1240), with marginal rubrics, plain red and blue initials, paragraphs etc. and additions *passim* and at fos. 63 ff. (added leaves). Includes copies of royal (Edgar–Hen. III), papal and episcopal charters, collected mainly at the beginning. Lacks other obvious arrangement.

Fos. iii + 88 (medieval foliation, i–lxx, with post-medieval continuation). 11½ × 8 in.
1071.   **Ditto,** 'Liber Pensionum' (A. 3).

10—M.C.

Register, 15th cent. (aft. 1433), of deeds etc. rel. the priory's spiritual possessions and privileges (appropriations of churches, grants of pensions etc.), 12th–15th cent., incl. copies of a number of royal, papal and episcopal documents *passim*. Rubrics, and blue initials decorated with red. C. Price, *Liber Pensionum Prioratus Wigorn*. (Worcester Hist. Soc., 1925) (abstract). The former fly-leaves (Poole, *l.c.*, 170) are now bound separately as *ib.*, Add. MSS. 7, 25.

Fos. 67 + 4. 14 × 9½ in.

1072. **Ditto** (A. 8, A. 10). (Parts of an ?) early 16th cent. cartulary, with uncompleted marginal rubrics, red or occasionally blue initials (the first of each section with elaborate decorative penwork) etc., and misc. additions *passim*. Arranged topographically and incl. copies of royal, papal and episcopal charters. Fos. 9–12 of A. 10 should precede fo. 1 of A. 8, and fos. 20–1 should similarly follow fo. 3.

Fos. (A. 8) 76; (A. 10) 22. 12 × 8½ in. Signature 'Browne Willis' in A. 10, fo. 22v.

❡ *Elemosinarius*

1073. **Ditto** (A. 9). Cartulary etc., of the almoner, 14th cent. (*temp*. Edw. III). Arranged topographically, in sections, with a list of rents at the beginning (pp. 9–12) and extensive misc. additions *passim*. J. Harvey Bloom, *Liber Elemosinarii* (Worcester Hist. Soc., 1911) (abstract).

Fos. 105 (post-medieval pagination, 1–210). 9¼ × 6½ in.

❡ *Other registers etc.*

1074. **PRO., Exch., Augm. Off.** (Misc. Bks. 63). Letter-book, *temp*. Hen. III–Edw. III. J. Harvey Bloom, *Liber Ecclesiae Wigorn*. (Worcester Hist. Soc., 1912) (abstract etc.).

1075. **Worcester, D. & C.,** Muniments (A. 5). Priory register, 1301–1408, arranged chronologically. J. M. Wilson, *The Liber Albus of the Priory of Worcester* (Worcester Hist. Soc., 1919) (abstract of fos. 1–162). *Id.*, *The Worcester Liber Albus* (1920) (popular extracts in English).

1076. **Ditto,** 'Registrum Sede Vacante' (A. 1). J. W. Willis Bund, *The Register of the Priory of Worcester during the vacancy of the See . . . 1301–1435* (Worcester Hist. Soc., 1897) (abstract).

1077. **Ditto,** 'Registrum Prioratus' (A. 2). Register, early 14th cent., of rentals,

custumaries etc., incl. copies of some early royal, episcopal and other charters. Ed. W. H. Hale, *Registrum . . . Prioratus Beatae Mariae Wigorn*. (Camden Soc., Old ser. xci, 1865). *FO:* T. Astle, 1765 (to whom is probably due the Italian binding, cf. BM., Stowe 937).

1078. **Ditto,** 'The Ledgers' (A. 6 (1), (2) and (3). Priors' registers, 1458–1540. Three vols.

WORCESTER co. Worc.
Hosp. of St. Wulstan *f. c.* 1085
F. T. Marsh, *Annals of the Hospital of St. Wulstan . . . together with a Chartulary etc.* (Worcester, 1890), edits original charters only (Bodl., Worcestershire ch. 12–108, rolls 1–2).

1079. **Birmingham, Reference Libr.** (No. 403957). 'Tenor cartarum de maner(io) de Chadewych et al(iis) terr(is)' etc. Abstracts, *c.* 1500, of deeds etc., incl. one or two royal and papal privileges, rel. Chadwich *al*. Chadwick in Bromsgrove and elsewhere in cos. Worc. and Warw. Arranged by grantors, whose names are entered in the left margin.

Roll of 2 membrs. 59 × 12 in. *FO:* the Dean and Governing Body of Christ Church, Oxford; George Cadbury, F.S.A. (with the manor of Chadwich).

WORKSOP co. Nott.
Aug. Priory *f. c.* 1120
1080. **Untraced** (Presumed destroyed by fire at Worksop, 1761). Cartulary in the possession, 16th–17th cent., of the Talbot fam., earls of Shrewsbury, and later, by descent with the priory's site, of the Howard fam., earls of Arundel and dukes of Norfolk, 17th–18th cent. (*T*). Extracts down to fo. 80 are in: (*a*) BM., Harley 4028, fo. 130, where it is described as *penes* George Lascelles of Kniveton, 1618, but the property of the (3rd) earl of Pembroke (d. 1630), husband of Mary Talbot; (*b*) Bodl., Dugdale 11 (*SC.* 6501), fo. 37 (*penes* Alathea (Talbot), 1649, widow of the 2nd earl of Arundel); (*c*) *Mon. Angl.* vi, 118–20 (*penes* John Selden, *c.* 1655, who was steward and reputedly also husband of Elizabeth (Talbot), widow (d. 1651) of the 8th earl of Kent); and (*d*) Bodl., Dodsworth 126, fos. 140v, 146; 127, fo. 118v (*SC.* 5067–8) (from a transcript by St. Loo

Kniveton, d. 1628). Mary, Elizabeth and Alathea Talbot were daughters and co-heiresses of Gilbert, 7th earl of Shrewsbury. The eventual sole heiress was Alathea, cf. D. M. Barratt, 'The Library of John Selden', *Bodl. Libr. Record* iii (1950–1), 136 etc.

¶ *Inventories*

1080A. **Untraced.** Index of charters, 1449, by C. Fleming, prior, of which an early 17th cent. transcript is deposited by the Earl of Winchilsea with Northamptonshire Record Soc. (Finch–Hatton MS. B. 215, pp. 365–71). Perhaps incorporated in No. 1080.

WORMSLEY   co. Heref.
Aug. Priory   *f. c.* 1216
1081.   **BM., Harley 3586,** fos. 67–145. Gen. cartulary, 14th cent. (aft. 1336), with later 14th cent. continuation (fos. 79v ff., aft. 1374) and occasional subsequent additions. Red paragraphs, boxing of titles etc. Arranged mainly topographically, with a group of royal charters (fos. 128–9, incomplete) followed by charters *de Bladis*, *de Feno* and rel. churches, chantries etc. (incl. copies of some episcopal documents) at the end. A Table of headings at fo. 67, in the later hand, shows sections entitled *Bulla Privilegiorum* and *Confirmacio possessionum nostrarum et ordinacio ordinis nostri*, with part of that for Wormsley (incl. copies of further royal and episcopal charters), to be lacking at the beginning. *Mon. Angl.* vi, 398 (*l*), lists the heads of the extant sections.
    Fos. 78 (post-medieval numeration, 1–77, from fo. 68; wants leaves at the beginning and aft. fos. 127, 129, 137). 11¾ × 8 in. *FO:* R. Harley, 1st earl of Oxford (from Brampton Castle, co. Heref.), 1722.

WYMONDHAM   co. Norf.
Ben. Abbey   *f.* (as a priory) bef. 1107
1082.   **BM., Cotton Titus C. viii.** Gen. cartulary, 13th cent. (*temp.* Hen. III), with rubrics, red initials, and some additions *passim*. Arranged apparently by places and subject matter, with an incomplete section of papal and episcopal charters at the beginning (fos. 6–15), followed by another of royal and baronial charters (fos. 16–21), and incl. copies of a few further royal charters at fos. 34v–36v. Extracts, 1628, are

in BM., Harley 294, fo. 181v. *Mon. Angl.* iii, 327 (*s*), lists the more important contents.
    Fos. ii + 107 (15th cent. foliation, xvii–cxi, from fo. 5). 10 × 7 in. *FO:* Sir W. Le Neve, 1628; Sir E. Walker (*T*); Sir Wm. Dugdale (?).

WYMONDLEY, LITTLE   co. Hertf.
Aug. Priory   *f.* (as a hosp.) 1203–7
1083.   **BM., Add. 43972.** Gen. cartulary, mid-13th cent., with marginal rubrics etc. and additions *passim*. Arranged topographically in two parts: (1) fos. 12 ff., rel. lands, rents etc. held *in dominico*; (2) fos. 53 ff., rel. other possessions. Preceded (fos. 2–11) by a rental, and includes copies of a few papal, royal and episcopal charters at the beginning and elsewhere *passim*. H. I. Bell, *Brit. Mus. Quart.* x (1935–6), 95–8 (discussion).
    Fos. iii + 78 (wants a few leaves *passim*). 9⅛ × 7 in. *FO:* T. Lloyd; Sir T. Phillipps (MS. 3627).

YARMOUTH, GREAT   co. Norf.
Hosp. of St. Mary   *f.* bef. 1278
1084.   **Oxford, Bodl., Gough Norf. 20** (*SC.* 18076), fos. 1–31. Register of deeds etc., *c.* 1400, with spaces for initials and titles. Includes (fos. 14v–23) a rental of 1398, with later revisions, and (fos. 28v–31) constitutions in English. Bound (fos. 32 ff.) with a notarial translation into English, 1614.
    Fos. 31. 9⅜ × 6½ in. *FO:* the Mayor & Aldermen of Great Yarmouth; H. Borrett, 1710.

YARMOUTH, GREAT   co. Norf.
v. also GORLESTON.

YORK, See of   *f.* 625
1085.   **BM., Lansdowne 402.** Cartulary, *c.* 1309 (*temp.* Archbp. W. Greenfield), with rubrics, red and blue decorated initials, and a few additions at the end. Contains copies of royal, papal and other charters, 11th–14th cent., rel. the temporalities of the See, numbered consecutively and incl. some leases by the archbps. A contemp. Table (fos. 2–7) includes the titles of 40 charters now lacking at the beginning.

Fos. 131. $11\frac{1}{2} \times 8\frac{5}{8}$ in. *FO:* Sir James Ware; Henry, 2nd earl of Clarendon; James, 1st duke of Chandos; James West, 1763.

YORK co. York
Minster (Cath. Church) *f. c.* 627
1086. **BM., Cotton Claud. B. iii.** Gen. cartulary (fos. 3–134), 13th cent. (*c.* 1280), with rubrics, spaces for initials, and misc. additions (fos. 134–65, 198–206). Opens (fo. 3) with a section of royal charters, followed (fo. 6v) by the title: 'Hic incipiunt carte, ordinaciones, confirmaciones, resignaciones et quieteclam (aciones) ac alia scripta Decanatui Ebor. spectancia.' A contemp. Table (fos. 208–13) classifies the material according to the dignitaries it concerns. Fos. 166–97 are a separate late 13th cent. compilation containing terriers, rentals etc. of the prebends; ed., in translation, T. A. M. Bishop, 'Extents of the Prebends of York (*c.* 1295)', *Miscellanea iv* (Yorks. Arch. Soc., Record ser. xciv, 1937 for 1936), 1–38.

Fos. 213 (3–134 with contemp. pagination, 1–264). $12\frac{1}{2} \times 8\frac{3}{4}$ in.
1087. **York, D. & C.,** Muniments, 'Magnum Registrum Album'. Gen. cartulary, 14th cent. (*temp.* Edw. III), with rubrication of the early leaves, subsequent titles underlined in red, and spaces for initials throughout. Preceded (fos. 1–33) by Hugh Cantor's chronicle of the See, ed. J. Raine, *Historians of the Church of York* ii (Rolls ser., 1886), 98–227. Twenty-two preliminary leaves contain extracts from Domesday and a contemp. Table, classified according to subject matter. For a later Table see No. 1096 below. *Mon. Angl.* vi, 1175–99, and Raine, *op. cit.* iii (1894), 1–210 *passim*, print extracts.

Fos. 22 + 392 (contemp. foliation in four parts, 1–74, 1–100, 1–100, 1–118, perhaps with reference to an earlier division for binding). $11\frac{1}{4} \times 9\frac{3}{4}$ in.
1088. **Ditto,** 'Doomsday Book'. Misc. register of rights, privileges etc., mid-14th cent., with rubrics and red initials. Title (fo. 1): 'Infrascripta iura competunt ... Decano et Capitulo ... ex privilegiis, libertatibus, immunitatibus, et consuetudinibus legitime prescriptis' etc. Includes copies of royal and papal charters, compositions, ordinations, extents etc., grouped roughly in these classes. Fos. 126–152 contain additions.

Fos. xi + 152. $14\frac{3}{4} \times 9\frac{3}{4}$ in.
1089. **BM., Cotton Vit. A. ii,** fos. 94–156. Misc. late 14th cent. register with rubrics, red paragraphs, occasional red initials, and some additions (mainly at the end). Contains statutes etc. of the cathedral and a formulary, followed by a collection of misc. charters etc., incl. copies of royal and papal documents and of grants and leases by the Dean & Chapter, apparently for the most part concerned with rights in churches, tithes, rents etc.

Fos. 63 (imperf.). $9\frac{1}{4} \times 6\frac{1}{4}$ in. (the leaves shrunk and mutilated by fire, 1731, and now mounted).

⁋ *Inventories*
1090. **York, D. & C.,** Muniments (M. 2 (2).20). 'Inventorium pixidum et capsarum.' Inventory of the muniments, late 15th cent., arranged by pressmarks, with indexes of places etc., chantries and presses at the end.

Fos. 103. $12\frac{3}{4} \times 8\frac{1}{2}$ in. Paper.
1091. **Ditto** (M. 2 (2).16). Inventory similar to, and apparently contemp. with, No. 1090, but with a different internal arrangement and a single general index at the end.

Fos. 86. $12\frac{3}{4} \times 8\frac{1}{2}$ in. Paper.
1092. **Ditto,** 'Extents' (M. 2 (2)). A 15th cent. register of terriers of lands etc. of individual dignitaries, incl. (fos. 3–18v) a repertorium, arranged by subject matter, of the relevant muniments, with references either to No. 1087 or to original documents. Also includes some copies of charters etc., partly added, *passim*.

Fos. 70. $16\frac{1}{4} \times 11\frac{1}{2}$ in. Paper.
⁋ *Vicars Choral*
1093. **Ditto,** 'Cartulary of the Vicars Choral'. Cartulary (pp. 1–106), late 13th cent., with incomplete rubrication and spaces for initials. Contains copies of title-deeds etc., arranged topographically, followed by misc. 14th cent. etc. additions, mainly of documents rel. litigation, with some obits.

Fos. 152 (paginated 1–302 + 2). 12×8 in.
⁋ *Other registers etc.*
For other registers at York, see H. T. Riley, *HMC. First Report* (1870), App., 97.
1094. **Durham U.L., Cosin V. v. 9,** fos. 135–50. A late 14th cent. quire con-

taining copies of charters and other documents rel. the appropriation of Rotherham church. *FO:* the Rev. George Davenport, 17th cent.; Durham Cathedral (Bp. Cosin Libr.), *c.* 1670.

1095. BM., Cotton Galba E. x, fos. 91–147. Chapter registers, 1396–7 and 1500, *sede vacante.*

1096. York, D. & C., Muniments (M. 2 (4). 26). Tables, 15th cent., of No. 1087 and other registers. Paper.

YORK co. York
Ben. Abbey of St. Mary *f.* 1088–9
1097. BM., Add. 38816, fos. 21–39. A collection of misc. 12th cent. quires, written in several hands with rubrics, decorated initials in various colours, and many excisions. Perhaps originally a single compilation. The first quire (fos. 21–8) contains copies of three royal charters to the abbey, Will. II–Hen. II, and the remainder contain the conclusion of the rule of St. Benedict (fo. 29), followed (fo. 29v) by Stephen of Whitby's history of the foundation, a list (*c.* 1180?) of abbeys in fraternity, and some misc. additions. *BM. Cat. Add. MSS.* 1911–1915, 251–3.

Fos. 19. $11\frac{3}{4} \times 8\frac{1}{8}$ in. *FO:* Sir John Savile; Sir T. Phillipps (MS. 24354); George Dunn.

1098. Oxford, Bodl., Dodsworth 76 (*SC.* 5018), fos. 56–64. Fragm. of a rubricated late 13th cent. cartulary (fos. 56–60 with red and blue decorated initials), containing copies of 56 deeds rel. various places. Fos. 61–4, in another hand, have a 15th cent. foliation, lv–lvi, lix–lx. A photostat copy is in Leeds, Yorks. Arch. Soc. MS. 618. W. H. Turner & H. O. Coxe, *Cal. Charters and Rolls . . . in the Bodl. Libr.* (Oxford, 1878), 693–8 (calendar).

Fos. 9. $8\frac{3}{8} \times 6\frac{1}{2}$ in. *FO:* Christopher, baron Hatton.

1099. Ditto, fo. 121. Copies, 13th–14th cent. of six deeds rel. Sandtoft. Perhaps part of a roll. Turner & Coxe, *op. cit.,* 693. *Mon. Angl.* iii, 617–8.

Fos. 1. $11\frac{3}{4} \times 7\frac{7}{8}$ in. *FO:* as No. 1098.

1100. BM., Harley 236. Cartulary, 14th cent. (*temp.* Edw. II), perhaps the first part of a larger compilation. Arranged in sections by subject matter (royal charters, compositions and tithes, Appleton etc.,

leases in Richmondshire, manor of Hudswell, various churches etc.), with additions down to *temp.* Edw. III etc. *passim,* incl. (fo. IV) a 16th cent. index. *Mon. Angl.* iii, 540 (*h*) lists the contents.

Fos. 55 + some unnumbered blank leaves (later medieval foliation, xiii–lxxxv, from fo. 2; wants xxv–xxvi etc.). $8\frac{1}{2} \times 6\frac{5}{8}$ in. *FO:* Sir S. D'Ewes.

1101. York, D. & C., MS. xvi. A. 1. Cartulary (fos. 111–318), 14th cent. (*temp.* Edw. III), with red paragraphs, underlining of titles, boxing of headings etc. Arranged topographically by wappentakes, which are all in the North Riding, and enlarged, 15th–16th cent., by the addition of further sections of deeds at the end (fos. 319–386) and an elaborate abstract of contents at the beginning (fos. 1–110). Wants groups of leaves *passim* and at the end.

Fos. x + 386 (15th–16th cent. foliation, x–ccccxlv, from fo. 111). $12\frac{7}{8} \times 9\frac{1}{4}$ in. (mutilated). *FO:* T. Atkinson; F. Hildyard, bookseller.

1102. Manchester, Rylands Libr., Lat. MSS. 220–1. Cartulary, similar to No. 1101, with similar enlargements, now bound in great disorder in two vols. The headings etc. in the 14th cent. part are underlined in red and the paragraphs are alternately red and blue. The wappentakes are in the West and (mainly) East Ridings.

Fos. xxiv + 417 (wants many leaves *passim*). $12\frac{1}{4} \times 9$ in. *FO:* J. Towneley; the Rev. T. D. Whitaker; R. Heber; Sir T. Phillipps (MS. 8135).

1103. York, D. & C., MS. xvi. A. 2. Cartulary, mid-14th cent., in two apparently contemp. parts with an elaborate late medieval abstract of contents, now severely mutilated, added at the beginning: (1) fos. 1–43, with headings etc. in the hand of the text, copies of deeds arranged by obedientiaries etc.; (2) fos. 44–101, with red paragraphs, boxing of headings etc., copies of deeds *de Communa* arranged topographically.

Fos. 23 (excl. stubs) + 104 (late medieval foliation, i–clxi; wants leaves *passim*). $12\frac{3}{4} \times 9\frac{3}{8}$ in. *FO:* the Rev. J. Lewis.

1104. Untraced. Fragm. of a 15th cent. cartulary reported, in 1895, to be at Birch Hall, co. Essex; see *HMC. Fourteenth Report,* App. ix, 270. Not found among papers of the Round fam. deposited at

Chelmsford, Essex R.O., or remaining at Birch Hall.

Fos. ii+6.

¶ *Other registers etc.*

1105.   **Oxford, Bodl., Dodsworth 76** (*SC.* 5018), fos. 122–3. Leaves from two registers, containing copies of pleas, writs etc., 13th–14th cent. *FO:* as Nos. 1908–9.

YORK   co. York
Hosp. of St. Leonard   *f.* 1135

1106.   **BM., Cotton Nero D. iii**, fos. 3–218. Vol. i (cf. No. 1107) of a 14th–15th cent. gen. cartulary with rubrics and blue initials decorated with red (sometimes illuminated). Contains copies of royal, archiepiscopal, papal and other general charters, incl. some rel. churches, *de Travis, de Nona Garba* etc., followed (fo. 69) by material for the city of York, in alphabetical order of places, and (fos. 205 ff.) an added section of further royal etc. charters written in contemp. hands. A photostat copy is in the Bodleian Libr. *Mon. Angl.* vi, 607 (*c*), lists heads of sections.

Fos. 242 (incl. unnumbered blank leaves). $15\frac{1}{2} \times 11$ in.

1107.   **Oxford, Bodl., Rawlinson B. 455.** Vol. ii (cf. No. 1106). Copies of deeds etc. rel. the West and East Ridings, arranged in alphabetical order of places under either head. Extracts, 17th cent., in Bodl., Dodsworth 120B, fos. 1–116, include some from leaves now missing. A photostat copy is in BM., MS. Facsimiles 466.

Fos. 152 (17th cent. numeration, 1–232; wants groups *passim*). $16\frac{1}{2} \times 12$ in. *FO:* the Harley libr. (sale-cat. 1744, vol. iv, no. 20725).

¶ *Other registers etc.*

1108.   **Lichfield, D. & C.**, Muniments (QQ. 1). Roll of extents, 1287.

YORK   co. York
Guild of Corpus Christi.
        No cartulary recorded.

¶ *Other registers etc.*

1109.   **BM., Lansdowne 403.** 'Liber Ordinationis.' Register of members etc., 15th–16th cent., with copies of a few deeds, *temp.* Hen. VII–VIII, inserted at the beginning (fos. 9–14). Ed. R. H. Scaife, *The Register of the Guild of Corpus Christi* (Surtees Soc. lvii, 1872).

B. SCOTLAND

ABERDEEN
co. Aberd.
See of, *f.* bef. 1150, and Cath. Church, *f.* bef. 1157

C. Innes, *Registrum Episcopatus Aberdonensis*, 2 vols. (Spalding & Maitland Clubs, 1845), describes the cartularies and edits much of their contents. For those at Aberdeen, see also M. R. James, *Cat. Medieval MSS. Aberdeen U.L.* (Cambridge, 1932), xiv etc.

1110.   **Aberdeen U.L., MS. 247.** 'Registrum Rubeum.' Composite register comprising: (1) fos. 1–33 (with red underlining of titles, paragraphs etc.), inventory of the contents of the treasury, 1436, incl. (fos. 14–17) lists of *carte, littere* and *evidencie*; followed (fo. 19) by lists of obits, statutes etc.; (2) fos. 34–59, copies, *c.* 1362, of 14th cent. royal, episcopal and other charters to the cathedral, with later 14th cent. continuations; (3) fos. 60–100, copies, 15th–16th cent., in a number of hands, of misc. documents etc., incl. some royal and episcopal charters etc.

Fos. 84 (post-medieval foliation, 1–100; wants a few leaves *passim*). $11\frac{3}{8} \times 6\frac{3}{4}$ in.

1111.   **Edinburgh, NLS., Adv. 16. 1. 10** (A. 1. 38). 'Registrum Album.' Composite misc. register of the church and see, begun late 14th cent. (*temp.* A. de Tynninghame (?), bp. 1382–90) with continuations down to the 16th cent. in a number of hands. Some parts are rubricated, with red initials etc. Includes sections of royal and papal charters, grants by the bishops etc. An 18th cent. transcript is in *ib.*, Adv. 35. 3. 34, pp. 1–504.

Fos. 188. $11\frac{1}{4} \times 6\frac{1}{2}$ in.

1112.   **Aberdeen U.L., MS. 249.** 'Registrum Capellanorum Chori.' Cartulary, late 15th cent., with red decorated initials etc. and some later additions and interpolations towards the end; continued (fos. 98 ff.) on added quires etc., in a succession of hands, down to 1552. Arranged apparently by beneficiaries (i.e. individual prebendaries and dignitaries) and includes copies of some royal and episcopal chart-

ers. Fos. 81–3 contain inventories of jewels, books etc.

Fos. ii + 213. $10\frac{3}{8} \times 7$ in.

1113.   **Aberdeen U.L., MS. 248.** Cartulary of 16th cent. charters and other memoranda rel. the endowments of obits etc., begun *c.* 1544–50 by Alexander Galloway, 'rector a Kinkell', with later 16th cent. additions at the end. Rubrics, and initials and occasional miniatures in various colours. Includes a Table of fos. i–lii (the original compilation) at fos. lvii^v–lix, and an uncompleted kalendar of the obits at the beginning.

Fos. ii + 113. $10\frac{3}{8} \times 7\frac{1}{2}$ in. *FO:* Sir P. Lesley.

¶ *Other registers etc.*

1114.   **Edinburgh, NLS., Adv. 34. 4. 4** (Jac. V. 6. 4). Misc. 14th–16th cent. of constitutions, ordinances and other misc. documents (incl. royal charters) rel. the privileges of the see, inquisitions, lists of bounds etc. Partly duplicates material in No. 1111. An 18th cent. transcript is in *ib.*, Adv. 35. 3. 4, pp. 505 ff.

1115.   **Aberdeen U.L., MS. 251.** 'Registrum Assedationum', 1543–58 etc. Preceded by constitutions and ordinances of the chapter, 1540.

ABERDEEN
co. Aberd.
Parish Church (Coll., 1540) of St. Nicholas.

1116.   **Aberdeen, City Charter Room.** Register of grants, rentals, statutes etc., begun apparently at the end of the 15th cent. and continued in a series of 16th cent. hands. The material is mainly contemp., with notarial attestations, but includes some 14th cent. items. A number of the leaves are mutilated. Ed. J. Cooper, *Cartularium Ecclesie S. Nicholai Aberdonensis*, 2 vols. (Spalding Club, 1888–92).

Fos. vi + 114. $14\frac{1}{2} \times 9\frac{3}{4}$ in.

ARBROATH
co. Forfar
Tiron. Abbey
f. 1178

C. Innes & P. Chalmers, *Liber S. Thome*

de Aberbrothoc, 2 vols. (Bannatyne Club, 1848–56), edits Nos. 1117–18.

1117.   **The Earl of Northesk,** lodged (1954) with Messrs. Lindsay, Howe & Co., W.S., Edinburgh. Fragms. of a 13th cent. cartulary (*temp.* Alex. II–III), with additions. Finely written with rubrics, alternate red or blue initials and consecutive red numeration of the entries, corresponding to that of No. 1118. Contents: (1) copies of royal and other charters arranged by reigns and numbered *i* (incomplete)–*xxxi*, *xciii* (incomplete)–*civ*, *cxvii–cxxvi* (10 fos.); (2) charters of bps. of St. Andrews etc., numbered *cxliiii–clxviii* (a quire of 6 fos.); (3) charters of bps. of Brechin and Aberdeen, numbered *clxxxiv–ccii* (5 fos., consecutive); (4) misc. additions in later 13th–14th cent. etc. hands, incl. copies of further episcopal, royal and papal charters, with parts of the 'Statuta Concilii Scoticani' and of a list of taxations of benefices (13 fos.).

Fos. 34. $10\frac{5}{8} \times 7\frac{3}{8}$ in.

1118.   **Edinburgh, NLS., Adv. 34. 4. 2** (A. 5. 13). 'Registrum Vetus.' Cartulary (fos. 34–129), mid-14th cent., with rubrics, red initials and consecutive red numeration of the entries, preceded and followed by misc. contemp. and later additions. Contains copies of royal, episcopal, papal and other charters, arranged partly by reigns and partly by grantors, with a Table at fos. 34–8. A 17th cent. abstract by Sir J. Balfour is in *ib.*, Adv. 33. 2. 9, fos. 41–63, and transcripts (17th–18th cent.) are in *ib.*, Adv. 34. 1. 10, 35. 3. 2; BM., Add. 33246, fos. 96–362; and in the possession of the Earl of Dalhousie, Brechin Castle.

Fos. 138. $8\frac{3}{4} \times 5\frac{3}{4}$ in. *FO:* Sir J. Balfour.

1119.   **BM., Add. 33245.** Register (fos. 30–186), 16th cent. (aft. 1531), of royal and other (incl. some episcopal) charters and documents, compositions, inquisitions, leases, bounds etc., 13th–16th cent., apparently rel. the abbey's rights, privileges etc. in lands, rents, churches etc. Rubrics, red and blue decorated initials (of which a few have been excised) etc. Fos. 1–29 contain an added 16th cent. topographical index. A note at fo. 29v shows the book to have been in the hands of Richard Hay, 1696.

Fos. 186 (contemp. foliation, ii–clxvii, from fo. 30; wants xxv–xxxii, lxxix).

11×7 in. *FO:* the Hamilton fam., dukes of Hamilton.

¶ *Other registers etc.*

1120.   **Edinburgh, NLS., Adv. 34. 4. 3** (A. 1. 24). 'Registrum Nigrum.' Register of leases etc., 1288–*c.* 1500 (mainly 15th cent.). *FO:* Sir J. Balfour.

1121.   **Arbroath, Burgh Muniments.** Register of leases etc., similar in date and scope to No. 1120, in which the contents are largely duplicated. *FO:* the regality of Arbroath; the Earl of Panmure, 1748; presented by the Hon. Wm. Maule, 1822.

1122.   **Ditto.** Register of Abbot G. Hepburn, 1503–13. *FO:* as No. 1121.

1123.   **Ditto.** Register of Abbots J. and D. Beaton, 1518–36. *FO:* as No. 1121.

BALMERINO   co. Fife
Cist. Abbey   *f. c.* 1227

1124.   **Edinburgh, NLS., Adv. 30. 5. 3** (A. 5. 27). Cartulary, 14th cent. (aft. 1331), with rubrics etc., and occasional additions. Arranged in two sections: (1) fos. 1–20, copies of royal and other charters; (2) fos. 21v–27v, copies of papal privileges to the abbey and Cistercian order. A 16th cent. transcript is in *ib.*, Adv. 33. 2. 5 (*FO:* Col. Charles Fairfax) and others, 18th cent., are in *ib.*, Adv. 35. 3. 13, pp. 133–92, and in the possession of the Earl of Dalhousie, Brechin Castle. Ed. W. B. D. D. Turnbull, *The Chartularies of Balmerino and Lindores* (Abbotsford Club, 1841).

Fos. i+27. $8 \times 5\frac{1}{4}$ in. *FO:* Sir J. Balfour.

BRECHIN   co. Angus
See of, and Cath. Church   *f.* bef. 1150

1125.   **The Earl of Dalhousie,** deposited at Edinburgh, Scottish R.O., Hist. Room (Dalhousie Collection). Gen. cartulary, early 16th cent., with an addition of 1552 at the end. Contains copies of charters and other documents, mainly 15th–16th cent., rel. the cathedral's endowments, incl. some royal, episcopal, papal etc. material *passim*. Ed. C. Innes, *Registrum Episcopatus Brechinensis* i (Bannatyne Club, 1856).

Fos. iii+151. $11\frac{3}{4} \times 9$ in. *FO:* the Earl of Panmure.

CAMBUSKENNETH   co. Stirl.
Aug. Abbey   *f. c.* 1140

1126.   **Edinburgh, NLS., Adv. 34. 1. 2** (A. 4. 6). Authenticated transcript, 1535, of

225 of the abbey's charters, made because the originals were in danger of destruction by damp. Red and blue decorated initials and some illuminated borders etc. Arranged in alphabetical order of places and subject matter, with a contemp. Table on 6 unnumbered preliminary leaves, and the entries, incl. copies of royal and episcopal documents, individually attested by Sir J. Foulis, clerk of the Register, under confirmation of the Great Seal, the cord for the attachment of which remains. Transcripts, 18th cent., are in *ib.*, Adv. 35. 3. 7, 34. 1. 2a, and in the possession of the Earl of Dalhousie, Brechin Castle. Ed. Sir Wm. Fraser, *Registrum Monasterii de Cambuskenneth* (Grampian Club, 1872).

Fos. xii + 166. 12½ × 8½ in. *FO:* the Earl of Mar, 1693.

COLDINGHAM co. Berw.
Ben. Priory *f.* bef. 1139
No cartulary recorded.
⁋ *Inventories*
1127.   **Durham, D. & C.,** Muniments (Misc. Ch. 1223). Inventory, 12th–13th cent., of 41 episcopal and other charters.
Roll of 1 membr. 15¼ × 5 in.
1128.   **Ditto** (Misc. Ch. 1224). Inventory, 12th–13th cent., of 45 royal and baronial charters.
Roll of 1 membr. 12½ × 5 in.
1129.   **Ditto** (Misc. Ch. 2646). Inventory, first half of the 13th cent., of 102 royal, episcopal and baronial charters. Cf. No. 1130.
Roll of 3 membrs. *c.* 48 × 5 in. (mutilated).
1130.   **Ditto** (Misc. Ch. 2647). Continuation of No. 1129, listing 33 further baronial charters.
Roll of 1 membr. 12 × 5 in.

COLDSTREAM co. Berw.
Cist. Priory (Nuns) *f.* bef. 1166
1131.   **BM., Harley 6670.** Gen. cartulary, 1434, made by John Laurence, notary public, 'cum propter vetustatem (cartarum) tum propter metum Anglorum'. Written in a rather rough hand with rubrics etc. and arranged topographically, incl. copies of one royal charter (Alexander II) and several of the earls of Dunbar etc. Transcripts, 18th cent., are in NLS., Adv. 34. 4. 1, pp. 64–134 and in the possession of the

Earl of Dalhousie, Brechin Castle. Ed. C. Rogers, *Chartulary ... of Coldstream* (Grampian Club, 1879).
Fos. 57. 7 × 5 in. *FO:* the Earl of Haddington.

COUPAR ANGUS co. Perth
Cist. Abbey *f.* bef. 1164
C. Rogers, *Rental Book of Cupar Angus with a Breviary of the Register*, 2 vols. (Grampian Club, 1879–80) edits Nos. 1132–3, partly in abstract. See also D. E. Easson, *Charters of ... Coupar Angus*, 1166–1608 (Scottish Hist. Soc., 1947).
1132.   **Untraced.** Cartulary of which a 17th cent. 'Breviarium' by Sir J. Balfour is in NLS., Adv. 33. 2. 9, fos. 27–38. The extracts, from fos. 1–32, are of 12th–13th cent. royal, papal, episcopal and other grants.
⁋ *Other registers etc.*
1133.   **Edinburgh, Scottish R.O.,** Hist. Room (R. 2/3). 'Registra Assedationum', 1443–1559. 2 vols. Paper.

CRAIL co. Fife
Coll. Church *f.* 1517
1134.   **Edinburgh, NLS., Adv. 34. 4. 6.** Transcript, 1528, of the charters of constitution and endowment, with inventories of plate, ornaments, books etc. Conventional pen work decoration of initials and some later additions and interpolations. Calendared by C. Rogers, *Register of the Collegiate Church of Crail* (Grampian Club, 1877).
Fos. 118 (unnumbered). 12 × 9 in. Exchanged, 19th cent., by the burgh of Crail for a transcript.

CROSSRAGUEL co. Ayr
Clun. Abbey *f.* (as an oratory) bef. 1214–16
1135.   **Untraced.** Cartulary *penes* the Earl of Cassillis, 1729, see F. C. Hunter Blair, *Charters of ... Crosraguel* i (Ayrshire & Galloway Arch. Association, 1886), xvii.

CULROSS co. Perth
Cist. Abbey *f.* bef. 1217
1136.   **Destroyed.** Cartulary which belonged to the Lady Colville of Culross, containing 'a list of all the mortifications dedicated by the earls of Fife to the Abbacy of Culross'. For the circumstances of its

destruction by fire, 17th cent., see 'A Delver in Antiquity' (W. B. D. D. Turnbull), *Fragmenta Scoto-Monastica* (Edinburgh, 1842), 14–15, citing Lord Fountainhall, *Decisions* i, 544, dated 12 Jan. 1693.

DEER   co. Aberd.
Celtic Monastery   *f.* 6th cent.
No cartulary recorded.
¶ *Other registers etc.*
1137.   **Cambridge U.L., Ii. 6. 32.** 'The Book of Deer.' Gospel-Book etc., 9th–10th cent., with the legend of the abbey's foundation and five notes of grants in Middle Irish and Latin added, 12th cent., in blank spaces, margins etc., at fos. 3–5, 40. Ed. J. Stuart, *The Book of Deer* (Spalding Club, 1869). J. Fraser, 'The Gaelic *Notitiae* in the Book of Deer', *Scottish Gaelic Studies* v (1938–42), 51–66. D. E. Easson, *Medieval Religious Houses: Scotland* (1957), 192. *FO:* T. Gale, D.D. (?); Bp. J. Moore.

DRYBURGH   co. Berw.
Praem. Abbey   *f.* 1150
1138.   **Edinburgh, NLS., Adv. 34. 4. 7** (A. 5. 51). Cartulary, 15th cent., with spaces for initials and headings, apparently transcribed from an earlier compilation which, when copied, lacked one or more leaves at the beginning and others at the end. Arranged roughly topographically, with copies of royal and episcopal charters included *passim*, and of papal ones grouped at fos. 74–94. The entries, of which the latest is dated 1338, are numbered consecutively *vi–cclxxxxiiii* with about 33 others unnumbered at the end. An 18th cent. transcript is in the possession of the Earl of Dalhousie, Brechin Castle. Ed. J. Spottiswoode, *Liber S. Marie de Dryburgh* (Bannatyne Club, 1847).
Fos. 112. $10\frac{3}{4} \times 7\frac{3}{4}$ in. Paper. *FO:* Sir J. Balfour.

DUNFERMLINE   co. Fife
Ben. Abbey   *f. c.* 1070
1139.   **Edinburgh, NLS., Adv. 34. 1. 3a** (A. 4. 4). Composite register, 13th–16th cent. The original compilation (fos. vi–xxvi, lxxv–lxxvi, lxxx–lxxxix, mid-13th cent. (*temp.* Alex. III), is written in double columns with rubrics and alternate red and blue initials, and contains copies of royal,

episcopal and other charters to the abbey, arranged by grantors. The rest of the MS. consists of additions, incl. a rubricated late 13th cent. etc. section of papal bulls (fos. ci–cxi), a 15th cent. index (fos. 11–15) and copies of *acta* of the abbots and other misc. documents. Transcripts, 18th cent., are in *ib.*, Adv. MS. 35. 3. 9 and in the possession of the Earl of Dalhousie, Brechin Castle. Ed. C. Innes, *Registrum de Dunfermelyn* (Bannatyne Club, 1842).
Fos. 169 (34 + cxxxv, in two consecutive post-medieval foliations). $12\frac{1}{2} \times 9$ in. *FO:* Sir J. Balfour.
¶ *Other registers etc.*
1140.   **Edinburgh, Scottish R.O.,** Hist. Room (R. 2/3). 'Registrum Assedationum', 1557–85. Innes, *op. cit.*, 486–92.
1141.   **The Marquess of Tweeddale** (heritable baillie of the regality of Dunfermline), deposited *ib.* (room 51, shelf 13). Register of charters and a few tacks by the commendators, 1555–85. Innes, *op. cit.*, 465–84.

EDINBURGH   co. Midloth.
Aug. Abbey, Holyrood   *f.* 1128
No cartulary recorded.
¶ *Other registers etc.*
1142.   **Edinburgh, Scottish R.O.,** Hist. Room (R. 2/4). Register of grants by the commendators, 1545–67. C. Innes, *Liber Cartarum Sancte Crucis* (Bannatyne Club, 1840), prints extracts.
1143.   **Edinburgh, City Charter Room** (bay B, shelf 11). Register of grants by the commendators, 1570–9. Innes, *op. cit.* (extracts).

EDINBURGH   co. Midloth.
Coll. Church & Hosp. of the Holy Trinity   *f.* bef. 1460
v. also SOUTRA.
1144.   **Edinburgh, City Charter Room** (bay C, shelf 12). Misc. register of *acta* etc., 1504–94, incl. (fo. 20) an inventory, 1580, of registers, charters etc. preserved 'in cubiculo . . . prepositi'. Ed. D. Laing, *Registrum Domus de Soltre* etc. (Bannatyne Club, 1861), 55–258 etc.
¶ *Other registers etc.*
1145.   **Ditto** (bay C, shelf 12). Register of grants by the college, 1543 etc. (only 25 fos. written).

EDINBURGH co. Midloth.
Parish Church (Coll., 1466–9) of St. Giles.
1146. **The Earl of Dalhousie**, deposited at Edinburgh, Scottish R.O., Hist.
Room (Dalhousie Collection). Register of
charters, rentals etc., begun in 1368 with
copies of 10 charters, to which there is a
preface and Table at fo. 7, and a rental (fos.
13–14). Continued in a series of hands
down to the second half of the 15th cent.,
incl. copies of some royal and episcopal
charters. The original order of the opening
leaves has been disturbed. Ed., with material from other sources, D. Laing, *Registrum Cartarum Ecclesie S. Egidii de Edinburgh*
(Bannatyne Club, 1859).
Fos. i + 38 (numbered 1–39; wants fo. 38
and a leaf aft. fo. 12). 12½ × 10 in. *FO:* the
Earl of Panmure.
¶ *Other registers etc.*
1147. **Edinburgh, City Charter
Room** (bay A, vol. 42). Register of *acta*,
rents, obits etc., 1500–79. Marguerite
Wood, 'An Addition to Laing's Chartulary of St. Giles', *Book of the Old Edinburgh
Club* xxviii (1953), 51–8 (description).

EDINBURGH co. Midloth.
Aug. Hosp. of St. Anthony, Leith *f.* 1418
No cartulary recorded.
¶ *Other registers etc.*
1148. **Edinburgh, NLS., Adv. 34. 5. 5**
(Jac. V. 7. 25). Rental etc., 15th–16th cent.
J. G. Dalyell, *A Brief Analysis of the Chartu-
laries of . . . Cambuskenneth, Chapel Royal
of Stirling, Preceptory of St. Anthony at Leith*
(Edinburgh, 1828), 79 ff.

ELGIN co. Moray
Cath. Church *f. c.* 1224
v. MORAY, See of.

ELGIN co. Moray
Leper Hosp. ('Domus Dei') *f.* bef. 1237
1149. **Edinburgh, NLS., Adv. 34. 7. 2**
(W. 7. 23). Authenticated copies, 1548, in
several hands, of relevant extracts from the
cartularies of the see of Moray (Nos. 1171–2
below).
Fos. *c.* 75. 5¾ × 5¾ in.

GLASGOW co. Lanark
See of, *f. c.* 1115, and Cath. Church,
f. bef. 1197
C. Innes, *Registrum Episcopatus Glasguen-
sis*, 2 vols. (Maitland & Bannatyne Clubs,

1843), edits Nos. 1150–1. Extracts, 1556,
are in NLS., Adv. 34. 4. 5, of which later
copies are in BM., Harley 4631, vol. i, fos.
122–68 and NLS., Adv. 29. 5. 3. Others,
1766, with copies of numerous original
documents, are in Glasgow U.L., MSS. F.
6.2 and 3. For further extracts in Glasgow
City Archives, see Innes, *op. cit.* i, pp. iii ff.
1150. **Aberdeen, Blairs Coll.** 'Registrum Vetus.' Gen. cartulary (fos. i–xxiiii),
early 13th cent. (aft. 1202), with some pen-
work decoration of initials and misc.
additions in blank spaces *passim*. Contains
copies of royal and other, followed by
papal charters, with later 13th cent. continuations down to fo. lxvii, and a mid-13th
cent. Table of fos. i–xxx on two preliminary leaves. Fos. 68 ff., of coarser vellum, contain a few 15th cent. additions.
A 17th cent. transcript is in the possession
of the Earl of Dalhousie, Brechin Castle.
Fos. 4 + 85 (wants fos. xxxviii, l, without
apparent loss of material). 8¾ × 6 in. *FO:*
the Scots College, Paris; George Chalmers
(as a loan); the Right Rev. A. Cameron;
the Right Rev. J. F. Kyle, Buckie.
1151. **Edinburgh, Scottish R.O.**,
Hist. Room (R. 2/3). 'Liber Ruber.'
Transcript (fos. lxv–clvii), early 15th cent.,
of No. 1150, with marginal titles and uncompleted red initials. Preceded (fos. ix–
xv, xviii–lxi) by two similarly written
sections of supplementary material, incl.
copies of further royal, papal and episcopal
charters etc., and with misc. additions (fos.
i viii, clvii^v–clxxxviii) down to 1476, incl.
(fos. clxxv–clxxxii) inventories, 1432, of
jewels, ornaments, relics and library books.
Fos. 188 + some blank unnumbered
leaves at the end. 9½ × 6¼ in. *FO:* the Scots
College, Paris; George Chalmers.
¶ *Other registers etc.*
1152. **Aberdeen, Blairs Coll.** 'Liber
Protocollorum magistri Cuthberti Sim-
onis, notarii publici et scribae capituli Glas-
guensis', 1499–1513. Ed., with No. 1153,
J. Bain & C. Rogers, *Liber Protocollorum*,
2 vols. (Grampian Club, 1875). *FO:* as No.
1150 above.
1153. **Ditto.** Rental of the See, 1509–
70. Ed. Bain & Rogers, *op. cit. FO:* as No.
1150, but retained by the successors of the
Right Rev. A. Cameron at Edinburgh
until aft. 1875.

GLASGOW co. Lanark
Coll. Church of the BVM. and St. Anne
('Our Lady College') *f.* 1525
1154. **Glasgow, City Records Room**
(press 29). Notarial copy, 1549, in book
form, of the foundation and other 16th
cent. charters etc. of endowment. Ed. J.
Robertson, *Liber Collegii Nostre Domine*
(Maitland Club, 1846).
Fos. 51. 13 × 9¼ in.
1155. **Ditto.** A second copy of No.
1154.
Fos. 88 (lacks a further leaf). 12¾ × 8¾ in.

HOLYROOD co. Midloth.
v. EDINBURGH.

INCHAFFRAY co. Perth
Aug. Abbey *f.* (as a priory) 1200
1156. **The Earl of Kinnoull,** lodged
(1954) with Messrs. Condie, Mackenzie &
Co., W.S., Perth. Gen. cartulary, 15th cent.
Contains copies of 66 royal, baronial etc.
charters, numbered consecutively, followed (fos. 43–51) by a section of 17 further royal, episcopal etc. charters rel. the
abbey's churches. Ed. C. Innes, *Liber Insule
Missarum* (Bannatyne Club, 1847).
Fos. iii + 51. 7⅞ × 5⅝ in.
¶ *Other registers etc.*
1157. **Ditto.** 'Registrum Assedationum', 1554–5 etc.

INCHCOLM co. Fife
Aug. Abbey *f.* (as a priory) *c.* 1123
No cartulary recorded.
¶ *Other registers etc.*
1158–1159. **The Earl of Moray,** Darn-
away Castle (Moray Charters 42. 3 *al.* 'The
Great Transumpt', 42. 4). Two notarial
transcripts, 1420 & 1423, in roll form, of
respectively 22 and 19 charters, incl. episcopal, papal and royal documents. Five
entries are copied in both. 18th cent.
versions are *ib.*, and in NLS., Adv. 35. 2. 5,
pp. 1–55. Ed. D. E. Easson and A. Mac-
donald, *Charters of Inchcolm* (Scottish Hist.
Soc., Third ser. xxxii, 1938).

JEDBURGH co. Roxb.
Aug. Abbey *f.* (as a priory) *c.* 1138
No cartulary recorded.
¶ *Other registers etc.*
1160. **Edinburgh, Scottish R.O.,**
Hist. Room (R. 2/3). Register of charters

and leases by the abbots, commendators
etc., 1479–1596.
1161. **Lord Sinclair,** deposited *ib.*,
Hist. Room (R. 2/3). Similar to No. 1160,
for the years 1542–94. *FO:* George Cane.

KELSO co. Roxb.
Tiron. Abbey *f.* (at Selkirk) *c.* 1113
1162. **Edinburgh, NLS., Adv. 34. 5. 1**
(A. 5. 22). Gen. cartulary (fos. 8–171), 14th
cent. (aft. 1316), with rubrics etc. and plain
red initials. Arranged mainly topographically with copies of the foundation etc.
charters at the beginning and of other
royal, with episcopal and papal charters,
grouped mainly at the end. Fos. 1–7 contain an added rental, and fos. 171v ff. misc.
additions. Transcripts, 18th cent., are *ib.*,
Adv. 35. 3. 6 and in the possession of the
Earl of Dalhousie, Brechin Castle. Of the
latter, a 19th cent. copy is NLS., Adv.
22. 2. 2. Ed. C. Innes, *Liber S. Marie de
Calchou*, 2 vols. (Bannatyne Club, 1846).
Fos. 219. 8 × 5½ in.

LEITH co. Midloth.
v. EDINBURGH.

LINCLUDEN co. Kircudbr.
Coll. Church *f.* 1389
No cartulary recorded.
¶ *Other registers etc.*
1163. **Edinburgh, Scottish R.O.,**
Hist. Room (R. 2/4). Register of charters
and leases by the provost and prebendaries,
1547–64, with some other misc. material.
W. McDowall, *Chronicles of Lincluden*
(Edinburgh, 1886), 106 ff. (abstract).

LINDORES co. Fife
Tiron. Abbey *f.* 1191
1164. **Lt-Col. W. W. S. Cuning-
hame, D.S.O., D.L., J.P.,** Caprington
Castle. Gen. cartulary (fos. 29–74v), mid-
13th cent. (aft. 1253), with uncompleted
rubrication and red initials decorated with
blue or green. Preceded (fos. 3–28) and
followed (fos. 74v–88) by misc. 13th–15th
cent. additions, the former on added quires
etc. Includes copies of royal, episcopal etc.
charters *passim*, and of papal ones at fos.
65–74v. Ed. J. Dowden, *Chartulary of
Lindores* 1195–1479 (Scottish Hist. Soc. xlii,
1903).
Fos. 86 (post-medieval foliation, 3–87 +
1). 7½ × 5 in.

1165.   **Edinburgh, NLS., Adv. 34. 7. 1**
(W. 7. 20). Cartulary, early 16th cent. (aft.
1502), of royal, papal, episcopal and other
charters to the abbey, and of some grants
etc. by it, with a few later additions at the
end (fos. 28v–31). An 18th cent. transcript
is in the possession of the Earl of Dalhousie, Brechin Castle. Ed. W. B. D. D.
Turnbull, *The Chartularies of Balmerino and
Lindores* (Abbotsford Club, 1841).
    Fos. 31. 5⅝ × 4¼ in. (leaves mounted).
Paper. *FO:* Sir J. Balfour.

MAY, Isle of   co. Fife
Ben. (afterw. Aug.) Priory   *f.* bef. 1153
    (afterw. transferred to Pittenweem)
    v. also Nos. 804, 1178.
⁋ *Other registers etc.*
1166.   **Untraced.** Register of deeds of
alienation etc., 16th cent. Used by J.
Stuart, *Records of the Priory of the Isle of May*
(Soc. of Antiquaries of Scotland, 1868).
FO: W. Baird, Elie.

MELROSE   co. Roxb.
Cist. Abbey   *f.* 1136
    C. Innes, *Liber de Melros*, 2 vols. (Ban-
natyne Club, 1837), edits Nos. 1167–8 with
some additional material.
1167.   **Edinburgh, NLS., Adv. 34. 4.
11 (A. 5. 47).** Parts of a late 13th cent. cartulary (*temp.* Alex. III?), with rubrics and
red or sometimes green initials, incl. copies
of royal, papal and episcopal charters
passim. Transcripts, 18th cent., are in *ib.*,
Adv. 35. 3. 13, pp. 1–105 and in the possession of the Earl of Dalhousie, Brechin
Castle.
    Fos. 44 (medieval foliation, viii–lviii,
lxii; wants leaves *passim* aft. fo. xxxviii).
9⅝ × 7 in. *FO:* the Rev. H. Malcolm.
1168.   **BM., Harley 3960.** Cartulary,
15th cent. (aft. 1440), with red initials and
paragraphs, and some additions in a slightly
later hand at the end (fos. 100, 102–9).
Arranged topographically and incl. copies
of numerous royal and occasional papal and
episcopal charters *passim.*
    Fos. i + 111. 14½ × 10½ in.
⁋ *Other registers etc.*
For Nos. 1169–70 see Sir W. Fraser,
Memorials of the Earls of Haddington i
(Edinburgh, 1889), liii–iv, note.
1169.   **The Earl of Haddington,** Tyn-

inghame. Register of grants, leases etc. by
the commendators, 1547–1609.
1170.   **Ditto.** Entry-Book, 1571–94.

MORAY, See of   *f.* bef. 1124,
and Cath. Church at Elgin, *f. c.* 1224
    C. Innes, *Registrum Episcopatus Moravi-
ensis* (Bannatyne Club, 1837), edits Nos.
1171–2. Transcripts, 18th cent., are in
NLS., Adv. 35. 3. 5, 34. 4. 12, and in the
possession of the Earl of Dalhousie,
Brechin Castle. A 19th cent. index is in
NLS., Adv. 34. 3. 27.
1171.   **Edinburgh, NLS., Adv. 34. 4.
10 (A. 1. 40).** Composite register in two
main parts: (1) fos. 1–115, cartulary (fos.
1 34), late 13th cent., of the cathedral,
with rubrics, red initials and a few additions at the end, incl. copies of royal, papal
and episcopal charters *passim;* followed by
misc. quires from other registers etc., containing copies of charters and other documents rel. the church and see, among
which is misbound, as fos. 65–6, a contemp. Table; the whole perhaps put together at the end of the 14th cent., after the
cathedral's destruction; (2) fos. 119 ff.,
copies of charters of alienation by Bp. P.
Hepburn, late 16th cent.
    Fos. 169. 11¼ × 7 in.
1172.   **Ditto,** Adv. 34. 4. 9 (A. 1. 41).
'The Red Book', 16th cent., containing:
(1) fos. 1–94, a transcript of pt. 1 of No.
1171; (2) fos. 96–154, misc. *acta* of the bp.
and chapter, 1492–1538; (3) fos. 155 ff.,
copies of deeds of dilapidation by Bp. P.
Hepburn, as in No. 1171, pt. 2.
    Fos. vi + 320. 10½ × 7½ in.

NEWBATTLE   co. Midloth.
Cist. Abbey   *f.* 1140
1173.   **Edinburgh, NLS., Adv. 34. 4.
13 (A. 7. 9).** Gen. cartulary, 14th cent. (aft.
1339), with red paragraphs etc. Arranged
topographically, with copies of royal and
episcopal charters included *passim* and of
papal ones to the abbey and Cistercian
order, followed by some additions, at the
end. A contemp. Table on six leaves at the
beginning is followed by three further
leaves of additions. A copy of a transcript
by Richard Hay, 1696, is in the possession
of the Earl of Dalhousie, Brechin Castle.
Ed. C. Innes, *Registrum S. Marie de
Neubotle* (Bannatyne Club, 1849). See also

Anon., 'The Vicissitudes of a Scottish Chartulary', *The Scotsman* (newspaper), 11 Aug. 1896.

Fos. 87 (unnumbered). $10\frac{1}{8} \times 7$ in. *FO:* Robert, 1st marquis of Lothian, 1688; bought from J. McEwan by 'D.H.', 1723.

PAISLEY co. Renfrew
Clun. Abbey *f.* (as a priory) *c.* 1163

1174. **Edinburgh, NLS., Adv. 34. 4. 14** (Jac. V. 6. 16). Gen. cartulary, 16th cent. (aft. 1529), with some rubrication of the earlier pages. Arranged according to subject matter, in part topographically, with copies of royal, papal and episcopal charters included *passim* and a contemp. Table on nine unnumbered preliminary leaves. A transcript, 1696, is in *ib.*, Adv. 34. 1. 10, of which a copy is in the possession of the Earl of Dalhousie, Brechin Castle. Ed. C. Innes, *Registrum Monasterii de Passelet* (Maitland Club, 1832).

Fos. 14+274 (contemp. foliation, i–cclxxi+3). $10\frac{7}{8} \times 7\frac{1}{2}$ in. *FO:* the Cochrane fam., earls of Dundonald.

PITTENWEEM co. Fife
Aug. Priory *f.* bef. 1318
v. MAY.

ST. ANDREWS co. Fife
See of, *f.* 1109, and Aug. Cath. Priory, *f.* 1144

1175. **Untraced.** Gen. cartulary (fos. 20–152), 13th cent., written partly in double columns, with rubrics, coloured initials and a few additions. Arranged by grantors and followed by sections of 14th cent. (fos. 152v–69) and later additions. An 18th cent. transcript is in NLS., Adv. 17. 1. 3a. Ed. T. Thomson, *Liber Cartarum Prioratus S. Andree in Scotia* (Bannatyne Club, 1841).

Fos. 195. Small folio. *FO:* Sir A. Gilmour, 17th cent.; the Earl of Panmure, 1729; Lord Panmure, 1841; not found at Brechin Castle, nor with the Earl of Dalhousie's law agents in Edinburgh, 1954.

1176. **Untraced.** 'Magnum Registrum', incl. a history (fos. 58–99), copies of charters (mainly rel. the priory's privileges and churches) and other misc. material. An 18th cent. Table (printed by Thomson, *op. cit.*, xxv–xxx) and extracts are in BM., Harley 4628, fos. 214–42.

Fos. 121.

¶ *Other registers etc.*

1177. **Wolfenbuettel, Cod. Helmstedt 411.** Letter-book of J. Haldenstone, prior 1418–43. A photostat copy is in St. Andrews U.L. Ed. J. H. Baxter, *Copiale Prioratus S. Andree* (St. Andrews Univ. Publns. xxxi, 1930). *FO:* Flacius Illyricus; Count Heinrich Julius of Brunswick-Wolfenbuettel, 1597; the University of Helmstedt, until 1810.

1178. **Edinburgh, NLS., Adv. 17. 1. 3** (W. 1. 2). Register of charters, leases etc., 1553–65 etc., of: (1) St. Andrews priory, fos. 1–197; (2) Pittenweem priory, fos. 198–296; (3) the archbishopric, with additions rel. St. Andrews priory down to 1574 (fos. 104 in another foliation). Paper. *FO:* G. Martine, M.D.

SCONE co. Perth
Aug. Abbey *f.* (as a priory) *c.* 1120

W. Smythe, *Liber Ecclesie de Scon* (Bannatyne & Maitland Clubs, 1843), edits Nos. 1179–80.

1179. **Edinburgh, NLS., Adv. 34. 3. 29** (A. 5. 4). Gen. cartulary, 14th cent., with red and sometimes blue or green initials, touching of letters etc. and representations of *bullae.* Contains copies of 83 charters etc., 1164–1326, with the papal, royal and episcopal documents grouped mainly at the beginning and one or two additions, *temp.* David II etc., at the end. Transcripts, 18th cent., are in *ib.*, Adv. 35. 2. 5, 9a. 1. 13.

Fos. 32. $9\frac{3}{4} \times 6\frac{3}{4}$ in. *FO:* David Murray, 1st viscount Stormont (D); Sir J. Balfour.

1180. **Ditto, Adv. 34. 3. 28** (W. 3. 8). Uncompleted 15th–16th cent. cartulary, with spaces for initials and some decorative pen-work etc. Contains copies of 148 royal, papal, episcopal and a few other charters and documents. Transcripts, 18th cent., are in *ib.*, Adv. 35. 2. 5 and BM., Add. 33246, fos. 1–74.

Fos. 76+*c.* 50 blank leaves at the end. $11\frac{1}{2} \times 7\frac{1}{2}$ in. Presented by David Murray, 7th viscount Stormont, 1773.

¶ *Other registers etc.*

1181. **The Earl of Mansfield,** lodged (1954) with Messrs. Condie, Mackenzie & Co., W.S., Perth. Register of rentals, 1465–1566.

SOUTRA co. Midloth.
Aug. Hosp. of the Holy Trinity *f.* 1164
1182. **Edinburgh, NLS., Adv. 34. 4. 1**
(W. 4. 14). Cartulary, late 14th cent., with
crude pen-decorated initials. Contains
copies of 59 royal, episcopal and other
charters to the hospital, 12th–14th cent.,
with one or two additions at the end. At
fo. 25 there is a notarial attestation of the
accuracy of the copies, 5 Feb. 1399/1400.
An 18th cent. transcript is in *ib.*, Adv.
35. 2. 4, pp. 1–66. Ed. D. Laing, *Registrum
Domus de Soltre* etc. (Bannatyne Club,
1861), v–xii, 1–54.
    Fos. 27. $9\frac{7}{8} \times 6\frac{1}{4}$ in.

1183. **Edinburgh, City Charter
Room** (bay A, vol. 31). Notarial trans-
cript of No. 1182 made, 1516, by George
Newton for the provost of Holy Trinity
College, Edinburgh, to which the hospital
was annexed in 1462.
    Fos. 17. $12\frac{1}{4} \times 9\frac{1}{2}$ in.

STIRLING co. Stirl.
Chapel Royal
1184. **Edinburgh, NLS., Adv. 34. 1. 5**
(W. 1. 10). Register, 16th cent., containing
copies of about 13 papal, episcopal etc.
documents, 1501–11, rel. the chapel's
erection into a collegiate church etc., with
inventories (fos. 35–8) of jewels, service-
books etc., 1505. The leaves are attested
individually by Sir J. Primrose, clerk of the
Privy Council. A list of contents on the
back flyleaf notes: hat 'Beside those con-
teined in this register there are eleven
bulls'. An 18th cent. transcript is in the
possession of the Earl of Dalhousie, Brechin
Castle. J. G. Dalyell, *A Brief Analysis of the
Chartularies of . . . Cambuskenneth, Chapel
Royal of Stirling* etc. (Edinburgh, 1828),
49 ff.
    Fos. ii + 50 (numbered, 1–51; wants 49).
$13\frac{3}{4} \times 10$ in.

TORPHICHEN co. W. Loth.
Preceptory of Knts. of St. John *f.* bef.
1153 (?)
    No cartulary recorded.
❡ *Other registers etc.*
1185. **Untraced.** Register of grants,
leases etc., 1581–96. (J. B. Gracie?),
*Abstract of the Charters and other Papers
recorded in the Chartulary of Torphichen* 1581–
96 (Edinburgh, privately, 1830). *FO:* the
Sandilands fam., barons Torphichen; R.
Williamson, 1599; the Hamilton fam.,
earls of Haddington, 1616; J. Ferguson; J.
Maidment; J. B. Gracie (as of the barony of
Drem), 1830.

Part Two

SECULAR CARTULARIES

SECULAR CARTULARIES

ALGAR of Haslewick in Inkpen, co. Berks.

1186.   **The Earl of Craven,** deposited at Reading, Berkshire R.O. (D/EC. T. 18). Copies, *c.* 1400, of 22 deeds rel. Inkpen, 13th–14th cent. Endorsed 'copie (cartarum?) abbate de Titchefeld'.
Roll, 48 × 9¾ in.

ANLABY of Anlaby, co. York.

1187.   **Cambridge, Fitzwilliam Museum, MS. 329.** Cartulary, 1450, of lands in co. York, made by Thomas Anlaby, with later additions. Miniatures, marginal drawings of seals, tombs, shields of arms etc. Arranged topographically and incl. misc. genealogical and other material (fos. i–xiii). Contemp. binding, with painted shields of arms, and carrying-case. M. R. James, 'The Anlaby Chartulary', *Yorks. Arch. J.* xxxi (1934), 337–47.
Fos. 3 + 149. 11¼ × 7½ in.

ASPHALE, Roger de; rector of Stonham Aspall, co. Suff.

1188.   **BM., Harley 498,** fos. 2–4, 24–9. Copies 13th–14th cent., with marginal titles, of about 25 grants, *temp.* Edw. I.
Parts of a roll, originally *c.* 5 ft. × 8½ in. Now cut into pieces.

BARFORD ST. MARTIN, co. Wilts *v.* BLAUNCHARD.

BASSET of Weldon, co. Northt.

1188A.   **BM., Sloane Roll xxxi. 4.** Copies, 13th cent. (aft. 1237), with rubrics, red paragraphs etc., of deeds etc., 12th–13th cent., rel. various counties incl. some royal charters (from *temp.* Matilda). Made apparently for Ralph Basset (d. *c.* 1256) with additions down to *temp.* Hen. IV.
Roll of 8 membrs., mainly joined at the top. 26 × 9¼ in. etc.

BEAUCHAMP, earls of Warwick.

1189.   **BM., Add. 28024.** Cartulary, 1395–6, arranged topographically, with a list of the places (which are in a number of counties) at fo. 68v, and incl. copies of royal (from *temp.* Hen. I) and some episcopal

charters. Fos. 1–2, 197–9, contain an index and abstract by Wm. Dugdale, 1640, whose extracts are in Bodl., Dugdale 6 (*SC.* 6496), pp. 417 ff. *BM. Cat. Add. MSS.* 1854–1875, ii, 399 (description).
Fos. 199. 16 × 11 in. Paper. *FO:* the North fam., barons North and earls of Guilford, 17th–19th cent.

BEAUCHAMP, barons Beauchamp; of Hatch, co. Som.

1190.   **The Marquess of Ailesbury,** deposited at Taunton, Somerset Arch. Soc. Libr. Register, late 13th cent., of extents, custumals, fees etc. Ed. (in translation) H. C. Maxwell Lyte, *Two Registers . . . of Beauchamp of Hatch* (Somerset Record Soc. xxxv, 1920), 1–56.
Fos. 47. 8¼ × 6¼ in.

1191.   **PRO., Exch., Augm. Off.** (Misc. Bks. 58). Register, 14th cent. (aft. 1341, with additions), mainly of documents rel. the family's advowsons, fees, homages and other rights and privileges, but incl. some copies of deeds rel. grants of land, 12th–14th cent. Blue initials decorated with red, red and blue paragraphs etc. Ed. (in translation) Lyte, *op. cit.,* 57 ff. *PRO. Deputy Keeper's Eighth Report,* App. ii, 147–51 (calendar).
Fos. i+61. 14⅛ × 9¼ in.

1192.   **Bradford, City Art Gallery & Museums.** Inventory and abstract, early 15th cent., of deeds and other muniments etc. rel. cos. Devon, Som., Dors., Middlx. and Kent, incl. some entire copies of documents. In all, 313 entries.
Roll of 14 membrs. 30 ft. 6 in. × 10 in. Presented by Viscountess Swinton (cf. No. 678 above).

BEK, Antony; dean of Lincoln 1329–37; bp. of Norwich 1337–43.

1193.   **BM., Harley 3720.** Part of a misc. private register and memorandum book, *temp.* Edw. II–III, incl. copies of royal, papal and other letters and documents addressed or relating to him in his official capacities.
Fos. 27. 8⅞ × 5¾ in.

BERKELEY of Wymondham, co. Leic.
1194.   **BM., Harley 265.** Cartulary, 15th cent. (aft. 1458), rel. Wymondham, Edingthorpe and other places in cos. Leic. and Norf. Arranged topographically, and comprising material *temp*. Edw. I–Hen. VI.
Fos. 2 + 144 (damaged by damp). 9 × 6¼ in.

BISHOP, Nicholas; of Oxford.
1195.   **Cambridge U.L., Dd. 14. 2.** Register, 1432 with additions, of deeds, rentals etc. rel. Oxford, arranged by parishes. Annotated by B. Twyne. *Cambr. U.L. Cat. MSS.* i, 520–2 (list of headings etc.).
Fos. 317. 7½ × 5⅛ in. *FO:* Bp. J. Moore.

BLAUNCHARD, John; archdeacon of Worcester 1371–83.
1196.   **BM., Stowe 882.** Cartulary, late 14th cent., of deeds 1221–1387 etc., rel. the manor of Barford St. Martin, co. Wilts, etc. Small red initials with mauve decoration etc. *BM. Cat. Stowe MSS.* i, 603 (description). E. Bernard, *Cat. MSS. Angliae* ii (1697), 356, no. 9059.
Fos. 76 (excl. blank leaves). 12½ × 9 in. *FO:* William, 9th earl of Derby; G. Brander; T. Astle.

BLEWBURY, William de; of Blewbury, co. Berks; *clericus.*
1197.   **PRO., Exch., K.R.** (Transcripts of Deeds & Charters, E. 132/9). Copies, late 13th cent., of deeds etc. rel. Blewbury, incl. a charter of Walter, bp. of Salisbury.
Roll of 2 membrs. *c.* 60 × 10½ in.

BOARSTALL, co. Bucks.
v. REDE.

BODRIGAN of Bodrigan in Gorran, co. Cornw.
1198.   **The Earl of Mount Edgcumbe,** deposited at Truro, Cornwall R. O. Copies, 14th cent., of 175 deeds, 1174–1319, mainly rel. Tremoderet in Roche and elsewhere in E. Cornwall. A transcript, 1927, is in the Royal Institution of Cornwall, Truro.
Roll of great length, *c.* 9½ in. wide.

BOHUN, Humphrey (1276–1322); 4th earl of Hereford and 3rd earl of Essex.

1199.   **PRO., Duchy of Lanc.** (Miscellanea, DL. 41/10/12). Part of an inventory, 1307–8, of charters, 12th and 13th cent., received by W. de Rolleston, constable of Pleshey Castle from his predecessor A. de Kenebauton (Kimbolton).
Indented roll of 1 membr. (lacks at least one other), 9½ in. wide. Written on both sides.

BOHUN of Fressingfield, co. Suff.
1200.   **BM., Harley 2201.** Cartulary, late 15th cent., compiled apparently for Edmund Bohun, with additions. Contains material rel. Fressingfield from *temp.* Edw. III.
Fos. 89. 12¼ × 8½ in. Paper.

BOOTH *al.* **BOTHE,** John de; of Barton, co. Lanc.
1201.   **Untraced.** Cartulary, 1403–4, from which extracts, 1630, down to fo. 44 (entry no. 221), are in Bodl., Dodsworth 149 (*SC.* 5090), fos. 150–65.

BOYS *al.* **BOSCO,** Warin de; of Turvey, co. Bedf.
1202.   **Col. N. V. Stopford Sackville, O.B.E.,** deposited in Northamptonshire R.O. (box 1374). Copies, 13th–14th cent., of 205 deeds, 13th cent., rel. Turvey.
Roll of 13 membrs., 7 in. wide.

BRAY, Henry de (b. 1269); of Harlestone, co. Northt.
1203.   **BM., Cotton Nero C. xii,** fos. 158–81. Book of evidences, early 14th cent. (aft. 1309), incl. copies of deeds. Red underlinings and red and blue paragraphs. Less complete than No. 1204 but includes some material not found there. Ed. Dorothy Willis, *The Estate Book of Henry de Bray* (Camden Third ser. xxvii, 1916).
Fos. 24 (lacks the opening leaf and at least 8 others at the end). 8¼ × 6 in. *FO:* Sir Wm. Dugdale (?).
1204.   **BM., Lansdowne 761.** 'Transcripta Cartarum et Memorandorum.' Autograph copies, 1322 etc., of deeds and other misc. evidences and memoranda rel. Harlestone etc., mainly 14th cent., with additions down to the 16th cent., mainly at the end (fos. 87 ff.). Red underlinings, paragraphs etc. Ed. Dorothy Willis, *op. cit.*
Fos. 94. 8⅜ × 5⅝ in. *FO:* R. Stafford, 16th–17th cent.; H. Powle.

BRAY, Robert.

1205. **The Earl of Winchilsea,** deposited in Northamptonshire R.O. (Finch Hatton 510). 'Irrotulamentum terrarum' etc. Copies, late 14th cent., of 22 deeds, 13th cent.–*c.* 1375, rel. lands acquired in and aft. 1362 in Rothwell and Rushton, co. Northt.

Roll of 5 membrs. *c.* 72 × 10½ in.

BRAYBROOKE of Braybrooke, co. Northt.
v. also GRIFFIN.

1206. **BM., Sloane 986.** Cartulary, late 13th cent. (aft. 1274), with rubrics etc. and spaces for initials. Arranged topographically by counties (Northt., Bedf. and Bucks., with some material for Leic., Linc., Essex, Hertf. and London), and incl. copies of three charters of King John (fos. 67v–72).

Fos. i + 79. 9 × 6¾ in. *FO:* John Griffin, 15th cent.

BRIAN, Roger fil., de Throcking.
v. THROCKING.

BROCAS
v. THWAITES.

BROKESBY
v. BROOKSBY.

BROMLEY of Bromley in Whitmore, co. Staff.

1207. **Untraced.** Copies, 14th cent. (aft. 1348), of 63 deeds rel. Bromley, Butterton and Bucknall, co. Staff., mainly *temp.* Edw. II–III. An incomplete transcript and translation, 1912, by C. Swynnerton is at Stafford, Wm. Salt Libr. Calendared by *id.*, 'A Domestic Cartulary . . . of Bromley etc.', Wm. Salt Arch. Soc., *Coll. Hist. Staffordshire* 1913, 219–76.

Roll of 5 membrs. 86 × 9 in. *FO:* the Rev. C. Swynnerton, 1913.

BROOKSBY *al.* **BROKESBY,** Bartholomew.

1208. **Oxford, Bodl., Wood empt. 7** (*SC.* 8595). Cartulary, 1445, of lands in co. Leic., arranged topographically, the material being mainly 14th cent. Illuminated initial (arms of Brooksby), fo. vii. Some other pen-decoration in black, tricked with red. A partial transcript, 17th cent., is in

London, Coll. of Arms, Vincent 109. Noticed by J. Nichols, *Hist. Leicester* iii, pt. 2 (1804), 969.

Fos. xiv + 191. 10¼ × 7 in. *FO:* R. Sheldon.

BYLNEY of Haveringland, co. Norf.

1209. **William H. Robinson Ltd.,** 1952 (Cat. no. 82, pt. ii (1952), item 586). Abstracts of deeds, 15th cent., in various hands, rel. Haveringland.

Roll, *c.* 9 ft. long. Written on both sides. *FO:* Sir T. Phillipps (MS. 17653).

BYRON, Sir John le; of Clayton in Droylsden, co. Lanc.

1210. **Oxford, Bodl., Rawlinson B. 460.** 'The Black Book of Clayton.' Cartulary, 15th cent. (aft. 1445) with additions, rel. lands in co. Lanc. Arranged topographically, the earliest material being 13th cent. A transcript, 1665, by C. Towneley is in Manchester Reference Libr. (Farrer MSS.). W. D. Macray, *Cat. MSS. Bibl. Bodl.* v (1) (Oxford, 1862), 690.

Fos. 138. 9⅝ × 7 in. *FO:* Frankland Scholefield, 1699.

CHAMBERLAIN of Shirburn, co. Oxon.

1211. **The Earl of Macclesfield (?),** Shirburn Castle. 'The Chamberlain Evidences.' Cartulary, apparently in book form, of which a modern transcript (112 deeds etc., 1290–1424, rel. Shirburn) is in the Bodleian Libr. (H. E. Salter papers). Noticed by H. E. Salter, *The Boarstall Cartulary* (Oxford Hist. Soc. lxxxviii, 1930), v.

CHASTELAYN

1212. **The Incumbents of Hadleigh,** co. Suff., deposited at Bury St. Edmunds, Bury and W. Suffolk R.O. (Acc. 422/24). Copies, 15th cent., with additions, of 22 undated deeds (mainly 14th cent.?) rel. grants to the Chastelayn and Waleys fams. in Hadleigh, Kersey etc., incl. one by Richard, prior of Kersey. Noticed, but attributed to Kersey Priory, in 'Hadleigh Deanery and its Court', *Proc. Suffolk Inst. Arch.* xv (1915), 19.

Roll of 2 membrs. *c.* 5 ft. × 8 in.

CHEDDAR of Bristol.

1213. **BM., Harley 316.** Cartulary, late 14th cent. etc., rel. lands in cos. Som. (incl.

Cheddar), Glouc. and Dors., *temp.* Edw. III–Ric. II. Arranged topographically and preceded (fos. 1–4) by part of a kalendar with added entries rel. the births of sons or Robert Cheddar.

Fos. 86. 14⅝ × 9¾ in. *FO:* Scipio le Squyer (if the MS. listed in Rylands Libr., Lat. MS. 319, fo. 109, as 'Chedder's lands').

CLAYTON, co. Lanc.
v. BYRON.

CLERVAUX of Croft, co. York.
1214.   **C. W. D. Chaytor Esq.,** Croft Hall. Cartulary etc., *c.* 1450, rel. lands in cos. York and Durham, made apparently for Richard Clervaux. Additions (fos. 1–3, 143 ff.) include (fos. 149 ff.) a late 15th cent. supplement. A. Hamilton Thompson, 'The Clervaux Chartulary', *Arch. Aeliana*, Third ser. xvii (1920), 186–228, notices and calendars the Durham material etc. Used by W. H. D. Longstaffe, *Hist. Darlington* (Darlington, 1854), lix–lxxx.

Fos. 167. 16 × 12 in.

COBHAM, DE; barons Cobham, of Cobham, co. Kent.
1215.   **The Marquess of Salisbury,** Hatfield (MS. 306). Cartulary, 13th cent. (*temp.* Hen. III), with 13th–14th cent. additions, containing copies of deeds, rentals etc. Some marginal rubrication and red etc. initials. *HMC. Hatfield* i (1883), 1 (a note).

Fos. 55. 10½ × 7¾ in.

COLTISHALL, Manor of; co. Norf.
1216–1223.   **Cambridge, King's Coll.,** Muniments (E.25.1–7 & E.27). Registers or memoranda books, late 15th cent., of misc. evidences, incl. deeds. Made perhaps *c.* 1478, when the college acquired the manor. Eight vols. of *c.* 40–80 leaves apiece. 12 × 9 in. approx. Paper.

CONSTABLE of Flamborough, co. York.
1224.   **Brig. R. C. J. Chichester-Constable, D.S.O.,** deposited at Beverley, Yorkshire East Riding R.O. Cartulary, early 13th cent., of deeds rel. Holme and Flamborough.

Fos. 31. 8½ × 7 in. *FO:* P. Le Neve.

CONSTABLE of Burton Constable, co. York.
1225.   **Brig. R. C. J. Chichester-Constable, D.S.O.,** deposited at Beverley, Yorkshire East Riding R.O. Cartulary, late 14th cent., rel. Halsham etc., co. York. Now bound up with a 16th cent. survey of the family's estates.

Fos. 43. 15 × 11 in.

COOK of Rustington, co. Suss.
1226.   **Cambridge, Trinity Coll., MS. O. 1. 25.** Cartulary, 15th cent. (*temp.* Edw. IV) with additions, of deeds and other evidences, 14th–15th cent., rel. Rustington and the manors of Rookley and Budbridge, Isle of Wight. Arranged topographically, with spaces for coloured initials. On fos. 57–61, 63, there are ten coloured drawings of coats of arms. M. R. James, *Cat. MSS. Trinity Coll.* iii (Cambridge, 1902), 30–1, no. 1049.

Fos. 85. 7½ × 5½ in.

CORNWALL, Edmund, 2nd earl of.
v. EDMUND.

COTTON, Walter; of Landwade, co. Cambr.
1227.   **BM., Add. 37669.** Cartulary, 15th cent. (aft. 1431), of deeds, 12th–15th cent., rel. Landwade, with additions (*temp.* Hen. VI) at the end. Red title (fo. 2) and paragraphs. Used by W. M. Palmer, 'Landwade and the Cotton Family', *Proc. Cambr. Antiq. Soc.* xxxviii (1938), 1–49.

Fos. ii + 44 (excl. blank leaves). 12⅛ × 8½ in. *FO:* Sir T. Phillipps (MS. 10309).

COURTENAY, earls of Devon and lords Courtenay.
1228.   **The Earl of Devon,** Powderham Castle. 'Transcriptum cartarum et scriptorum Domini Hugonis de Curtenay super maneriis suis' (fo. 22). Cartulary, 14th cent., with some rubrication, other red and blue decoration and additions. Arranged mainly topographically and incl. some genealogical and other misc. material. H. C. Maxwell Lyte, *HMC. Ninth Report,* pt. ii (1884), App., 403–6 (list of contents).

Fos. 142. 9¼ × 6¼ in.
1229.   **BM., Add. 49359.** Misc. 14th cent. register of fees, pleas, inquisitions, rentals and (fos. 61–73, 82–4 etc.) copies of

deeds, mainly 14th cent., with some coloured initials etc. and a few later additions. Preceded (fos. 3v–6v) by a French version of the 'Modus Tenendi Parliamentum' (transcribed, 17th cent., by Sir S. D'Ewes in BM., Harley 305, fos. 284–93) etc. Noticed by M. Coate, 'The Vyvyan Family of Trelowarren', *Trans. Royal Hist. Soc.*, Fourth ser. xxxii (1950), 114.

Fos. 95. 14 × 9½ in. *FO:* the Vyvyan fam.

CRANSLEY, co. Northt.
1230.   **Untraced.** 'Cartularium Villat(ae) en (*sic?*) Campis de Cransley', 14th cent. Written on both sides of a long strip of vellum and partially illegible. Bernard Halliday, sale cat. no. 243 (1939), item 1238.

CURTEYS, John; mayor of the Wool Staple of Calais (d. 1391).
1231.   **Messrs. Garrard & Allen** (solicitors) of Olney, deposited at Bedford, Bedfordshire R.O. (D.D.G.A. 95). Posthumous cartulary (aft. 1399) of his lands in Wymington and elsewhere in cos. Bedf. and Northt.

Fos. 109. 11½ × 8¼ in. Paper. *FO:* Richard Orlebar, 1814.

DARELL of Littlecote, co. Wilts.
1232.   **BM., Harley 1623.** Cartulary, 15th cent., of deeds, rentals etc. rel. lands in London and cos. Wilts, Dors., Hertf., Berks etc., *temp.* Edw. I–Hen. VI.

Fos. 40. 14¼ × 10¼ in.

DAVENTRE, Thomas fil. Walteri de; knt., of Daventry, co. Northt.
1233.   **PRO., Duchy of Lanc.** (Misc. Bks. 9). Cartulary, 1376–7, of deeds and other evidences, 13th–14th cent., rel. lands in Daventry, Tingrith (co. Bedf.) and Skirwith (co. Cumb.).

Fos. ii + 30. 13¼ × 8¼ in.

DESPENSER, Hugh le, earl of Winchester; and his son, Hugh, baron le Despenser; both executed in 1326.
1234.   **PRO., Exch., K.R.** (Accounts Various, E. 101/332/27, 101/333/2 & 6). Indentures rel. the delivery into the Exchequer, 1329–30, of deeds rel. lands in various counties, which are listed, in many cases with abstracts.

Two rolls (the first sealed) of 27 and 12 membrs., and three sheets of vellum joined and sealed at the foot.

DUDLEY
v. SUTTON.

DYNHAM, John de.
1235.   **BM., Add. 34792** (A). Cartulary, 15th cent., with spaces for rubrics and initials, of deeds etc., 13th–14th cent., rel. lands in Cardinham, Hartland and elsewhere in cos. Cornw. and Devon.

Fos. 30. 9½ × 7 in. Presented, 1895, by G. C. Boase.

EDMUND, 2nd earl of Cornwall (1250–1300).
1236.   **PRO., Exch., T.R.** (Misc. Bks. 57). Cartulary, early 14th cent., with spaces for small coloured initials, of the charters, deeds etc., incl. numerous royal grants and confirmations, which passed at his death to Edward I, as his next heir. Contemp. Table, on three preliminary leaves.

Fos. 3 + 71 (wants several leaves at the end). 12 × 8 in.

ESSEX, Earls of.
v. BOHUN, Humphrey.

FERMOR, Richard; of London and Easton Neston; merchant of the Staple of Calais.
1237.   **BM., Egerton 1938.** Part of a 16th cent. register of deeds and rentals, 1288–1530, rel. estates in cos. Bedf., Hertf., Northt. and Worc. Incomplete at the beginning and end.

Fos. 111 (contemp.(?) numeration, 145–255). 15 × 10½ in. Purchased of E. Lumley, 1861.

FITCHET
v. HYLL.

FITZ BRIAN, ROGER; of Throcking.
v. THROCKING.

FITZ LAMBERT, Thomas fil. Thome; of Moulton.
v. MOULTON.

FITZ WALTER, Thomas; knt., of Daventry.
v. DAVENTRE.

FOLJAMBE, of co. Derby.

1238. **The Duke of Rutland,** Belvoir Castle (Muniments, ii. 29. 3; formerly in drawer 37). Fragm. (the last quire) of an early 15th cent. cartulary, containing copies of deeds rel. Tideswell, Hucklow, Wormhill, Elton, Stanton etc., co. Derby.

Fos. 8. $11\frac{1}{2} \times 7\frac{1}{2}$ in.

FORT of Llanstephan, co. Carm.

1239. **PRO., Exch., K.R.** (Miscellanea, E. 163/9/39). Cartulary, 15th cent., of deeds *temp.* Edw. I–Ric. II, with one or two 15th cent. additions, rel. Llanstephan etc.

Fos. 11. $11\frac{3}{4} \times 8\frac{3}{4}$ in. Paper (except fo. 6, an inserted 14th cent. vellum leaf).

FRANCIS, Adam; lord mayor of London 1352–4.
v. also MONTAGU.

1240. **The Marquess of Salisbury,** Hatfield (MS. 291, fos. 1–106). Cartulary, 1362, with a preface and explanatory notes in French, containing abstracts of deeds etc., mainly 14th cent., rel. Edmonton and elsewhere in cos. Middx. and Essex. Arranged by manors, with pressmarks.

Fos. 106 (unnumbered). $14\frac{1}{4} \times 10\frac{1}{2}$ in.

(?) **FRAY,** John; baron of the Exchequer.
v. also Nos. 824–5 above (Rowney Priory).

1241. **PRO., Exch., Augm. Off.** (Misc. Bks. 62) **& K.R.** (Transcripts of Deeds & Charters, E. 132/29). Quires *ii–iii* of a 15th cent. register (*temp.* Hen. VI) of deeds and other evidences, arranged topographically. Contains material rel. Munden, Rowney, Wenden and other places in cos. Hertf., Essex, Northt. and Leic. A medieval foliation, running backwards, indicates that the whole compilation originally consisted of four quires.

Fos. 47 (24+23). $12\frac{3}{4} \times 9\frac{1}{2}$ in.

❡ *Other registers etc.*

Nos. 1242–5 appear to be associated with Nos. 824–5, 1241.

1242. **PRO., Exch., K.R.** (Ancient Deeds, DD: E. 211, box 11, item with superseded numeration TG. 14377). Roll of evidences, late 15th cent., rel. Munden etc.

1243. **Ditto** (Ancient Deeds, DD. 252). Roll of evidences, 15th cent. (*temp.* Hen. VI), rel. Cottered. Paper.

1244. **PRO., Chancery** (Ancient Deeds, CC: in C. 147, box 22). Roll of evidences, late 13th cent., rel. Munden.

1245. **Ditto** (Ancient Deeds, CC: in C. 147, box 22). Roll of evidences, mid-15th cent., rel. North Mimms.

GAINSFORD of Crowhurst, co. Surr.

1246. **BM., Harley 392.** Cartulary, 15th cent., of deeds etc. *temp.* Edw. III–Hen. VI rel. cos. Surr., Suss. and Kent.

Fos. 109. $9\frac{1}{2} \times 6\frac{5}{8}$ in.

GOLDINGHAM of Goldingham Hall, co. Essex.

1247. **Chelmsford, Essex R.O.** (D/DEx M 25). Register, *c.* 1315, of deeds and other evidences, 13th–14th cent., rel. Bulmer, co. Essex, and Kersey and Belstead, co. Suff. Followed (fos. 34 ff.) by added early 15th cent. copies of part of the material.

Fos. 44 (lacks a leaf aft. fo. 11). $10\frac{1}{2} \times 5$ in. (fos. 34 ff., 11×5 in.). Presented to Exeter City Libr. by R. P. Bishop, and transferred in 1940.

GOXHILL of co. Linc.

1248. **Peterborough, D. & C., MS. 23.** Cartulary, late 14th cent., of deeds, 12th–14th cent., rel. cos. Linc., York, Leic., Norf., Suff. and Essex. A transcript, 20th cent., is in Lincolnshire Archives Office (Foster Libr.).

Fos. 88. $12\frac{1}{8} \times 8\frac{1}{2}$ in.

GREGORY of Stivichall, co. Warw.

1249. **Major A. M. H. Gregory-Hood,** deposited at Stratford-upon-Avon, Shakespeare Birthplace Libr. ('Gregory Leiger-Book'). A mid-late 16th cent. register, with large red initials etc., of deeds and other evidences rel. co. Warw. Incorporates as pp. 7–18, 169–256, a late 14th cent. kalendar and parts of 13th and 14th cent. cartularies of Coventry Cathedral Priory (No. 275 above) and Stoneleigh Abbey (No. 936 above). Damaged by damp and largely illegible.

Pp. 327. $7\frac{5}{8} \times 6$ in. etc.

GRIFFIN of Braybrooke, co. Northt.
v. also BRAYBROOKE.

1250. **Northamptonshire R.O.** (box 1062). Cartulary, 16th cent., with elaborate pen-drawn initials, of deeds (mainly medieval) and other evidences rel. cos. Northt., Leic. and Som. Lettered, *c.* 1883, on the spine, 'UU'.

Fos. 131. 12½ × 9¼ in. Passed, 18th cent., to the Isham fam., barts.

1251.   **Ditto** (box 1062). Cartulary, 16th cent., with a few elaborate pen-drawn initials (grotesques), of deeds etc., mainly 16th cent., rel. the same counties as in No. 1250. Lettered similarly, 'TT'.

Fos. 259. 11½ × 9 in. *FO:* as No. 1250.

GURNEY, Thomas; of Halton, co. Bucks.
1252.   **Sir F. Dashwood, bart.,** deposited with Bucks. Arch. Soc. (Aylesbury, County Museum Muniment Room, box H/11). Copies and abstracts, 1457, with additions, of deeds and other evidences, 14th–15th cent., rel. co. Bucks. Includes genealogical notes, which are noticed by A. Vere Woodman, 'A Fifteenth-Century Pedigree', *Records of Buckinghamshire* xvi, pt. i (1953–4), 43–7.

Roll of 6 membrs., 24 × 11 in. etc., sewn together at the top.

HALE, Manor of, co. Lanc.
1253.   **Major G. I. Ireland Blackburne,** deposited at Preston, Lancashire R.O. (DDIb). 'The Hale Charter Roll.' Copies, mid-15th cent., of misc. evidences incl. writs, extracts from assize rolls, genealogical notes rel. the Ireland family and a few deeds, 13th–15th cent.

Roll of 3 membrs. 29 × 9⅞ in.

HARLESTONE, co. Northt.
v. BRAY.

HEBDEN of Hebden in Burnsall, co. York.
1254.   **Bodl., Yorks. Rolls 21.** Copies, 14th cent. (aft. 1312–13), with rubrics, and initials touched with red, of about 35 deeds, 12th–14th cent., rel. lands in the W.R., co. York.

Roll of 4 membrs. (the last detached). *c.* 70 × 8 in. *FO:* Sir T. Phillipps (MS. 35170).

HEREFORD, Earls of.
v. BOHUN, Humphrey.

HOO, DE; of Luton, co. Bedf.
1255.   **BM., Add. Roll 28721.** Copies, mid-14th cent. (aft. 1345) with a few additions, of deeds, 13th–14th cent., incl. a few royal charters etc., rel. cos. Bedf., Hertf. and Suss., arranged by places.

Roll of 14 membrs. *c.* 29 ft. × 9½ in. Written on both sides.

HOTOT of Clopton, co. Northt.
1256.   **Untraced.** Cartulary, 14th cent., cited by J. Bridges, *Hist. Northampton* ii (Oxford, 1791), 367–72, as 'MS. Dudley notat. A'.

Pp. 45. Folio. *FO:* the Dudley fam., barts.; George Baker (MS. E. E., 'picked up by Mr. (John ?) Caley on a bookstall in Edinburgh'); Sir T. Phillipps (MS. 12025).

HULL
v. HYLL.

HUNGERFORD of Farleigh Hungerford, co. Som.
1257.   **Taunton, Somerset R.O.** (DD/SAS). Cartulary, 15th cent. (aft. 1458) with additions, of deeds etc., 1205–1475 and n.d., rel. lands in cos. Wilts, Som. and Glouc., and in the parish of St. Martin-in-the-Fields, Westminster. Includes copies of 15th cent. documents rel. the foundation etc. of chantries in Farleigh Hungerford church and (added) Salisbury Cathedral. Used by J. E. Jackson, *Farleigh Hungerford* (1879).

Fos. 340. 18 × 12 in. *FO:* the Rt. Hon. Henry Hobhouse, P.C.

HUNTINGFIELD
1258.   **The Earl of Ancaster,** deposited at Lincoln, Lincolnshire Archives Office (3 Anc. 2/1). Cartulary, mid-14th cent. (aft. 1336) with additions, of deeds and other evidences, 12th–14th cent., incl. charters of King Stephen, rel. lands in co. Linc. etc. Made perhaps during the minority of Sir Wm. Huntingfield, baron Huntingfield 1351. Calendared in *Huntingfield Cartulary* (Lincolnshire Archives Office, 1956; mimeograph).

Fos. 34. 11½ × 7⅞ in.

HYLL *al.* **HULL,** Robert; and Isabella his wife, daughter and heiress of Sir Thomas Fitchet, knt.

1259. **PRO., Exch., Augm. Off.** (Misc. Bks. 60). Cartulary, 15th cent. (*temp.* Hen. IV), of deeds and other evidences, mainly rel. co. Som. and adjacent counties. Calendared by F. Palgrave, *PRO. Deputy Keeper's Eighth Report*, App. ii, 151–66.

Fos. 175. 12¾ × 9½ in.

1260. **Ditto** (Misc. Bks. 59). A fair copy (?) of No. 1259, of contemp. or slightly later date.

Fos. 106. 11½ × 8¼ in. Paper.

INCE, Richard de; of Ince, co. Lanc.

1261. **Col. C. G. Walmesley, D.S.O.,** deposited at Preston, Lancashire R.O. (DDWa. 11/1). Copies, mid-14th cent., of 65 charters etc., 1263–1326 and n.d., rel. Ince, Aspull, Pemberton and Wigan, co. Lanc.

Roll of 11 membrs., 8–9 in. wide; lacks at least one further membr. at the end.

KAY of Woodsome, co. York.

1262. **Untraced.** Cartulary, 15th cent. Royal octavo. Paper. *FO:* J. Wilson; Sir T. Phillipps (MS. 15080).

KELMARSH, co. Northt.

1263. **William H. Robinson Ltd.,** 1955. Two quires of a 15th cent. cartulary, containing copies of deeds rel. Kelmarsh, 13th–14th cent. Ends in the middle of an entry.

Fos. i + 18. 10¾ × 7¼ in. *FO:* George Baker (MS. F. F.); Sir T. Phillipps (MS. 12026 *al.* 18960).

KENDALE of co. Hertf.
v. WALEYS.

KNIVETON of co. Derby.

1264. **Lincoln, D. & C.,** Muniments (A/1/9). Cartulary, early 14th cent., with spaces for initials and additions, rel. lands in co. Derby. At the back are some genealogical notes down to 1618.

Fos. 4 + 116. 12 × 7⅞ in.

KNOLTON manor, co. Kent.
v. LANGLEY of Knolton.

LAMBERT, Thomas fil. Thome fil.; of Moulton.
v. MOULTON.

LANCASTER, Earldom and (1351) Duchy of.

Nos. 1265–1274 are noticed by R. Somerville, *Hist. Duchy of Lancaster* i (1953), xi, 29, 116–17 etc.

1265. **PRO., Duchy of Lanc.** (Misc. Bks. 11). A collection of misc. quires written in a series of 14th cent. hands, with partial rubrication, containing copies of charters and deeds housed in various places rel. the Duchy and its lands, *temp.* John–Ric. II.

Fos. 80. 14¼ × 10½ in.

1266. **Ditto** (Miscellanea, DL. 41/1/19, 41/1/38). Copies, 14th cent., of charters and deeds, *temp.* Hen. III–Edw. III, contained in boxes at Kenilworth Castle.

Rolls of 2 and 4 membrs., 12½ in. wide.

1267. **Ditto** (Misc. Bks. 12). Register, early 15th cent., with later additions and insertions, of charters and other evidences, *temp.* Hen. I–IV, rel. the Duchy and its lands in various counties. Contemp. Table, fos. 2–3.

Fos. 63 (lacks the opening 8 leaves of text bef. fo. 8). 15½ × 11 in.

1268. **Ditto** (Misc. Bks. 1). 'The Great Coucher Book,' vol. i. The first part (cf. No. 1269) of an early 15th cent. gen. cartulary (*temp.* Hen. IV), elaborately written with illuminated initials, coats of arms, borders etc. Arranged topographically by counties etc., with a section of royal charters at the beginning and another entitled *Partes Transmarinae*, followed by further copies of royal charters, at the end.

Fos. 453. 16 × 10¾ in.

1269. **Ditto** (Misc. Bks. 2). 'The Great Coucher Book,' vol. ii (cf. No. 1268). Arranged similarly by counties, with a concluding section for the honour of Bolingbroke, and incl. further copies of royal charters *passim*. Preceded by 20 leaves bearing elaborately executed coats of arms in tincture.

Fos. 23 + 490. 16½ × 10¾ in.

❡ *Inventories*

1270. **Ditto** (Miscellanea, DL. 41/1/35). Inventory, 14th cent. (aft. 1322), by Robert de Hoton *et al.* (cf. Nos. 1271–2, 1293), of charters, deeds etc. kept in the chapel of Tutbury Castle.

Roll of 8 membrs., 10¼ in. wide.

1271. **Ditto** (Miscellanea, DL. 41/1/37). Inventory, 14th cent. (aft. 1322), similar to No. 1270, of charters, deeds etc. as arranged in boxes and bags at Pontefract Castle. Cf. No. 1272.

Roll of 8 membrs., 11 in. wide. Apparently lacks about 3 membrs. at the head.

1272. **Ditto** (Miscellanea, DL. 41/1/36). A 15th cent. copy of No. 1271, supplying the material now wanting from it and the names of its compilers, Robert de Hoton *et al.*

Roll of 7 membrs., 10¼ in. wide.

1273. **Ditto** (Miscellanea, DL. 41/3/27). Inventory, 14th cent., by Simon Pakeman, of charters, deeds etc., early 12th–14th cent., contained in two large hanapers at the Savoy. Cf. No. 1274.

Roll of 3 membrs. (joined at the top), 9–11 in. wide.

1274. **Ditto** (Miscellanea, DL. 41/1/33). Inventory, 1376, by Simon Pakeman, of charters and deeds, *temp.* Edw. III, kept in a hutch in the treasury at the Savoy, cf. No. 1273.

Roll of 6 membrs., 11¼ in. wide.

LANDWADE, co. Cambr.
v. COTTON.

LANGLEY
1275. **BM., Harley 7.** Cartulary, late 15th cent., of deeds etc., *temp.* Hen. III–Edw. IV, rel. cos. Glouc., Warw., Northt., Salop, Oxon and Cambr. Genealogical notes at fo. 237v suggest that it was made for William Langley (d. 1483). *BM. Cat. Harl. MSS.* i, *ad loc.*, lists the titles of sections.

Fos. 237. 11¾ × 8½ in. Paper.

LANGLEY of Knolton, co. Kent.
1276. **Oxford, Bodl., Rawlinson B. 337.** Cartulary, 15th cent. (*temp.* Hen. VI, with additions ?), of deeds etc., *temp.* Hen. III–Edw. IV, rel. co. Kent. Contemp. binding (red leather). An abstract, 17th cent., is in BM., Stowe 924, fos. 245–54. W. D. Macray, *Cat. MSS. Bibl. Bodl.* v (i) (Oxford, 1862), 606, lists the principal places referred to.

Fos. 207 (lacks 181–2). 12 × 8 in. Paper. *FO:* J. Philipot, 17th cent.

LANNARGH-NANSKYLLY, of co. Cornw.
1277. **PRO., Exch., K.R.** (Miscel-

lanea, E. 163/21/1). Cartulary, *c.* 1500, in a dilapidated state, of deeds and other evidences, *temp.* Edw. I–Ric. III.

Fos. ii + 48, with numerous loose fragms. 8½ × 5½ in. Paper.

LE BYRON
v. BYRON.

LEGH, John de; of Norbury Booths Hall, Knutsford, co. Chest.
1278. **Manchester, Rylands Libr.** (Legh of Booths Ch. 326). Contemp. copies of twenty-two 13th–14th cent. grants etc. to John de Legh and Elena his wife etc. An added late 14th cent. memorandum relates to lands of the Mascy family of Sale. Calendared by F. Taylor, *Hand-list of Legh of Booths Charters* (Manchester, 1950), 280–2.

Roll of 3 membrs. *FO:* R. H. Wood.

LENNOX, Earldom of.
1279. **Untraced.** Cartulary among the records, 18th cent., of the burgh of Dumbarton. A transcript, of 116 charters etc. 1180–1398, in NLS., Adv. 35. 4. 9 (Jac. V. 4. 2), pp. 1–102, was edited, with another then in the possession of the Duke of Montrose etc., by J. Dennistoun, *Cartularium Comitatus de Levenax* (Maitland Club, 1833).

LUCAS of Little Saxham, co. Suff.
1280. **BM., Add. 7097.** Copies, 15th–16th cent., of surveys, rentals and charters, mainly 14th–16th cent., rel. co. Suff. Made perhaps by or for Thomas Lucas, solicitor general *c.* 1504–7.

Fos. 201. 12¼ × 8½ in. Paper. *FO:* T. Martin; A. C. Ducarel; C. Ord.

LUCY, barons Lucy; of Cockermouth, co. Cumb.
1281. **John Wyndham Esq.,** Leconfield Estate Office, Cockermouth Castle. Copies, 16th cent., taken apparently from a late 14th cent. compilation, of royal and private charters and other evidences, *temp.* John–Ric. II, rel. lands in cos. Cumb., Northumb. etc., incl. the honour of Cockermouth, barony of Multon of Egremont etc.

Roll of 18 membrs. (joined at the top). 32 × 11½ in. etc.

MACCLESFIELD, DE; of Macclesfield, co. Chest.

1282.   **BM., Cotton Cleop. D. vi.**
Cartulary, 15th cent. (*temp.* Hen. V, with contemp. additions) of deeds, 14th–15th cent., incl. copies of some royal charters etc., rel. lands of John de Macclesfield senior, keeper of the Great Wardrobe 1398–9 etc., and of his son John de Macclesfield junior, in Macclesfield, London and co. Essex. Fos. 196–203 contain rentals for Macclesfield town and hundred, 1414.
Fos. 220. $10\frac{1}{2} \times 7\frac{1}{4}$ in.

MAKENADE of Macknade, near Faversham, co. Kent.

1283.   **Untraced.** Cartulary in the hands of Martin James of Chancery, 1587, from which extracts are in London, Coll. of Arms, Glover's Collections B, fos. 124 ff. and BM., Harley 4757, fos. 100–5.

MARCH, Earls of.
v. MORTIMER.

MAULEVERER

1284.   **Brown fam. archives,** deposited at Northallerton, Yorkshire North Riding R.O. (ZFL). Copies, 15th cent., of about 90 deeds rel. lands in the W.R., co. York. A transcript by W. T. Lancaster is in Leeds, Yorks. Arch. Soc. MS. 404, fos. 159–204.
Roll of 6 membrs. $145 \times 9\frac{3}{4}$ in. *FO:* William Brown, F.S.A.

MIDDLETON, Barons.
v. WILLOUGHBY.

MOHUN, DE; barons Mohun, of Dunster, co. Som.

1285.   **BM., Egerton 3724.** Register, 14th cent. (*temp.* Edw. III), with rubrics, red paragraphs etc., of fees, terriers, extents etc. rel. lands in S.W. England. Followed (fos. 39–40) by an Anglo-Norman French poem entitled 'En sa veillesse set li prudhom.', and (fos. 41 ff.) by copies of misc. charters and deeds rel. fees, rents and other services.
Fos. xxxvii+90. $13\frac{1}{4} \times 9\frac{5}{8}$ in. *FO:* G. Matcham; Sir T. Phillipps (MS. 16566).

MOLEYNS of Stoke Poges, co. Bucks.

1286.   **BM., Egerton Roll 8762.** Abstracts, 14th cent., of fines, deeds etc., 1328–40, rel. lands in cos. Bucks., Surr. and Oxon, of Sir John Moleyns and Egidia his wife, grand-daughter and coheiress of Sir Robert Pugeys and Amicia de Stoke.
Roll of 5 membrs. *c.* $12\frac{1}{2}$ ft. $\times 7\frac{1}{2}$ in. *FO:* the Pierrepont fam., earls Manvers.

1287.   **Taunton, Somerset Arch. Soc. Libr.** Cartulary, 14th cent. (*temp.* Edw. III), of lands of Sir William de Moleyns in cos. Bucks., Oxon, Northt., Hertf., Wilts, Surr., Som. and London.
Fos. 290. $19 \times 12\frac{1}{2}$ in. *FO:* the Rt. Hon. Henry Hobhouse, P.C.

MONTAGU, earls of Salisbury.
v. also FRANCIS.

1288.   **PRO., Exch., Augm. Off.** (Ancient Deeds, BB. 108). Copies, mid-14th cent., of 15 royal and other charters, 1333–7 etc., to or rel. William Montagu, 1st earl.
Roll of 7 membrs., $11\frac{1}{2}$ in. wide.

1289.   **The Marquess of Salisbury,** Hatfield (MS. 293). Register, *c.* 1360 with additions, of charters and other evidences, *temp.* Edw. II–III, mainly rel. William Montagu, 1st earl (d. 1344), and presumably compiled for William, 2nd earl. Arranged apparently according to subject matter and incl. copies of numerous royal and some ecclesiastical and monastic documents.
Fos. 94 (unnumbered, and the original order apparently disturbed). $14\frac{5}{8} \times 10\frac{1}{4}$ in.
¶ *Inventory*

1290.   **PRO., Exch., K.R.** (Ancient Deeds, DD: E. 211, box 13, item with superseded numeration TG. 22987). Part of an inventory, mid-14th cent., of about 200 leases, bonds, acquittances, reliefs etc. rel. various persons and places. Arranged in lettered groups (*B–D*).
Roll of 7 membrs. (contemp. numeration, (iii)–ix), 6 in. wide.

MORDAUNT of Turvey, co. Bedf.

1291.   **Col. N. V. Stopford Sackville, O.B.E.,** deposited in Northamptonshire R.O. (SS. 258). Abbreviated copies, early 16th cent., of 162 deeds etc., 13th–14th cent., rel. Turvey.
Fos. 11. $12\frac{1}{4} \times 8\frac{1}{2}$ in. Paper.

MORTIMER, earls of March.

1292. **BM., Harley 1240.** 'Liber Niger de Wigmore', late 14th cent. (aft. 1379). Cartulary of deeds etc., 13th–14th cent., rel. lands in England, Wales and Ireland. Preceded (fos. 1–7) by indexes, and (fos. 8–34) by a Table similar to the inventories in No. 1294. Fos. 81–93, bound out of order, relate to the inheritance of Philippa, wife (1368) of Edmund Mortimer, 3rd earl (d. 1381), and daughter of Lionel, duke of Clarence. H. Wood,'The Muniments of Edmund Mortimer, Third Earl of March, concerning his Liberty of Trim', *Proc. Royal Irish Acad.* xl, section C (1931–2), 312–55, describes the MS., pp. 325–7, and calendars the Irish material (fos. 114 ff.). It is noticed by E. Owen, *Cat. MSS. rel. Wales in the BM.* ii (1903), 230; iv (1922), 925.

Fos. 125 (contemp. foliation, i–cclxxxiiii, from fo. 8; wants 67 leaves aft. fo. 99 (clix) and other smaller groups *passim*). 16 × 11 in.

¶ *Inventories*

1293. **BM., Egerton Rolls 8723, 8724.** Inventory, 14th cent. (*c.* 1330–40?), by Robert de Hoton *et al.*, of muniments of various lords of Mortimer etc. found in the Tower of London. Includes frequent abstracts of documents. For Hoton, cf. Nos. 1270–2.

Rolls of 4 and 7 membrs. (the second imperf. at the beginning, but apparently a continuation of the first), 10¼ in. wide. *FO:* the Pierrepont fam., earls Manvers.

1294. **BM., Add. 6041.** Two 14th cent. inventories (*c.* 1368–81), of muniments in the treasury at Wigmore. The second (fos. 49 ff., imperf. at the end) relates to the inheritance of Phillippa, wife of Edmund Mortimer, 3rd earl of March (cf. No. 1292), in whose lifetimes both appear to have been made. Each is preceded by an index. Owen, *op. cit.* iv (1922), 924–5.

Fos. i+106. 11¾ × 7½ in. 'Manuscript found in 1795 in opnning a vault in an Ruind Tower in R' (note on an old binding now destroyed). Presented by Thomas Thomson, deputy clerk-register of Scotland, 1809.

MOULTON, co. Linc.

1295. **Untraced.** Terrier and cartulary of Thomas fil. Thome fil. Lamberti of Moulton in Holland made, 1316, by Everard de Flete his steward.

Quarto. *FO:* Maurice Johnson, 1725 (cf. Bodl., Tanner 342, fo. 19).

MOULTON of Frampton, co. Linc.

1295A. **Oxford, Magdalen Coll.,** Muniments (Adds. 36). Bifolium (consecutive leaves) from a 14th–15th cent. cartulary, containing copies of about 20 deeds down to 1337.

Fos. 2. 16½ × 12½ in.

MOWBRAY, DE; dukes of Norfolk, earls of Nottingham, barons Mowbray and Segrave.

v. also SEGRAVE. No cartulary recorded.

¶ *Other registers etc.*

1296. **BM., Add. 24688,** fos. 7–50. Transcripts, late 15th cent. (aft. 1490), of lists of fees, inquisitions, terriers etc. rel. lands in cos. York, Lincoln etc. Preceded (fos. 7–12) by copies of documents rel. the sale of lands in these counties to Thomas Stanley, 1st earl of Derby.

Fos. 44. 12⅛ × 9¼ in. *FO:* Charles Devon.

MUGGE of Scorriton in W. Buckfastleigh, co. Devon.

1297. **BM., Add. Roll 28722.** Copies, 15th cent., of 13 deeds, 13th–15th cent., rel. Scorriton etc.

Roll of 2 membrs. 40 × 8½ in.

MUNDEN, co. Hertf.

v. (?) FRAY.

NANSKYLLY
v. LANNARGH-NANSKYLLY.

NARFORD, William and Petronilla de; of Narford, co. Norf.

1298. **BM., Stowe 776.** Cartulary, 13th–14th cent., substantially supplemented *temp.* Edw. II with occasional subsequent additions, rel. lands in cos. Norf. and Suff., mainly the inheritance of Petronilla as daughter and coheiress of Sir J. de Vaux *al.* Vallibus (d. 1287). Some red paragraphs etc. on the early leaves.

Fos. 54 (ii+52; two pairs of leaves excised aft. fos. 9, 10). 8½ × 6⅜ in. *FO:* T. Martin; T. Astle.

NEEL

1299.   **The Earl of Leicester,** Holkham Hall (Holkham Deed 22a). Abstracts, 1414–5, by Edmund Lucas, bailiff (m. Mary, daughter of Gilbert Neel), of 92 deeds, 13th–14th cent., rel. Holkham, Rainham and Weasenham, co. Norf. (fos. 13–23); with terriers, feodaries and lists of lands of the Neel fam., and terriers of lands of the prior of Walsingham and Ld. Wm. Calthorp.

Fos. 55. 12 × 8¾ in. Paper. Damaged by damp.

NEWDEGATE, John; serjeant-at-law; of Harefield, co. Middx. (d. 1528).

1300.   **F. H. M. Fitzroy Newdegate, Esq.,** Arbury, Nuneaton. Cartulary, late 15th cent. (*temp.* Hen. VII) with early 16th cent. etc. continuations and additions, of deeds and other evidences etc., 13th–16th cent. etc., rel. Harefield etc., co. Middx.; London; Batchworth etc., co. Hertf.; and cos. Surr., Bucks. and Linc. Includes misc. genealogical and other personal memoranda rel. the Newdegate and related families *passim.*

Fos. 135 + 5 (incl. some extraneous material; contemp. foliation, i–cxi, of fos. 15–126). 13¼ × 9¼ in.

NEWTON of Newton, and Pownall Hall, co. Chest.

1301.   **BM., Add. 42134** (A). Transcripts, 16th cent., of deeds, 13th–16th cent., with numerous contemp. notes, genealogical trees etc. Said to have been compiled by Humphrey Newton (1466–1537) and copied, with some additions, by his son William (d. 1574). A transcript etc., 1889, is in BM., Add. 42134(B). J. P. Earwaker, *East Cheshire* ii (1880), 263–7. T. H. Noyes, 'Some Notices of the Family of Newton', *Sussex Arch. Coll.* ix (1857), 312–42 (notices and extracts).

Fos. i + 32 (wants leaves aft. fos. 23, 29). *c.* 12 × 8 in. Paper.

NORFOLK, Dukes of.
v. MOWBRAY.

NORTHUMBERLAND, Earls of.
v. PERCY.

NORWICH, John de; knt.; baron Norwich (d. 1362).

1302.   **Oxford, Bodl., Top. gen. c. 62.** Cartulary, 1348, with additions, of deeds rel. lands in cos. Norf. and Suff., incl. (fos. 86 ff.) lists of fees, extents and rentals.

Fos. xviii + 126. 14 × 9¾ in. *FO:* T. Martin; J. Ives; G. Brander; C. Ord; Sir T. Phillipps (MS. 3796).

NOTTINGHAM, Earls of.
v. MOWBRAY.

OKEOVER of Okeover, co. Staff.

1303.   **Oxford, Bodl., Wood empt. 6,** (*SC.* 8594). Cartulary, 14th cent. (*temp.* Edw. II–III), with spaces for initials, of deeds rel. cos. Staff. and Derby, with some other misc. material. Made apparently for Sir Roger de Okeover (d. 1337). Used by G. Wrottesley, 'An Account of the Family of Okeover' etc., Wm. Salt Arch. Soc., *Coll. Hist. Staffordshire*, New ser. vii (1904), pt. i, 3–187.

Fos. iv + 57. 9 × 6½ in. *FO:* John Vincent (Bodl., Dugdale 15 (*SC.* 6505), p. 91); R. Sheldon.

OXFORD, Earls of.
v. VERE.

PAKENHAM, Thomas de.

1304.   **BM., Campbell Ch. xvii.** Copies, 14th cent. (aft. 1318), of 78 deeds, *temp.* Edw. I–II, rel. Ixworth Thorpe etc., co. Suff., mainly grants to Thomas's father, Sir Wm. de Pakenham.

Fos. 34 (31 + 3). 11⅛ × 8¾ in.

PEDWARDINE of Pedwardine, co. Heref.

1305.   **BM., Add. 32101.** Cartulary, late 14th cent. with occasional additions, of deeds etc. rel. lands in cos. Linc., Northt., Heref., Westm., Southt. etc., arranged in alphabetical order of places. Preceded (fos. 7–8) by a descent, 1395, of the families of Pedwardine and Cronn, made by Robert Pedwardine. A transcript, 1637, is in BM. Lansdowne 207C, fos. 16–91.

Fos. 93. 10⅝ × 6¾ in. *FO:* the Towneley fam.

PERCY, barons Percy of Alnwick and (1377) earls of Northumberland.

1306.   **The Duke of Northumberland,** Syon House, Brentford (Muniments, D. i. 1a). Cartulary, 14th cent. (*temp.* Edw. II–III, with additions down to 1377), of deeds etc. rel. lands in cos. York, Northumb., Suss. etc. Begun apparently *temp.* Henry Percy, 2nd baron, and arranged in sections by counties. Red and blue initials, paragraphs etc. Extracts are in Bodl., Dodsworth 74 (*SC.* 5016), fos. 1–110. Ed. Miss M. T. Martin, *The Percy Chartulary* (Surtees Soc. cxvii, 1911).

Fos. 183. 12 × 9 in. *FO:* Col. Charles Fairfax.

PETIGARD, Roger; of Sporle, co. Norf.
1307. **Norwich, Central Libr., MS. 17899** (78. x. 4). Cartulary, *c.* 1342 with later 14th cent. additions, of deeds rel. lands in Sporle and vicinity, arranged topographically.

Fos. 54. 9½ × 6¾ in.

PIERREPONT, Sir Henry; of Holme Pierrepont, co. Nott.
1308. **The Duke of Portland** (Welbeck MS. 67. C. 11), deposited in the British Museum (MSS. Loans No. 29/60). Cartulary, 1482, of deeds, 13th–15th cent., rel. lands in cos. Nott., Derby and York. Compiled by Thomas Wyse, chaplain, with an elaborate Table (fos. 2–27) and a few additions *passim.*

Fos. 311 (excl. blank leaves). 17¼ × 12 in. *FO:* Henry Pierrepont, 2nd earl of Kingston-upon-Hull and marquess of Dorchester, 1651 (see extracts in Bodl., Dodsworth 108 (*SC.* 5049), 91–106).

PUSEY of Pusey, co. Berks.
1309. **Capt. E. Bouverie-Pusey,** deposited at Reading, Berkshire R.O. (D/EBp T1). Copies, 13th cent., of 28 deeds, 1204–97 & n.d., rel. Pusey and elsewhere in co. Berks, the later entries being additions.

Roll of 3 membrs. 70 × 6 in.

REDE of Boarstall, co. Bucks.
1310. **Major Sir H. L. Aubrey-Fletcher, bart., D.S.O.,** Townhill, Chilton, Aylesbury. Cartulary, 1444, with rubrics, blue and red initials etc., and additions. Made for Edmund Rede the younger. Contains copies of deeds etc., 12th–15th cent., incl. some royal (English & Scottish) and episcopal charters etc., rel.

cos. Bucks., Oxon and Berks, preceded (fos. 1–19) by a Table. An abstract, 1668, by A. à Wood is in London, Coll. of Arms, Vincent 85. Ed. H. E. Salter, *The Boarstall Cartulary* (Oxford Hist. Soc. lxxxviii, 1930). *New Palaeographical Soc.,* First ser., pl. 121 (description).

Fos. 292. 13 × 9 in.

RICHMOND, Honour of.
No cartulary recorded.
❡ *Other registers etc.*
1311. **BM., Cotton Faust. B. vii,** fos. 72–136. Register, late 15th cent., of fees, fines and wards, extracts from Domesday and other misc. material, incl. coloured drawings of: (*a*) William I presenting a charter to Alan, earl of Brittany; (*b*) the latter with his retainers; (*c*) Richmond Castle. Cf. Nos. 1312–5. Ed. (down to fo. 132) R. Gale, *Registrum Honoris de Richmond* (1722).
1312. **Untraced.** The 'Gilling MS.', 15th cent. Similar to No. 1311. Noticed by R. E. G. Kirk, *HMC. Fifteenth Report,* App. vi (1897), xxxvii, when it was at Castle Howard. *FO:* Ld. Wm. Howard; the Howard fam., earls of Carlisle (Hodgson's sale-cat., 20 July 1944, lot 238).
1313. **BM., Add. 5466.** Similar to No. 1311, 16th cent. Written by J. Messenger. *FO:* John Jackson, F.S.A.
1314. **BM., Harley 3674.** Similar to No. 1311, without the drawings. Late 16th cent.
1315. **Oxford, Bodl., Dodsworth 46** (*SC.* 4188). Similar to No. 1314, *c.* 1630.

RIDWARE of Seal, co. Derby (formerly Leic.).
1316. **BM., Egerton 3041.** Cartulary, 1308–9 with additions, of deeds and other evidences, 11th–14th cent., rel. lands in cos. Derby, Staff., Berks and Suff., incl. copies of a few royal charters and writs, Will. II–Edw. II, and a number of marginal etc. pen drawings. Red titles and initials. Ed. I. H. Jeayes & G. Wrottesley, 'The Rydeware Chartulary', Wm. Salt Arch. Soc., *Coll. Hist. Staffordshire* xvi (1896), 229–302. Described by J. Nichols, *Hist. Leicester* iii, pt. 2 (1804), 999–1007. *BM. Cat. Add. MSS.* 1926–1930, *ad loc.*

Fos. ii + 73. 11 × 8 in. *FO:* the Gresley fam., barts.

SALISBURY, Earls of.
v. MONTAGU.

SAXHAM, co. Suff.
v. LUCAS.

SCROPE of Castlecombe, co. Wilts.
1317. **BM., Add. 28206.** Register, 15th
cent. (*temp.* Hen. VI–Edw. IV), of misc.
evidences, incl. some deeds, 13th–15th
cent., rel. the manors of Castlecombe,
Oxenden (co. Glouc.), Bentley (co. York)
etc. *BM.Cat.Add.MSS.*1854–1875,ii,443–
4, lists the major contents. G. P. Scrope,
Hist. Castlecombe (1852), prints extracts.
    Fos. 131 (excl. blank leaves; paginated,
1–346). $12\frac{1}{2} \times 8\frac{1}{2}$ in. Paper.
1318. **BM., Add. 28207.** Similar to No.
1317 and in part duplicating its contents,
with some later additions.
    Fos. 35. $11\frac{5}{8} \times 8\frac{3}{8}$ in. Paper.

SEFTON, Henry de.
v. INCE.

SEGRAVE, barons Segrave.
v. also MOWBRAY.
1319. **BM., Harley 4748.** Index, 15th
cent., of a cartulary known as 'The Red
Book'. Calendars the contents topographically, by counties (Warw., Leic.,
Northt., Derby, Cambr., Bucks.). J.
Nichols, *Hist. Leicester* ii, pt. 1 (1795), App.
xiii, 108–20, prints the Leicestershire material.
    Fos. 32. $11\frac{3}{4} \times 8\frac{1}{4}$ in. Paper. *FO:* P. Le
Neve.
¶ *Other registers etc.*
1320. **BM., Add. 37671.** Feodary,
rental etc., 14th cent., of lands of John,
lord Segrave (d. 1353), in cos. Leic., Warw.,
Derby and Hunt. *FO:* Sir T. Phillipps (MS.
18492, 'Ex Bibl. Manwaring of Peover').

SPILLMAN of Rodborough, co. Glouc.
1321. **Mrs. A. H. Miller,** Frampton
Court; deposited at Gloucester, Gloucestershire R.O. (D. 149). Cartulary, late 15th
cent. with additions, of 23 deeds, 1218–1331
etc. Ed. (in English) C. E. Watson, 'The
Spillman Cartulary', *Trans. Bristol &
Glouc. Arch. Soc.* lxi (1939), 50–94.
    Fos. 10. $8\frac{1}{2} \times 7$ in.

SPORLE, co. Norf.
v. PETIGARD.

STAFFORD, dukes of Buckingham.
    Nos. 1322–3 are noticed by A. J. Hor-
wood, *HMC. Fourth Report* (1874), App.,
325–6.
1322. **Lord Bagot,** deposited at Stafford, Wm. Salt Libr. (D. 1721/1/2). The
'Old Cartulary' *al.* 'Stafford MSS., vol. ii'.
Cartulary, late 15th cent. (*c.* 1483 ?) with
additions, of deeds and some other misc.
material rel. co. Staff. etc. Arranged topographically.
    Fos. *c.* 400 (unnumbered). $12 \times 8\frac{1}{4}$ in.
Paper. *FO:* the Rev. Stebbing Shaw, 1793;
S. Pipe Wolferstan; W. Hamper; William,
2nd baron Bagot, 1820.
1323. **Ditto** (D. 1721/1/1). The 'Great
Cartulary' *al.* 'Stafford MSS., vol. i'. Composite register, 16th cent. (*temp.* Hen. VIII)
with additions, containing sections of
deeds rel. various manors in co. Staff. and
misc. material rel. the Stafford fam.
    Fos. 415. $16 \times 10\frac{3}{4}$ in. Paper. *FO:* as No.
1322.

STRODE of Plympton, co. Devon.
1324. **Mrs. A. M. D. Grigg-Strode,**
Newnham Park; deposited in Plymouth
City Libr. Copies, 14th–15th cent., of 118
deeds, late 13th–early 15th cent., rel.
Newnham etc.
    Fos. 19. 16×11 in.

SUTTON or **DUDLEY,** barons Dudley;
of Dudley, co. Staff.
1325. **Untraced.** 'Cartularium familiae
de Sutton, D(omi)ni de Dudley de Man-
erio de Deythor in Wallia', 16th cent.
    Folio. Vellum. *FO:* Sir G. Nayler; Sir T.
Phillipps (MS. 7137).

TERRICUS TYEIS (*al.* Theodoricus
Teutonicus), of Cologne; burgher of
Stamford, co. Linc.
1326. **PRO., Exch., Augm. Off.**
(Ancient Deeds, BB. 16). Copies, 13th
cent. (*temp.* Hen. III), in two main hands,
of 55 contemp. deeds rel. his accessions in
Stamford etc. In a number of cases these
are described as sales made to secure the
settlement of debts to money-lenders.
Some later 13th and 15th cent. additions
on the verso concern rents payable to

Stamford nunnery, incl. extracts from a rental.
Roll of 6 membrs., 6½ in. wide.

THORP, John de; baron Thorp (d. *c.* 1324).

1327. **Cambridge U.L., Mm. 5. 35.** Cartulary, 14th cent. (aft. 1323), of deeds rel. cos. Norf. and Suff., arranged topographically. *Cambr. U.L. Cat. MSS.* iv, *ad loc.*, lists the places etc.
Fos. 152. 9¼ × 6½ in. *FO:* Bp. J. Moore.

THROCKING, Roger fil. Briani de; of Throcking, co. Hertf.

1328. **BM., Cotton App. xvii.** Cartulary, 13th–14th cent. (*c.* 1296?), with rubrics, red paragraphs etc., of deeds rel. Throcking etc. Preceded (fos. 1–4) by a Table and followed (fos. 124v ff.) by contemp. etc. additions.
Fos. 140. 9½ × 6¾ in.

THWAITES, of Thwaites and Denton, co. York.

1329. **Chatsworth Libr., co. Derby** (Trustees of the Chatsworth Settlement), Hardwick MS. 20. Cartulary, 15th cent. (*c.* 1450–60?), with page-headings and initials in red, of deeds rel. co. York. Arranged topographically, with a contemp. Table at fos. 6–10, and incl. copies of antecedent title deeds of the properties concerned (Brocas, Vavasour etc. fams.). Sotheby's sale-cat., 6 June 1898, lot 591 (description).
Fos. xx + 142. 11¼ × 8½ in. *FO:* the Fairfax fam., Denton; Sir T. Phillipps (MS. 10300); the Dukes of Devonshire.

TREGODEK

1330. **Sir John Carew Pole, bart.,** Anthony House, Torpoint (BD/10/72A). Cartulary, mid-15th cent., of deeds etc., 13th–15th cent., rel. lands in co. Cornw. of the heirs of Thomas Tregodek. A modern abstract is at Truro, Royal Institution of Cornwall.
Roll of 3 membrs., 11½ in. wide.

TRESHAM, William; of Rushton, co. Northt; speaker of the House of Commons (d. 1450).

1331. **Northamptonshire Record Soc.,** deposited in Northamptonshire R.O. Part of a 15th cent. cartulary (aft. 1448,

with an addition of 1455), of deeds rel. cos. Northt. and Bucks. Originally arranged topographically, but the order of the quires (now 12 in number, formerly upwards of 28) has been disturbed.
Fos. 234 (paginated, 1–468). 11½ × 9 in. Paper. Title, 19th cent., on the spine, 'Hales MS.'. *FO:* R. C. Maylam.

TROPENELL, Thomas (d. 1488).

1332. **The National Trust,** Great Chalfield. Cartulary, 1464 with additions, of deeds etc. rel. cos. Wilts and Glouc. Arranged topographically and incl. some other misc. material. Ed. J. Silvester Davies, *The Tropenell Cartulary*, 2 vols. (Wilts. Arch. & Nat. Hist. Soc., 1908).
Fos. 489 (paginated, 1–978). 14 × 11 in. *FO:* the Eyre and Danvers fams.; Ezekiel Dickinson, 1744; the Harman fam.; the Rev. J. Silvester Davies, 1888; W. Heward Bell, 1901; R. Fuller.

TUTBURY, Honour of.
No cartulary recorded.
¶ *Other registers etc.*

1333. **PRO., Duchy of Lanc.** (Misc. Bks. 4). Rentals, 1415, and a feodary, 15th cent.

VALOINES of Godmersham, co. Kent.

1334. **BM., Stowe 854.** Cartulary, late 15th cent., of deeds, *temp.* Edw. I–Hen. VI, rel. Godmersham and Wye. Apparently imperf. at the beginning, and has some 16th cent. rentals etc., for which see *BM. Cat. Stowe MSS.* i, 595, added at the end (fos. 17v ff.)
Fos. 20. 16 × 10¾ in.

VAUX *al.* **VALLIBUS,** Sir John de (d. 1287).
v. NARFORD.

VAVASOUR
v. THWAITES.

VERE, DE; earls of Oxford.

1335. **Oxford, Bodl., Rawlinson B. 248.** Cartulary, late 15th cent. (*c.* 1500?), of deeds, 12th–15th cent. (mainly *temp.* Edw. I–III), rel. various counties, incl. the inheritance of Elizabeth, daughter of Sir John Howard and wife of John, 12th earl. Arranged by families (de Vere, Howard,

Boys, Sutton, Scales, Warren, Plaiz), with a mutilated Table at fos. 1–5.

Fos. iii + 62. 12½ × 8¾ in. *FO:* P. Le Neve.

WALEYS
v. also CHASTELAYN.

WALEYS of Glynde, co. Suss.
1336. **Mrs. Humphry Brand,** Glynde Place. Copies, early 15th cent. (*temp.* Hen. V), of deeds rel. lands of the Waleys fam. in Glynde etc., and of the Kendale family in Hitchin etc. Made probably for Nicholas Morley, whose wife Joan was daughter and heiress of Sir John Waleys (d. 1418) and of Joan (d. 1420) grand-daughter of Sir Edward Kendale.

Two rolls, *c.* 24 ft. × 12 in., 22 ft. × 12 in., + 3 loose leaves. Paper. Formerly pasted on to a parchment backing made up of sections of the household accounts of John of Gaunt, but now bound as a volume (fos. 16 + 20, 18 × 13 in.).

WALTER, Thomas fil.; de Daventre; knt.
v. DAVENTRE.

WARWICK, Earls of.
v. BEAUCHAMP.

WENDEN, co. Essex.
v. (?) FRAY.

WHIXLEY, Manor of; co. York.
1337. **Geoffrey Dent Esq., M.C.,** Ribston Hall; deposited at Leeds, Yorks. Arch. Soc. Libr. Cartulary, in a series of 14th–15th cent. hands (*temp.* Edw. III–Hen. V), followed (fos. 135–67) by a survey. An abstract, 1910, is in Leeds, Yorks. Arch. Soc. MS. 346.

Fos. iv + 167. 8½ × 5½ in. Medieval binding (boards, covered with skin), with the initials 'T.B.' stamped on the back cover.

WILLOUGHBY, of Willoughby and Wollaton, co. Nott.
Nos. 1338–41 are noticed by W. H. Stevenson, *HMC. Middleton MSS.* (1911), 196–7, 269. The leaves from an early Latin Bible formerly used as covers are now BM., Add. 45025.

1338. **Lord Middleton,** deposited at Nottingham U.L. (Middleton MSS.). Vol. i (cf. Nos. 1339–40) of a cartulary, *c.* 1500, of deeds rel. lands in co. Nott. Contains material for Middleton, Cossington, Wigtoft and Sutton-upon-Trent. Illuminated initials, with arms, fos. 26, 54. Some later additions.

Fos. 69. 15¾ × 10 in. Paper (fos. 26–33, 54–60, vellum).

1339. **Ditto.** Vol. ii (cf. No. 1338). Material for Lenton, Radford, Gunthorpe, Lowdham and Sutton Passeys. Some later additions.

Fos. 112. 14 × 9¾ in. Paper, with occasional vellum.

1340. **Ditto.** Vol. iii (cf. No. 1338). Material for Sutton Passeys and Wollaton.

Fos. 165. 16 × 10¾ in. Paper with occasional vellum.

1341. **Ditto.** Misc. register, 1560–1630, incl. (fos. 35–85) a cartulary of Cossall.

Fos. 96. 11¾ × 8¼ in. Paper.

WILSTROP of Wilstrop, co. York.
1342. **Manchester, Rylands Libr., Lat. MS. 251.** Cartulary, 15th–16th cent., of deeds rel. lands in co. York, arranged topographically in two parts: (1) ff. 1–53, Wilstrop and other places, with a Table at fos. 4–6 which shows material for the city of York and Bustardthorpe to be wanting and the original order of the leaves to have been disturbed; (2) fos. 54–89, Tockwith etc., with a Table at fos. 86–7 and separate witness lists at fos. 55–6. Formerly bound with Rylands Libr. Lat. MS. 225 (Tockwith cartulary, No. 977 above). Noticed by G. C. Ransome, 'The Chartulary of Tockwith alias Scokirk', *Miscellanea* iii (Yorks. Arch. Soc., Record ser. lxxx, 1931), 157–8.

Fos. 89. 12⅜ × 8¼ in. Paper. *FO:* P. E. Towneley (?), 1831 (*P*).

WINCHESTER, Earls of.
v. DESPENSER.

WOLLASTON, William; of Wollaston, co. Northt.
1343. **The Governors of Wyggeston's Hosp., Leicester;** deposited at Leicester Museum (I D 50/xii/28). Register, 15th cent. (aft. 1451), of deeds and other

evidences, 13th–15th cent., rel. Wollaston etc., incl. some genealogical notes.

Fos. 25. 12 × 9 in. Paper.

WOODFORD of Brentingby, co. Leic. 1344. **BM., Cotton Claud. A. xiii.** Cartulary, 1449, of deeds, mainly 14th–15th cent., rel. cos. Leic., Staff., Rutl. etc.

A preface in English (fo. 1) rel. John de Woodford, the founder of the family's fortunes, who acquired Brentingby in 1317, is printed by J. Nichols, *Hist. Leicester* ii, pt. 1 (1795), 373–4.

Fos. 282. 10 × 6¾ in. *FO:* Sir Charles Smith, afterw. Viscount Carrington, 1638 (Bodl., Dodsworth 41 (*SC.* 4183), fo. 105); Samuel Roper.

INDEXES

The indexes relate to medieval MSS. alone; post-medieval transcripts, extracts etc. are not normally included. All references are to entry-numbers in the catalogue.

INDEX I: PRESENT OWNERS ETC. OF MSS.

A. CORPORATE

(An asterisk (*) signifies that a MS. is deposited on loan.)

ABERDEEN
  Blairs Coll. 1150, 1152, 1153
  City Charter Room 1116
  University Library MSS. 247, 1110;
    248, 1113; 249, 1112; 251, 1115
ABERYSTWYTH
  National Library of Wales
    MSS. 7851, 895
  Gwysaney MSS. 1, 594; 15, 39
  Peniarth MSS. 390, 93
ABINGDON
  Christ's Hospital Muniments 8
ARBROATH
  Borough Muniments 1121-3
AYLESBURY
  Buckinghamshire Arch. Soc., County
    Museum 1252*
BEDFORD
  Bedfordshire R.O. 138*, 1231*
  Parish Church of St. John v. 692
BEVERLEY
  Minster 51
  Yorkshire East Riding R.O. 1224*,
    1225*
BIRMINGHAM
  Reference Library 522, 1079; v. also
    277, 278, 960
BRADFORD, co. York
  City Art Gallery & Museums 1192; v.
    also 678
BRISTOL
  Baptist Coll. MS. Z. c. 23, 472
  Bristol R.O. 78
BUCKFAST ABBEY, co. Devon 85
BURTON-UPON-TRENT
  Museum & Art Gallery 92*
BURY ST. EDMUNDS
  Bury St. Edmunds & West Suffolk R.O.
    98, 1212*
CAMBRIDGE
  University Library
    MSS. Dd. 3. 87 (art. 20), 738; 8. 2
      (art. 1), 515; 9. 38, 807; 10. 18,
      483; 14. 2, 1195
    Ee 1. 1, 635; 3. 60, 119; 4. 20,
      847; 5. 21, 605; 5. 31, 181;
      5. 34, 850

CAMBRIDGE (University Library)—cont.
  MSS.—cont.
    Ff. 2. 29, 120; 2. 33, 117; 4. 35,
      121
    Gg. 4. 4, 109
    Ii. 6. 32, 1137
    Kk. 5. 29, 1022
    Ll. 1. 10 (fos. i–xxvi), 218; 2. 15,
      207
    Mm. 2. 20, 79; 4. 19, 118; 5. 35,
      1327
    Additional MSS. 3020, 3021, 964;
      3468, 361; 4220, 110; 4407(12),
      428; 6006, 123; 6845, 211; 6874,
      102; 6969, 963
    v. also 529
  Christ's Coll. Muniments 285–6
  Corpus Christi Coll. MSS. 7 (pp. 203–
    22), 845; 111 (pp. 55–131), 23; 189 (fos.
    195–201), 163; 286, 199A; 298 (pt. ii),
    189; 301, 199
  Gonville & Caius Coll. MSS. 376, 922;
    485, 360
  Jesus Coll. MS. 18, 133
  King's Coll. Muniments (College Books
    etc.) 145–50, (B. 121) 72, (E. 25,
    1–7) 1216–22, (E. 27) 1223, (O. 33–9)
    506–11
  Pembroke Coll. Muniments 153
  Peterhouse MS. 62, 649
  St. Catherine's Coll. Muniments 154
  St. John's Coll.
    MSS. Aa. 1. 59, 736; N. 6, 173
    Muniments 144, 155; v. also 602
  Trinity Coll.
    MSS. O. 1. 25, 1226; O. 2. 1, 366; O. 2.
      41 (pp. 81–159), 364; O. 9. 26,
      185; R. 5. 33 (fos. 77–87), 438
    Muniments 151, 152
  Trinity Hall MS. 1, 198
  Fitzwilliam Museum MS. 329, 1187
CANTERBURY
  Dean & Chapter
    Lit. MSS. C. 20, 212; E. 19, 196; E. 23,
      206
    Muniments 163A, 164–6, 168–72,
      174

B. PRIVATE

(An asterisk (*) signifies that a MS. has been deposited on loan with a public institution)

INDEX II : FORMER OWNERS ETC. OF MSS.

(The names of direct ancestors, predecessors etc. of present owners of MSS. are *not* included in this index unless cited, for special reasons, in the catalogue.)

ABINGDON, Earls of. *v.* BERTIE

AGARD(E), Arthur (1540–1615); deputy chamberlain of the Exchequer. 222

AGARD, Henry; of Foston; knt. 1617. 981

AILESBURY, Earls & Marquesses of. *v.* BRUCE

ALCHIN (? William Turner (1790–1865); librarian). 688

ALDERFORD, John; of Abbots Salford, 16th cent. 1068

ALFORD, Sir William; of Meaux, 17th cent. 655, 660

ALLEN, Thomas (1542–1632); of Gloucester Hall. 3, 205, 739, 940

ALLEYN, Sir John; 16th cent. 1037–8, 1040

ALMACK, Richard; of Long Melford; 1849. 377

ANDERSON, Thomas; W.S.; 1725. 670

ANDREWS, Richard; of Colne, 1719. 271

ANSTIS, John (1669–1744); Garter king of arms. 610, 737; *v.* also *sub* 828

ARCHER, Sir Simon (1581–1662); antiquary. 522

ARMYNE *al.* AYRMINE, Sir William (1593–1651); 1st bart. 657, 674

ARNOLD, Edmund; 17th cent. 904–5

ARUNDEL, Earls of. *v.* HOWARD

ARUNDELL fam., barons Arundell; of Wardour Castle, 17th cent. 888

ASHBURNHAM, Bertram (d. 1878); 1st earl of Ashburnham. Owned, 1849–78, London, BM. Stowe MSS., *qq. vv.* in Index I (A); 920

ASHMOLE, Elias (1617–92); antiquary. Owned Oxford, Bodl. MSS. Ashmole, *qq. vv.* in Index I (A); 803

ASHTON, Sir Ralph (d. 1644); 1st bart., of Whalley and Downham. 1028, 1030

ASHTON, Richard; of Downham, 1658. 1029

ASTLE, Thomas (1735–1803); keeper of the records in the Tower of London. 67, 76, 267, 272, 350, 489, 496, 610, 665–6, 716,

775, 860, 902, 911, 981, 1050, 1052, 1077 1196, 1298; *v.* also *sub* 307, 470

ASTON fam., of Aston Hall. 112

ATKINSON, Thomas; 17th cent. 1101

ATKYNS, Sir Robert (1621–1709); judge. 259

AUBREY, John (1626–97); antiquary. 514 (?)

AUBREY & AUBREY-FLETCHER fam., barts.; Dorton House. 5, 1310

AYRMINE. *v.* ARMYNE

BACON fam., barts.; of Redgrave. 96–7, 105, 118–19, 127, 129, 134

BACON, Francis (1561–1626); 1st viscount St. Alban. 844

BACON, Sir Nicholas (1509–79); lord keeper. 104, 126 (?)

BAIRD, William (d. 1864); of Elie. 1166

BAKER, George (1781–1851); historian of Northamptonshire. 1256, 1263

BAKER, Thomas (1656–1740); antiquary. 851

BALDWYN, Bernard; 17th cent. 471 (?)

BALFOUR, Sir James (1600–57); bart.; Lyon king of arms. 1118, 1120, 1124 1138–9, 1165, 1179

BARKER fam., of Sundorne. 476

BARLOW, Thomas (1607–91); bp. of Lincoln. 783

BARNARDISTON, Giles; of Clare, 1638. 261

BARNES, Jo.; 17th cent. 352

BARRINGTON fam., Barrington Hall. 473

BARRINGTON, John Shute (d. 1734); 1st viscount Barrington. 53

BARRINGTON, Shute (1734–1826); bp. of Durham. 143

BARROW, Isaac; of Spinney, 1638. 924

BARRY, William (d. 1781); rector of Clonmany. 978

BATMAN, Stephen (d. 1584); D.D. 610

BATTELEY, Charles; 1698. 115

BAYNHAM, Edmund Christopher; 1944. 103